ONE HUMAN FAMILY

THE BIBLE, SCIENCE, RACE AND CULTURE

Carl Wieland

ISBN: 978-1-921643-43-9

Cover design: Rik Hilverts

Layout and design: Nikala Drager and Jessica Spykerman

Style consistency and general proofreading: Kym Holwerda

CREATION
BOOK PUBLISHERS
Atlanta, Georgia, USA
www.creationbookpublishers.com

For further information on creation/evolution
and the Christian worldview go to
CREATION.com

ONE HUMAN FAMILY

THE BIBLE, SCIENCE, RACE AND CULTURE

Carl Wieland

www.onehumanfamily.me
www.onehumanfamily.us

CONTENTS

8 DIFFERENT PEOPLE, DIFFERENT LANGUAGE ____ 177

9 ECHOES OF GENESIS _____ 193

16 THE EFFECT OF RELIGION ON CULTURE _____ 315

17 RACISM TODAY—AND HOPE FOR TOMORROW

Acknowledgments and Dedication

Many people, especially CMI colleagues, were helpful in myriad ways at various stages of this book. It would be unrealistic to name them all, though Robert Zins deserves special mention. His perseverance and patience with me in critiquing in detail a particularly difficult part of the draft manuscript was exceptional.

Also, Lita Cosner and Jonathan Sarfati as first and last overall reviewer, respectively, were very helpful. To Jonathan, thanks also for many fascinating bits of extra information. The responsibility for any remaining deficiencies is of course mine.

Special thanks, too, is due my fellow Board members of *Creation Ministries International* (Australia) for their foresight in providing the 'time out' required to finally get the project done.

This work is dedicated to all who support the ministry of CMI, whether as donors, volunteers (including semi-volunteers) or both.

Carl Wieland

Bible quotes in this book are from the English Standard Version, © 2001 by Crossway Bibles,www.crossway.org.

FOREWORD
by Dr. Jerry Bergman

As Tufts University's Daniel Dennett wrote in 1995, Darwin's theory is a "universal acid" that corrodes everything, even "the fabric of our most fundamental beliefs"—especially belief in God. Darwinism has also corroded our belief in the Judeo-Christian teaching that we are all descended from one couple, Adam and Eve, which makes us all one race. The results of this corrosion in the belief that all humans are very closely related are documented in this book.

Most critiques of evolution focus on the theory's many scientific problems, but ignore the serious social consequences. This well-written and well-documented book also addresses this other very important side of the question. Dr. Wieland has clearly done his homework; although I have spent almost three decades researching the subject of racism and evolution, he has managed to come up with much new material. I applaud him for this achievement.

Jerry Bergman PhD

The author not only covers the problem of racism in America and Nazi Germany, but in much of the rest of the world as well. In addition, he documents how acquiescence to evolution has been a major cause of the church's acceptance of racism. He makes it clear that a straightforward reading of the Scriptures irreconcilably opposes any version of racism or Darwinism, and shows the many ways in which racists have tried to get around the clear teaching of the biblical text.

No advocate of the single causation theory, Dr. Wieland covers the many social and economic factors that influence racism in his well-reasoned and balanced approach. He also covers the science of genetics in such a way that a layperson can follow, yet informs and adds insight to keep a professional interested in his writing.

His currency with the world race problem is reflected in the section that covers reverse racism, or the use of racism to fight racism, the antithesis of Martin Luther King's cry to judge people by their character and not their shade of skin color.

Having documented that racism is, unfortunately, still alive and well in the world today, Dr. Wieland then offers solid solutions to the problem. This book is of immense value for this reason alone.

Biologist and social scientist alike, Dr. Bergman is the holder of 9 (7 of them graduate) earned degrees and has over 800 publications in 12 languages, including 20 books and monographs. He has taught at Bowling Green State University, at the University of Toledo, and at the Medical College of Ohio, where he was a research associate in the department of experimental pathology. He currently teaches at Northwest State College in Archbold, Ohio.

∞

INTRODUCTION: Humanity's big picture

In past ages, explorers were hailed as heroes after they returned to their European homeland with tales of strange and different people and their practices. These tales were the source of boundless fascination and awe. In this globalized, networked age, by contrast, we are exposed to people from other ethnicities, cultures and regions of the planet as never before. So much so that one can, unlike those in past eras, easily lose any sense of fascination or wonder at the rich variety of people. Their images flash with regularity across the various gadget screens of our lives. We think nothing of bumping into these various people at the supermarket, either, albeit minus some of the more exotic regalia that Discovery Channel might feature.

Familiar or not, though, human beings in their full array of diversity—you and me and those in all corners of the globe—present an amazing picture when we sit back and contemplate it.

Think only of the diminutive Khoisan[1] ('bushmen') of southern Africa's Kalahari Desert, made famous by the movie *The Gods Must be Crazy*. Then put next to them a couple of tall, blonde,

---

1. This term actually collectively refers to two groups of people, the pastoral Khoi (or Khoikhoi) and the hunter-gatherer San, who are the ones generally referred to with the term 'bushmen'.

Canada

lanky Swedes from Stockholm. Contemplate not just the physical differences, but the huge gulf between their cultures. The bushmen are nomadic hunter-gatherers, a far cry from Sweden's advanced industrial economy. In the same vein, consider the Masai[2]—lean, tall tribesmen existing on mostly milk and blood[3] from their herds on the steamy African savannah. Then next to them, place in your mind's eye the short, stocky Inuit (formerly called Eskimos) subsisting for centuries in an icy wasteland, nourished by the blubber and flesh of the marine creatures they hunt.

Amidst all this immense, almost overwhelming, diversity, we will find a common thread, and an underlying unity at all levels—genetic, cultural, linguistic,

Namibia

---

2. Alternative spelling, 'Maasai'.
3. Pun earlier in the sentence intentional (well, after I noticed it, anyway). ☺

intellectual and spiritual.

This book will demonstrate that there are no 'races' in the sense that Darwin, for example, thought of them, and as large numbers of people still do. There is in a very real sense only one 'race' of human beings. This is despite the many subgroups, tribes and factions within the human family. At the same time, genes still matter in explaining group differences, and this book does not espouse some 'politically correct' approach, or total avoidance of a term like 'race', which still conveys meaningful information.

Sweden
iStockPhoto

It will also show that there are ideas on race and racism still commonly held today that simply don't fit the facts. This is not just from a biological and biblical standpoint, but also a practical sociological one.

No portion of the ideological spectrum is immune from such misconceptions, and what follows in these pages will likely not fit easily into the liberal/conservative categories into which many like to shoehorn things.

This is not 'just another creationist book'. Nor is it some over-idealistic let's-all-get-together-and-sing-Kumbaya[4] approach to the very real and deep problems and issues that tear people and communities apart. It dares to grapple with issues of race and culture that are largely taboo subjects today, including the starkly differing outcomes in different groups, and the effects

---

4.   An African-American spiritual song from the 1930s, popular in the '60s with peace movements etc., that has associations with human unity and spirituality. It is sometimes used, like here, to gently satirize excessively naïve views of how to solve the world's problems.

Vietnam
iStockPhoto

of different religions on those outcomes. From the reactions of early reviewers, these excursions will likely be the most fascinating—and at the same time the most controversial—aspects of the book.

Cards on the table

The reader may not yet share my belief that what purports to be the true history of humankind—Genesis, as revealed by the Creator of the universe—fits the facts of the real world. Despite claims to the contrary, this is a view shared by substantial numbers of educated and scientifically qualified people. Some things presented in this book will likely be new and surprising to you. It might start you thinking afresh about other things you may have thought were settled.

Regardless, I like to think that few will not find it fascinating—satisfying for some, perhaps challenging for others. Maybe even life-changing, as we take that history of humanity seriously, plug in the facts of the real world, and see what emerges.

Over the years, I have spoken on this subject to many thousands of people in various parts of the world. Experiencing the reactions of many of them tells me that the proposition in these pages will, for more than a few, provide a whole new way of looking at the world—in particular, its people. The message of this book is basically simple. It could almost be summarized in the main title's three words. History suggests that ideas with the potential to profoundly, even radically, impact thought and behavior are rarely complex at their core. When laid out and followed through in all its fascinating outworkings and implications, I believe that this concept of *one human family* is much more than some motherhood mantra. I am convinced that boldly grasping hold of it offers a real way forward in all aspects of this often emotion-charged issue—race and racism.

Caveats

This book is meant to be simple, in the sense of making sometimes technical concepts straightforward and, where possible, easy to understand. That occasionally means having to make incursions into that borderland close to the line where the simple becomes simplistic. Things can also appear overly simplified some time after publication when, as often happens, ongoing research deepens and complicates a phenomenon.

Kenya

Such additional knowledge can also overturn a 'known fact' completely. I recall a medical lecturer in my undergraduate years telling me in casual conversation, "You know, 50% of the cardiac physiology I was taught only ten years ago has now been shown to be wrong." I probably thought, naïvely, how fortunate I was to be living at that time in history, when we finally had the truth about the subject. But a decade or two after that incident, maybe 50% of what *he* had taught *me* about cardiac physiology was already having to be overhauled in the light of more information. That's simply the way that human knowledge progresses, even in relatively uncontroversial areas of observational science, i.e. the study of how things work in the present world. Imagine how much more things could (and do) miss the mark in historical (or forensic) science, i.e. trying to establish what happened in the past. The conclusions in such fields—paleontology (study of fossils), archaeology, trying to reconstruct alleged evolutionary genealogies, historical geology, and more—are crucially dependent on interpretations. So they are inevitably skewed by the worldviews and prejudices of the investigators—as well as by the preconceptions inherited from an earlier layer of education.[5]

Subjectivity of interpretation is even more of an issue, of course, in the book's forays into cultural and historical/sociological issues. I found these at once important, exciting, and risky to tackle. In the absence of divine inspiration, there can be no perfect or unbiased description of such a hugely complex thing as human affairs. Facts are facts, and absolute truth exists; I don't hold to some postmodern view of 'differing truths'. But in either framing thoughts (or perceiving

Masai dancers

them) on things such as culture—and the way that history is viewed, even for those who lived through it—everyone is a product of a unique set of inputs.

It was remarkable, for example, what differing reactions I had

---

5.   See creation.com/its-not-science.

to the several drafts of the apartheid chapter from various South African reviewers. The distinctions were not just between 'black and white', but also between those Europeans of an Afrikaner/ Boer heritage and those of English extraction. Yet all had lived through exactly the same era of history.

So then, rather than try to live up to some idealized notion of perfect objectivity, I have not hesitated from making this an intensely personal account at many points, with all the risks—and benefits, from several reviewers' accounts—that entails. I dare to suggest, too, that even those tempted to too-hastily assign the author to one or other of the many 'boxes' we mentally construct in this 'race debate' may be in for some surprises. And payoffs, also, if wise enough not to allow themselves to be derailed before the unfolding journey has revealed the strength of the overall case. By that I mean the 'big picture' of humanity—the *one human family* that emerges in these pages as we contemplate the most fascinating subject of all—ourselves.

∞

1 RACE AND THE ORIGINS DEBATE

THE MAN CAGED IN A ZOO

In 1906, a man called Ota Benga, a dignified human being from Central Africa's Congo, of a tribe whose members are often called 'pygmies', was put on display in New York's Bronx Zoo. There he shared a cage with an orangutan and a parrot, to be ogled by the masses as an example of a living 'ape-man' or 'missing link'.[1] Large crowds thronged to see this 'primitive creature', justifying the commercial instincts of the promoters.

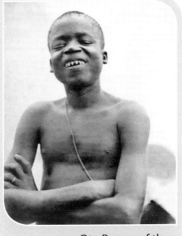

Ota Benga of the Mbuti people.
Public domain

What can explain such a horrendous action, one that would have required the consent if not involvement of many in positions of authority? A *Scientific*

---

1.   For a fuller account with documentation, see creation.com/otabenga.

American article of the time referred to pygmies as "ape-like little black people" and said that

> "Even today, ape-like negroes are found in the gloomy forests, who are doubtless direct descendants of these early types of man, who probably closely resembled their simian ancestors … ."[2]

Further on (p. 107), the same source called the Congo pygmies

> "small, ape-like, elfish creatures, furtive and mischievous … [who] live in the dense tangled forests in absolute savagery, and while they exhibit many ape-like features in their bodies, they possess a certain alertness, which appears to make them more intelligent than other negroes … . They have seemingly become acquainted with metal only through contact with superior beings … ."

Neither the display nor the huge interest in it would have taken place if people in that society had not already been primed by such authoritative opinions to believe that there were sub-humans in various parts of the planet.

So, was this a mere blip on the radar, some momentary aberration within the world's foremost bastion of freedom and democracy? The destructive thought patterns that gave rise to this outrageous action are not something safely tucked away in the long-gone past, as will be seen. The belief system that spawned it is still with us, and so are the patterns themselves, to greater or lesser degree—if perhaps buried a little deeper within our collective consciousness than before.

Myths about bias on origins

I placed my cards on the table earlier regarding where I'm coming from in all this. I've told you what my bias is, in other words. Perhaps that has already created a wall of resistance to any new ways of looking at things. If so, that may be because you think I can't be 'neutral'. But neutrality in that sense is well known to

---

2. Munn and Company (Ed.), The Government Philippines Expedition, *Scientific American,* July 23, p. 65, 1904.

be a myth among people who make a living thinking about such things (philosophers). All reasoning, in science or philosophy or anything else, takes place within some sort of framework. That framework is inevitably based on a foundation of ideas that are believed to be true, without actual proof (though generally for reasons that seem strong to their holder).

For example, the starting assumption of those who are convinced that the world around us must have generated its own order and complexity (i.e. evolved from some primeval simplicity) is that there is no supernatural realm. For them, it is an article of faith that the natural world of matter and energy is all there is, all there ever was, and all there ever will be.[3] The issue, then, is not whether one has a starting belief or bias. It's pretty well compulsory to have one. Even 'Who cares?' qualifies as one. It means you have assumed that the issue will not affect you and/or that the evidence either way will not be strong enough to warrant a decision, so it's not worth investigating.

Ota Benga with a pet chimpanzee he brought from the Congo.
Public domain

The issue, then, is this: how well does the framework built on any particular belief/bias foundation withstand the test of reality? In other words, how well does it fit the facts of the real world when we interpret them within that particular framework?[4]

3.   This starting assumption, or religious position, if you like, is known as either 'naturalism' or 'materialism' (obviously not the same thing as when people talk about 'materialism' in the sense of craving the latest BMW).

4.   As with virtually all reasoning, there is an inevitable element of circularity. But if you're using a framework to interpret facts with a starting belief that is way off base, it shouldn't last long. If you are continually head-butting against reality, you would hopefully become exhausted from having to construct ever more exotic hypotheses to try to salvage your core belief.

So, whether you share the same foundation at present or not, come along for the ride, if only as an exercise. Come see how the structure built on that foundation (that Genesis gives us true history) makes sense—even if only for the sake of discussion at this point. If you care about the issue of race, about how people and nations think about and care about each other, you won't want to miss the opportunity to see how having the right foundational beliefs can make a huge difference.

The biblical beginnings of humanity

Most people in Western culture are at least vaguely familiar with the book of Genesis. They know that it claims that all people started off with Adam and Eve, and not that long ago. If true, it would mean that we are all extremely closely related. So, as far as the Bible is concerned, in an overarching sense there can only be one 'race' of people (though we will explore some important caveats to and nuances of that statement).

Sure, some who profess to believe the Bible have been known to distort what it says, often to try to justify exploiting or 'dissing' other groups. One such twist on Genesis is to invent imaginary groups created before Adam was, then claim that these gave rise to 'the other races'. But clearly, that is not what is taught in the Bible at all. Adam was "the first man" (1 Corinthians 15:45); Eve was "the mother of all [the] living" (Genesis 3:20).

The Apostle Paul says in the New Testament that all nations were "made from one man" (Acts 17:26). A few renderings of that verse based on a different set of manuscripts, among them the King James, say that God has "made of one blood all nations of men". But manuscriptal arguments to one side, this is just another way of saying the same thing. We often use the word 'blood' as a figure of speech to mean genetic relatedness. Pedigreed animals are said to have 'bloodlines'. We talk about whether an aunt or uncle is a 'blood relative', rather than merely being related to us by having married a blood relative. In short, the Bible plainly teaches that all people were made from one line of descent, i.e. from one man and (implied) one woman.

But, many will say—look at all those *differences*. People tend to see such things as the shape of our eyes, or the color of our skin or eyes, as 'separately evolved'. They think that the differences arose from people groups having been separated for thousands, even tens of thousands, of years—so they *must* be substantial.

DARWINISM'S EFFECT ON RACISM

Darwin believed this, as we will see. Of course, discrimination and exploitation of others perceived as being 'different' had been with humanity for a very long time before he published *On the Origin of Species by means of Natural Selection*[5] in 1859. And it is important to stress up front that this book is about the consequences of rejecting the Bible's 'Genesis big picture' concerning the history of humanity. Such rejection of the facts of Genesis, or ignoring of their straightforward implications, has taken place even in overtly Bible-centered cultures with little or no evolutionary influence, as we shall see.

However, since Darwinism is the most sophisticated and potent expression of this rejection, it is no surprise to hear that *The Origin* led to a huge *increase* in racist thinking and behavior. That is undeniably true. Renowned Harvard paleontologist Stephen Jay Gould (1941–2002), a thoroughly committed evolutionist and opponent of creationists—and staunch antiracist—wrote:

> "Biological arguments for racism may have been common before 1850, but they increased by orders of magnitude following the acceptance of evolutionary theory."[6]

Following Darwin, it became increasingly 'obvious' that various easily identifiable groups of people, i.e. 'races', were either less evolved than other groups or (particularly if it was your own group) more evolved. *Ergo*, some groups were more human than their counterparts, others less so.

---

5.   Mostly shortened in referring to it as 'The Origin of Species' or 'Origin of Species', or simply 'The Origin'.
6.   Gould, S.J., *Ontogeny and Phylogeny,* Belknap-Harvard Press, Cambridge, Massachusetts, pp. 127–128, 1977.

Many religious folk, perhaps secretly glad to be released from the moral strictures of biblical accountability, readily absorbed this new evolutionary doctrine into their belief system. For them, advancement along evolution's ladder of progress, as it was perceived, became progress toward some sort of proto-New-Age godhood for all. At the least, it was part of a divine plan for the betterment, even perfection, of humanity. Either way, being part of a more biologically 'advanced' group meant either that your group was closer to the divine or was the recipient of divine favor in some way.

Large numbers came to see the world in terms of a stark 'struggle for existence', in which only the 'fittest' individuals and groups survived and prospered. ('Fittest' does not refer to physical strength or exercise capacity, by the way. It simply means those most suited, however that may come about, to the task of surviving and prospering, and more particularly, passing on their characteristics to the next generation—i.e. those with the greatest reproductive success.)

The full title of Darwin's book was *On the Origin of Species by means of Natural Selection, or the Preservation of Favoured Races in the Struggle for Life.* Darwin meant not just races of people (though he definitely did not exclude these, as his later works made plain), but plants and animals as well. When it came to races of humans, there was no shortage of people ready to take him at his literal word, namely that some races were less favored than others. So, if it looked like some races were not being preserved (whether or not others were helping them through the exit door), it must have been either 'natural' (they being the less fit) or else 'divinely ordained' by their evolutionized idea of God.

One of Darwin's close friends was Charles Kingsley,[7] a clergyman who greatly helped him by promoting the idea that one could believe in evolution at the same time as being a 'good Christian'. In a book of sermons, Kingsley wrote:

"The Black People of Australia, exactly the same race

---

7.   Grigg, R., Darwin's quisling, Charles Kingsley, *Creation* **22**(1):50–51, 1999, creation.com/kingsley.

as the African Negro, cannot take in the Gospel ... All attempts to bring them to a knowledge of the true God have as yet failed utterly ... Poor brutes in human shape ... they must perish off the face of the earth like brute beasts."[8]

Unfit to breed

Another outcome of Darwinian thinking was eugenics or 'racial hygiene'.[9] Eugenics is based on the belief that we must actively interfere in the evolutionary process by ensuring that 'defective' people do not give rise to offspring. At the very least, this would be by way of compulsory sterilization. More drastic methods of ensuring the absence of offspring were not precluded in this broad ideology.

The motivation of eugenicists was more than just ensuring the biological vigor of humanity. It was inextricably intertwined with ensuring the 'purity of the race', which meant of course the dominant group in Western Europe. So from the start, the definitions of which groups of people were defective or inferior kept straying into areas with strong racial overtones.

Today, such ideas, sometimes grouped under the label of 'Social Darwinism', are not openly popular. This is especially so among the world's 'intellectuals', those who strongly influence media opinion.[10] This is only partly a result of scientific discoveries to do with our biology, specifically our genes—discoveries which make ideas of racial inferiority/superiority untenable, as we will see. (Chapter 5 looks at a major additional reason for the unfashionable status of racism today among intellectuals.) Such discoveries were not a prediction from evolutionary thinking. In fact, theories of

8.   Kingsley, C., *Sermons on National Subjects*, Sermon XLI, Macmillan & Co., pp. 414–417, 1880, cited in Paton, J.G. *Autobiography*, Ed. by Paton, J., Banner of Truth Trust, Edinburgh, pp. 263–265, 1965.

9.   Originally the German *Rassenhygiene*, coined in 1895 by eugenicist Alfred Ploetz (1860–1940).

10.   The term 'intellectuals' as used here does not refer to all intelligent people but is restricted to those mostly involved in shaping public opinion, who generally contribute little to society other than their ideas and opinions, as in Thomas Sowell's book *Intellectuals and Society* (2010).

human evolution have had to be substantially re-jigged to cope with the accumulation of evidence that we *are* all astonishingly closely related. We will be looking at this evidence in Chapter 2, as well as carefully considering our external differences, like skin color. That's because these differences still lead many to wonder how we could in fact all be closely related, or how such differences could arise within a framework of biblical creation.

Meantime, though many biblioskeptics would like to blame Christianity for all social evils, it's obvious that a straightforward biblical view of human origins would have, all along, pointed to the *close biological relatedness* of all people groups. Widespread acceptance of this and its implications would, then and now, have made most popular notions about 'race' logically untenable. And it's easy to conclude that it would have made (and still can make) a big difference to our world. Given the suffering caused by racist attitudes and interracial conflict, it's hard to imagine that anyone wouldn't want to see that sort of outcome.

Was Darwin misunderstood on race?

The out-of-fashion nature of openly racist ideas in public discourse, coupled with the widespread enthusiasm for evolution in those same circles, encourages the claim that racism/eugenics involved some sort of inappropriate or mischievous misapplication of Darwinism. Darwin himself is said to have been misunderstood, misused, misquoted, you name it. So let's look at the facts. I'll try to be as fair to him as possible.

Actually, in one sense, it really doesn't matter what the founder or popularizer of a belief system personally believed. If most people have *understood* him to say that he believed XYZ, and have been persuaded by him about XYZ, then acted on it, the effect is the same as if he *had* held and taught that view. Nevertheless, despite the best efforts of 'Darwin revisionists' to show otherwise, he hasn't been misrepresented in the above, or in the considerably greater details to follow.

The evidence suggests that Darwin was a gentle—perhaps even squeamish, but at any rate tenderhearted—sort of fellow.

He found slavery, for instance, distasteful, even abhorrent. But, as will be shown, the 'racial' implications of his theory were not only obvious to onlookers, they were well understood and even expounded by him.

As a child of his times, the economic and political dominance of Western Europe would have been prominent in Darwin's worldview. This would have especially applied to Britain in those heady days of an empire upon which the sun never set.

RACISM AND EVOLUTION BEFORE DARWIN

Preceding centuries had seen a plethora of voyages of discovery. In that golden age of exploration, a fascinated Europe had learned of many different types of society. It was easy and tempting to construct a hierarchy of societies among them. At the bottom were the 'primitive' nomadic hunter-gatherers. Then, only slightly less primitive, and still nomadic, were the tenders of herds of animals. Next came agricultural societies, and so on. This hierarchy was capped by what was then modern industrial culture, obviously the most sophisticated and hence 'advanced'.

All of this had deeply penetrated the popular consciousness before Darwin published his theory. Europe's own recent history had shown movement from agrarian to industrial on this scale, so all societies on Earth must have reached their present status by moving along a similar path in time. I.e. the hierarchy could easily become associated with a timeline concept. Never mind that the Bible taught that agriculture and metalworking existed from the earliest times (Genesis 4:2, 22); the Bible itself was already beginning to be brought into disrepute by this same hierarchical reasoning. (The bulk of the Old Testament seemed to be associated with nomadic herdsmen,[11] and since these were 'obviously' towards the bottom of the scale of sophistication, so too, one would expect the texts to reflect a low level of understanding.)

Since the 'obviously lower' societal structures were generally

---

11. This was, in any case, a caricature. Moses was as much an Egyptian courtier as he was a herdsman, considering how he spent his first 40 years. David was a king, and the prophets were from all sorts of professions;

Darwin's grandfather Erasmus produced a complete theory of evolution.
Left: Fathom Media, Right: Public domain

seen to be associated with 'non-white' peoples, it made perfect sense to construct a similar hierarchy among the various 'races'. If you were English, to mentally place the white Englishman at the top of such a scale as the most sophisticated being was not just in your evident self-interest—it seemed to fit the facts. The reason that a particular, say, tribal culture was not as far along this timeline of culture was clearly that its inhabitants were somehow in themselves less capable.

Again, all of this was before any well-developed evolutionary consciousness arose in the West, but it provided part of the fertile seedbed in which Darwinism later flourished. It was like a ready-made framework into which Darwin's transformist ideas in biology, including human biology, could be inserted.

Consider, too, that well before Darwin, evolutionary ideas had been hovering in the ether, as it were. His own grandfather, Erasmus, had produced a fully fledged theory of evolution in his *Zoonomia*.[12] In even more ways than this, the time was ultra-ripe for Darwin's notion of ape-like creatures becoming people, as will be seen.

---

12. Grigg, R., Darwinism: it was all in the family, *Creation* **26**(1):16–18, 2003, creation.com/erasmus.

For centuries before, as explorers were coming back from distant lands with tales of strange new peoples, obvious questions included, "Where did such people come from? Who are they?" The common idea that most thinkers of the day turned to the Bible for answers is not borne out by the evidence. A consideration of Genesis history would have informed Europeans that the indigenous people of the Americas, for instance, had arrived there by migration/dispersion at some time after the Babel incident. They were the descendants of the small group that had survived the year-long global Flood catastrophe. These, in turn, had descended from Adam and Eve (some 1,600 years earlier), who were miraculously created during those six earth-rotation days, in which "heaven and earth … and all that is in them" (Exodus 20:11) were put in place. All roughly 6,000 years ago.

Instead, a lot of speculation was based on early Greek ideas, such as the *Scala Naturae* (stairway or ladder of nature) or 'Great Chain of Being'. This was the idea that there was a natural order into which all entities in existence fitted. At the bottom were inorganic things like rocks and soil, then simple life forms, and as one went progressively higher up the scale, more and more complex creatures. Man was towards the top, but deity of some sort capped the whole scheme. This pagan idea became absorbed into the thinking of many Christians. For them, the deity at the top was of course the biblical God. Angels were slotted into the space between man and God; after all, didn't Psalm 8:5 say that man was "a little lower than the heavenly beings"?

Blended with other Greek ideas such as the inevitable perfection or harmony of nature, it made sense that there would be no gaping discrepancies or 'gaps' between the categories on this divine scale. Various types of new creatures were being discovered that could close some of the gaps—for example, more man-like primates that could be interpolated between man and some of the less man-like ones.

So an idealistic notion that nature must reveal a smooth continuum took hold of the popular imagination. It was further fueled by the widespread deistic thought of the day. Deism was the non-biblical belief that a remote creator made everything a long time ago, set all the laws in motion, but then had nothing further to do with the world thus created. Miracles were regarded as distasteful interferences that such a creator would not stoop to perform. He (or she or even it, for all we could know of such a being) had no need to, either, since the postulate was that he had made everything in perfect harmony. We only had to keep searching and everything missing in that harmonious balance of divinely produced laws and objects would eventually become evident.

In the 15th and 16th centuries, there were seamen's stories circulating of men in the Americas with tails.[13] This seemed to be able to further smooth out nature's inevitable continuum, and many thought that more such discoveries of 'in-between forms' lay in store. We just had to keep looking and wait.

Like our social scale discussed earlier, this 'natural scale' was originally not evolutionary, in the sense that one type had turned into a higher one. It was simply the way things had been ordained, a perfect order. But like the hierarchy of societies and of the groups that inhabited them, it was another ready-made mental construct onto which evolutionary ideas, both Darwinian and pre-Darwinian, could become seamlessly grafted.

In such a hierarchy of nature, then, it was obvious where other peoples 'discovered' by Europeans would be placed—whether having tails or not. With their lower-technology cultures and their strange (to Europeans) customs, they were clearly going to be seen as 'closer to the animal' on this scale, compared to 'real' people.

As we've seen, it was easy to imagine that cultures always progressed from simple to complex. No one in the intellectual circles of the day had ever seen an example of a culture or society losing some of its edge to become a less sophisticated one. So if cultures get more sophisticated as one goes forward in time,

---

13. See e.g. Lunde, P., Ponce de Leon and an Arab Legend, accessed at www.saudiaramcoworld.com, 17 October 2010.

then, extrapolating backwards, they must get increasingly less so. It was therefore easy to see tribal societies in particular as having necessarily come from something even more rudimentary. From there, it was just a small mental step to the idea that the individuals within those societies, already seen as somehow lower on the 'natural order', had themselves come from a much lower rung still.

Stanford History Professor George M. Fredrickson (1934–2008) wrote that since the Middle Ages Europeans had had a belief that groups of people existed who "were so wild and uncouth that they wandered in the forests and had no society of any kind."[14] Such imaginary 'ultra-barbarians' or 'pure savages' represented a mental slot into which real, newly discovered peoples were later pigeonholed. This included the various Amerindian groups, as well as the so-called 'Hottentots' (as Europeans initially called the Khoisan of the South African Cape). Perhaps 'shoehorned' would be a more apt term than pigeonholed, though, because in hindsight the notion that they were bereft of any society or religion, as required by the 'pure savage' idea, seems bizarre. Fredrickson writes that "the literature of sixteenth and seventeenth century exploration is filled with comments likening American Indians, Eskimos and 'Hottentots' to wild beasts".[15]

The idea of development from the animal kingdom (perhaps still restricted to these 'other races', rather than one's own favored group) was therefore not that strange at all to Europeans pre-Darwin.

This was all very convenient, too, when it came to exploiting them, along with their land and its resources. And it is what happened to the Aboriginal inhabitants of Tasmania, an island state off the southern part of the Australian continent. They were regarded as "wild beasts whom it is lawful to extirpate",[16] and were

---

14.   Fredrickson, G.M., *White Supremacy: A Comparative Study in American and South African history*, Oxford University Press, p. 9, 1981.
15.   Ref. 14, p. 11.
16.   Clive Turnbull, *Black War: The Extermination of the Tasmanian Aborigines*, F.W. Cheshire, Melbourne, 1948.

virtually wiped out by the European settlers. Their extermination was far advanced *before* Darwin's book was published in 1859; the last full-blooded Tasmanian died in the late 1870s.

An investigation by a freelance author specializing in Australian colonial history indicates, from documentation available from the time, that the settlers heartily agreed with one Captain Betts, who wrote, *pre-Darwin,* that the indigenous Tasmanians 'may almost be said to form the connecting link between man and the monkey tribes'.[17]

The church's acquiescence

Then, as now, the popular scientific and intellectual views of the day contaminated large segments of the Church—regardless of Genesis. The "clergymen in the early days of the colony ignored the aborigines, believing them to be so far beneath the level of humanity as to be not worth teaching".[17] Genesis-related qualms could be stilled by various 'accommodations' (such as the 'pre-Adamite races' mentioned earlier) with Scripture. Like today, given the means and opportunity, there were any number of theologians motivated to pretend that Genesis was saying or intending something different from the obvious—that all people on Earth are closely related.

In the centuries before Darwin, there were other currents of popular thought which also made it easier to bypass the straightforward reality of Genesis. Pagan Greek thought in particular often dominated in an ostensibly Christian culture. For example, in the standard version of the 'Galileo myth', a benighted dogmatic church opposed 'science'. Whereas, in fact, Galileo was a strong believer in the inerrancy and authority of the Bible, and his views on heliocentrism were initially well received by the church. The main problem was the way in which Greek thought on the nature of the universe had become entwined with theology. This was encouraged by the scientific and philosophical establishment of the day. It parallels the way in which Christians

---

17. Robert Travers, *The Tasmanians—The Story of a Doomed Race*, Casella Australia, Melbourne, 1967.

are being urged today to embrace 'theistic evolution'.[18]

A similar phenomenon reigned when it came to ideas about the 'natural inferiority' of some people compared to others. For example, Aristotle had taught that some people were 'slaves by nature'. Rather than using the plain teaching of Scripture to reject this outright, the intellectual climate of the time meant that even the well-known thirteenth-century Christian philosopher Thomas Aquinas tried to reconcile this with Christian thought. He suggested that this natural inferiority of some people was one of the punishments for sin. Note that, as will be seen later, Aquinas had denounced slavery. So, justifying this was probably not his agenda; more likely it was a perceived but totally unnecessary need to 'harmonize' Scripture with the intellectual climate of the day. But his approach continued to be expounded for another 500 years or so, and was applied by many who *were* trying to justify the enslavement and exploitation of native people groups.[19]

There were also other, more ingenious ways of trying to 'harmonize' these intellectual views of the day—i.e. that some people were *naturally* inferior 'barbarians'—with the Bible. One was to suggest that, yes, all men started equal, but after that some groups went backwards, for reasons that were certainly not biblically stated. As with theistic evolution, such readings had to be imposed onto the text of Scripture, and did not arise naturally from it. The idea of the biblically non-existent 'curse on Ham' (see p. 44) was one attempt to provide a cause for such degeneration. It was used to justify slavery, particularly in the American South, and, to a lesser extent, segregation and white supremacy in the context of southern Africa (Chapter 15).

Aristotle's doctrine that some people are 'natural slaves' was consciously invoked by big-name Spanish intellectuals; for instance, to justify Spain's conquest and domination of the South American Indians. In a famous mid-16th-century debate, the great Spanish jurist Juan Gines de Sepulveda appealed to this teaching in claiming that slavery was the natural condition

18.   For a comprehensive list of articles and documentation, see creation.com/galileo.
19.   Maxwell, J.F., Slavery and the Catholic Church, Barry Rose, London, 1975.

of people who had both 'inborn rudeness' and 'inhuman and barbarous customs'. Civilized people, he claimed, were the 'natural lords' of such savages. It was therefore justified to use force against any of them who refused this 'overlordship'. The official Spanish crown doctrine towards the natives remained one of 'peaceful persuasion', but Sepulveda's arguments helped create an atmosphere in which that doctrine was often half-heartedly and ineffectually applied.[20]

The European Renaissance (14th to 17th centuries) that followed Aquinas's time, far from removing the fog of classical philosophy obscuring the biblical framework, greatly enhanced it. Greek thinkers, including their belief in 'natural inferiority', were more popular than ever. Fredrickson 's words are again pertinent; he writes that "the Renaissance was a time of intellectual ferment in which many traditional and orthodox ideas were being questioned—and among these was the doctrine of the unity of mankind."[21] He had previously stated that despite the attempts to justify beliefs in the natural inferiority of 'barbarian peoples' (such as Sepulveda's appeal to Aristotle, and the theological attempts at invoking a non-existent curse on Ham):

Bust of Aristotle, the Greek philosopher who taught that some people were slaves by nature.
Public domain

"such views could rarely be followed to their logical outcome in the sixteenth and seventeenth centuries because of *the strong countervailing force of Christian belief in the essential unity of mankind* [emphasis added]."[14]

20. Fredrickson, G.M., Ref. 14.
21. Ref. 14, p. 10.

This underscores the fact that the Bible acted overall as a *restraining influence* on racism.

The so-called Enlightenment, mostly centered on the 18th century, followed hot on the heels of the Renaissance, and increasingly eroded a biblical understanding of our origins. Ethnohistorian Dr. Rainer Baehre explains that before that century:

> "the view was widely held that all humanity had descended from Adam and Eve, including 'the savage.' Natural philosophy eroded this theological perspective during the Enlightenment, as the 'nature' of race and civilization began to be studied by philosophers, zoologists, anatomists, and physicians. Reflecting Enlightenment progressivism, they ranked living things from the basest to the highest and most perfect forms in the Great Chain of Being and raised the possibility of multiple creations. While the majority position of monogenesis prevailed into the 19th century, it was increasingly challenged by polygenesis [the unbiblical idea that various races had separate origins—CW], whose advocates included Voltaire, Montesquieu, and Hume [all skeptics who wrote against Christianity—CW]. Polygenesis was sometimes used to justify slavery, anti-Semitism, and European domination of indigenous peoples."[22]

During both the Renaissance and the Enlightenment, many in the churches favored whatever the prevailing view was in the wider society, over and above the biblical account. The widespread acquiescence of 'religious' folk to Darwinism in the 19th century thus had ample precedent. It was in fact mostly scientists that held out against this tide, not 'churchians'.

Supremacism: same scene, different actors

The impetus that Darwin gave to the existing racist beliefs of his time is not hard to understand. His theory purported to give a mechanism, a seemingly rational *scientific* and biological

---

22.   Baehre, R.K., Early anthropological discourse on the Inuit and the influence of Virchow on Boas, *Etudes/Inuit/Studies*, **32**(2):13–34, 2008.

basis, for understanding how animals had progressively turned into humans. The 'hard science' of those like Isaac Newton had achieved amazing transformations in understanding and harnessing nature. And now the well-deserved glamour of all that scientific progress could rub off to the benefit of Darwin's (not-so) new idea.

Darwinism also meant that one could drop polygenism, and accept a single origin for mankind (to which a lot of evidence could already be seen to point)—without abandoning one's desired belief in huge 'racial differences'. And, even better for many, without having to go back to the long-abandoned belief in a divine, recent creation of Adam and Eve. Darwinism's substitute way of having one's cake and eating it too was simple. For one thing, the point of origin was pushed way backwards in time from the biblical 6,000 or so years. The obvious physical differences between the various 'races' of mankind were explained as the result of many tens of thousands, if not hundreds of thousands, of years of physical separation, while evolving in isolation from one another.

Darwinian evolution was not supposed to have any fixed speed. And Darwin also understood that there was no inevitable progress involved in his theory. It was being driven by random factors such as natural variation. (Darwin did not know about mutations, used in modern evolutionary theory as the only ultimate source of variation available that could potentially create real novelty. But these are not guided by any goal or purpose either.) Natural selection,[23] though unguided, could perhaps be said to effect non-random change, in the sense that only traits suited to an environment prevail. But the environments that give rise to various selection pressures arise and change at random. So with nothing but randomness behind it all, groups separated from each other would naturally evolve in different directions and at different rates.

23.   As seen later, in this book natural selection is taken as a straightforward logical consequence of biological variation and reproduction. But it is a culling, not a creative process, incapable of the type of change microbes-to-man evolution demands. See creation.com/muddy.

In short, there was every reason to expect that some groups would have distinct biological advantages that others did not. The latter had not progressed as far in the direction of humanness as others. Some were more human, and some less human, than others. No prizes for guessing that the 'most human' or 'most evolved' ones would be Darwin's own race. And Darwin very much understood and believed these sorts of things about races, as will be seen.

Leading Darwin historian Peter Bowler is Professor of the History of Science at Queen's University, Belfast.[24] He stated in a recorded interview that:

> "... by the time he [Darwin] writes *The Descent of Man* in 1871 it's pretty clear that he by that time shares the growing suspicion or conviction of many Europeans. The non-white races simply do not have the capacity to be elevated properly into civilised human beings, that they are mentally and morally at a more limited level. In a sense they are stuck at an early stage in the biological evolution of the human species."[25]

Referring to the natives he met at Tierra del Fuego, at the tip of South America, Darwin wrote:

> "I could not have believed how wide was the difference between savage and civilised man: it is greater than between a wild and domesticated animal, inasmuch as in man there is a greater power of improvement. ... These poor wretches were stunted in their growth, their hideous faces bedaubed with white paint, their skins filthy and greasy, their hair entangled, their voices discordant and their gestures violent. Viewing such men, one can hardly

---

24. In the UK and British Commonwealth countries like Australia, 'Professor' means head of department. By contrast, a junior lecturer in the UK would be a 'professor' if in the same sort of role in the US.

25. Speaking on CMI's 2009 year of Darwin documentary, *The Voyage that Shook the World*. Along with other Darwin experts on that documentary, Bowler attempted a disclaimer due to embarrassment at featuring in a 'creationist' film. The published transcripts (see creation.com/darwin-historians-not-misrepresented) confirm that all of them were accurately represented.

FEATURE

Black People and the 'Curse on Ham'

Many people in Christian societies, including South Africa and the US, have sought to justify 'black' people being inferior based on the idea that Ham, one of Noah's three sons, was cursed. It was also used to justify their enslavement, because the curse involved being a 'servant of servants'. Especially in the USA, the obvious contradiction of slavery with the idea that 'all people are created equal' needed to be rationalized. The 'curse' idea was virtually unknown in places like Brazil, where there was no need to justify slavery on the basis of 'race' (see Chapter 4), since they had no Declaration of Independence teaching equality of people. Even many today who do not consciously hold to ideas of inferiority/superiority still believe that black skin color arose from this 'curse on Ham'.

The biblical account this is based on indicates that Ham obviously transgressed against his father by the standards of the prevailing culture, leading to Noah's pronouncement of the curse (Genesis 9:22–27).

However, there are major problems with the idea that this has to do with dark skin.

The Bible says nothing about skin color in Ham* or his descendants. That idea comes from the alleged association of the names of certain descendants with particular nations, some much more tenuous than others.

In fact, the curse was not on Ham at all, but on Canaan, his son. Anyone looking for later fulfilment of Noah's pronouncement could perhaps find some indication of this in the destiny of the Canaanites, the descendants of Canaan. Even this may be stretching a point, though, since the Israelites never made reference to any such thing in relation to their conquest of the land of Canaan.

In any case, the Bible does not indicate that this curse had any divine imprimatur, without which it could hardly have been effective. Noah, despite his track record, seems to have let his guard down in

iStockPhoto

getting drunk, and so shortly after his stunning preservation in the Flood. Not everything recorded in the Bible is approved by it.

"The Bible does not indicate that this curse had any divine *imprimatur* ..."

I once had a discussion with a fellow passenger flying out of Cairns in Australia's tropical Far North. The well-groomed Aboriginal man was a community leader among his people, and a strong Bible-believer. When I asked him his views on the solution to the many social problems of his people (see p. 263 ff.), he said it was, ultimately, the gospel of Jesus Christ. I was surprised to find on talking further, though, that he had accepted the idea of the 'curse on Ham' as the explanation for his own and his people's skin color. Hearing that this had no biblical foundation seemed liberating for him. This is not surprising, as the 'curse' theory readily implies an inferior status for darker skin.

*Some have claimed the name 'Ham' means 'black', but this is not so; it means 'burnt' as in 'sunburnt'. And Ham's descendants included the Egyptians (descended from Ham's son Mizraim) who were neither black nor perpetual servants, but instead had a vast empire lasting centuries.

make oneself believe that they are fellow-creatures, and inhabitants of the same world. It is a common subject of conjecture what pleasure in life some of the lower animals can enjoy: how much more reasonably the same question may be asked of these barbarians! At night … [they] sleep on the wet ground coiled up like animals."[26]

Prof. Bowler was referring to Darwin's views on the Fuegians when he said, in the very next section of the transcript of the interview quoted a moment earlier (unedited, *sic*):

"So their way of life may offer us a so fossilised relic of what our own ancestors lived like in the distant prehistoric past. But now Darwin and many of his contemporaries are beginning to realise that what they

26.   Darwin, C., *The Voyage of the Beagle: Journal of Researches into the Natural History and Geology of the Countries Visited During the Voyage of HMS Beagle Round the World, Under the Command of Captain FitzRoy, RN,* (1845), Wordsworth Classics reprint, London, pp. 196, 203–204, 1997. See also creation.com/darwin-and-the-fuegians.

needed to claim that they are biologically relics of the past. They are in fact equivalent to earlier stages in the ascent from the apes who have been preserved in isolated locations, preserved with those earlier levels of mental and moral development."[27]

Biblical antiracism: not a convenient afterthought

It is not infrequently claimed that the antiracist stance of most modern creationism is a mere overlay to biblical Christianity, something conveniently 'tacked on' now that antiracism is fashionable, even 'politically correct'.

So far from being the case, however, the Bible is intrinsically antiracist. Especially so in view of its Genesis history of mankind—the *one human family* doctrine that forms the theme of this book. This has been made more than clear by the history of European racism already touched on, in particular the citations from Professor Fredrickson about this doctrine's restraining influence. No wonder, then, that when Darwinism provided a seeming excuse for the removal of this restraint, racism exploded.

The writings of German zoology professor Ernst Haeckel (1834–1919) serve to further highlight both the racist impulses of the evolutionism of the day and *the intrinsic antiracism of Genesis*. Haeckel, who is now known to have fraudulently doctored drawings of embryos to promote belief in evolution,[28] was Darwin's chief evangelist on the European continent. His influence was huge, particularly in his own country of Germany.

Haeckel's pro-evolution book *The History of Creation* (original German: *Natürliche Schöpfungsgeschichte*) is heavily racist, and would be an embarrassment to evolutionists today. He divided

---

27. This part of his filmed interview did not feature on the documentary itself, but is included in the DVD 'extras' menu. See creation.com/darwin-historians-not-misrepresented for the transcript in context. In the interests of total accuracy, especially in view of the allegations of misrepresentation, we chose not to edit the text, even where it is an obvious misspeak.

28. See Ojala, P.J. and Leisola, M., Haeckel: legacy of fraud to popularise evolution, *J. of Creation* **21**(3):102–110, 2007, creation.com/haeckel-fraud. Also search for 'Haeckel' on creation.com. Unfortunately, some of these doctored drawings still appear in textbooks aimed at convincing people of the truth of evolution.

humans into twelve different species, subdivided into 36 different races. Referring to an earlier classification of the human races than his own, he wrote:

> "All these five races of men, according to the Jewish legend of creation, are said to have descended from 'a single pair'—Adam and Eve, and in accordance with this are said to be varieties of one kind or species. ... The excellent paleontologist Quenstedt[29] is right in maintaining that, 'if Negroes and Caucasians were snails, zoologists would universally agree that they represented two very distinct species, which could never have originated from one pair by gradual divergence.'"[30]

Haeckel's attempted ridicule of the biblical account shows that the Bible is antiracism, and that this was noted well before that stance became fashionable.

That his views were driven by ideology more than science is shown in the very same work (pp. 433–434), where Haeckel confirms that there were anthropologists in strong disagreement with his stance on race:

> "... there can be no doubt that the innumerable races and varieties of our domestic dog differ in a much greater degree from one another than the different genera and species distinguished by the zoologist in his systematic arrangement of the Dog-tribe. And yet they are generally regarded only as varieties of one single species—*Canis familiaris*. In the same way most anthropologists dogmatically and firmly hold to the so-called 'unity of species' for all the races of Men, and unite them into one species, as *Homo sapiens*. However, the unprejudiced and critical enquirer, when carefully comparing them, cannot rid himself of the

29. Friedrich August von Quenstedt (1809–1889).
30. Haeckel, E. *The History of Creation, or the development of the Earth and its inhabitants by the action of natural causes*, vol II, English edition translated from the 8th German Edition by Prof. Ray Lankester, Fellow of Exeter College, Oxford, 1909, pp. 412–413. See also Niekerk, E. van, Ernst Haeckel: a hostile witness to the truth of the Bible, creation.com/haeckel2, 3 March 2011.

conviction that the morphological differences between them are much more important than those by which, for instance, the various species of bears, wolves, or cats are distinguished in the zoological system."

But then, that should not surprise us. Most of the German scientists of the time also rejected evolution. From an admiring biography of Haeckel comes the following:

Ernst Haeckel in 1860, aged 26.
Public domain

"Darwin's ominous book [Origin of Species] had been available in Bronn's translation for two years. The German professional zoologists, botanists and geologists almost all regarded it [Darwin's theory] as absolute nonsense. Agassiz, Geibel, Keferstein, and so many others, laughed until they were red in the face..."[31]

Despite this failure to impress scientists, Haeckel's books, aimed at lay audiences, became hugely popular. They were laced with all manner of visual and literary deceit in addition to his faked embryo diagrams; for example, drawings and detailed descriptions of a whole group of creatures (the so-called Monera) that never existed. Also, a depiction of a similarly non-existent 'speechless ape-man' (hence his name for it, *Pithecanthropus alalus*).[32] It is not unrealistic to suggest that through his books, he was almost single-handedly responsible, far and above any other individual factor, for turning Germany into an evolution-believing country.

The rise of Social Darwinism following the acceptance of evolutionary biology caused a resurgence of antisemitism, too. A book by two BBC journalists about the history of philosophy

31.   Bölsche, W. *Haeckel—his life and work*, 1906.Translated by Joseph McCabe (1867–1955) Philadelphia, George W. Jacobs & Co. Publishers, p. 138.
32.   Grigg, R, Ernst Haeckel: Evangelist for evolution and apostle of deceit, *Creation* **18**(2):33–36, 1996, creation.com/haeckel.

states:

> "[It] threatened the liberal, Enlightenment-grounded assumptions behind Jewish integration in Central Europe. When combined in Vienna with the ability of the Governing Mayor, Karl Lueger, and his Christian Social cronies to harness the really not very modern resentment by the 'little man' of Jewish success, this 'biological turn' in the form of 'scientific' anti-Semitism, effectively destroyed the emancipatory assumptions of Jews (and their allies)."[33]

Darwin was a Social Darwinist

The story of 'Social Darwinism' is complicated a little by the fact that the man who was predominant in pushing the philosophy of struggle for improvement onto human society was Herbert Spencer. He was the one who actually coined the term 'survival of the fittest'.[34] Spencer was, strictly speaking, a Lamarckian[35] evolutionist. That means that he believed that the struggle to survive caused improvements to arise, i.e. they were not from random variations. By way of aside, Darwin himself, in early editions of the *Origin,* embraced Lamarckianism—e.g. a giraffe's neck getting longer through repeated stretching to reach the higher leaves—as the source of at least some of the variation. But there is no doubt that Darwin himself, tenderhearted or not, was a thoroughgoing Social Darwinist. He wrote:

> "At some future point, not distant as measured by centuries, the civilised races of man will almost certainly exterminate and replace the savage races throughout the world. At the same time the anthropomorphous apes, as Professor Schaaffhausen has remarked, will no doubt be

---

33.   Edmonds, D., and Eidinow, J., *Wittgenstein's Poker: The Story of a Ten-Minute Argument Between Two Great Philosophers.* New York, NY: HarperCollins, 2001, p. 103.
34.   Darwin adopted the term in later editions of *The Origin.*
35.   Named after Jean-Baptiste Lamarck (1744–1829), whose pre-Darwinian theory of evolution held that characteristics acquired during the lifetime of the organism—by the action of the environment, or through use and disuse—could be inherited.

exterminated. The break will then be rendered wider, for it will intervene between man in a more civilised state, as we may hope, than the Caucasian, and some ape as low as a baboon, instead of as at present between the negro or Australian and the gorilla."[36]

He personally leaned towards the view that man represented a single species, and not several, as others were urging. For one thing it looked as though they could all interbreed, though he was not quite certain of this. But Darwin had no compunction in conceding as follows:

"From these several considerations, it may be justly urged that the perfect fertility of the intercrossed races of man, if established, would not absolutely preclude us from ranking them as distinct species."[37]

Translated into today-speak, he is saying that even if it could be established that all human races were inter-fertile[38] (as he suspected would turn out to be the case), it might still be possible to classify them as separate species. This gives some indication of the huge biological differences he felt existed between the various groups of people on Earth.

Roman Catholic ethicist Benjamin Wiker, commenting on Darwin's *Descent of Man* (with extensive citation from it), summarizes a major thrust of Darwin's viewpoint thus:

"The European race, following the inevitable laws of natural selection, will emerge as the distinct species, human being, and all the transitional forms—such as the gorilla, chimpanzee, Negro, Australian aborigine and so on—will be extinct."[39]

Darwin's chief public promoter, Thomas Huxley, the scientist who became known as 'Darwin's bulldog', wrote:

36. Darwin, C., *The Descent of Man, and Selection in Relation to Sex* (1st ed.), London: John Murray, 1871, pp. 200–201.
37. Ref. 36, p. 116.
38. It's now well established that all peoples everywhere are inter-fertile, of course.
39. Wiker, B., *Moral Darwinism: How We Became Hedonists*, InterVarsity Press, Illinois, USA, p. 250, 2002.

"No rational man, cognizant of the facts, believes that the average negro is the equal, still less the superior, of the white man."[40]

The consequences of such thinking were soon obvious. We have already seen Gould's comment about the turbo-boost that Darwin's book provided to racist thinking. For Gould to say that racism (the sort that argued for biological inferiority of the other group) increased by 'orders of magnitude' means that it was amplified a hundredfold, a thousandfold, or more.[41] This was a worldwide phenomenon, but was particularly starkly illustrated in Australia's colonial history. The country's Aboriginal people had already suffered considerably due to the sorts of pre-Darwin/anti-Genesis notions discussed earlier. But their treatment took a massive nosedive post-Darwin.

ABORIGINALS—BEARING THE BRUNT

An unusual book was published in 1974, called *Aborigines in White Australia: A Documentary History of the Attitudes Affecting Official Policy and the Australian Aborigine 1697–1973*.[42] Apart from a few introductory/editorial comments, it consists almost entirely of substantial excerpts from documents. These are parliamentary transcripts, court records, letters to editors, anthropological reports, and so forth.

Far from showing a progressive enlightenment in the attitudes of the colonists as time goes on, one can see a distinct change for the worse after 1859, with a marked increase in callousness, ill-treatment and brutality towards Aboriginal people being evident in official attitudes. This is not lost on the editor of the above book, who writes:

"In 1859 Charles Darwin's book *On the Origin of Species* popularized the notion of biological (and therefore social) evolution. Scholars began to discuss

40. Thomas H. Huxley, *Lay Sermons, Addresses and Reviews*, Appleton, New York, USA, p. 20, 1871.
41. One order of magnitude means 10 x; two is 100 x; three is 1,000 x; and so on.
42. Edited by Sharman Stone, Heinemann Educational Books, Melbourne, 1974.

civilization as a unilinear process with races able to ascend or descend a graduated scale. The European was … the 'fittest to survive' … [The Aboriginal] was doomed to die out according to a 'natural law', like the dodo and the dinosaur. This theory, supported by the facts at hand [i.e. that Aboriginal folk were dying out from ill-treatment and disease—CW] continued to be quoted until well into the twentieth century when it was noticed that the dark-skinned race was multiplying. Until that time it could be used to justify neglect and murder."

From the book's transcript of an interrogation of a policeman during a Royal Commission of Inquiry in 1861 (p. 83), we read concerning the use of force against tribal Aboriginals:

"'And if we did not punish the blacks they would look upon it as a confession of weakness?'

'Yes, that is exactly my opinion.'

'It is a question as to which is the strongest race—if we submit to them they would despise us for it?'

'Yes …'"

The influence of evolutionary thinking can also be seen in another excerpt from *Aborigines in White Australia*, on page 100. The writer quoted, also author of an 1888 book, is justifying the killing of the native population in the State of Victoria. He writes:

"As to the ethics of the question, there can be drawn no final conclusion."

He says that this is because it is

"a question of temperament; to the sentimental it is undoubtedly an iniquity; to the practical it represents a distinct step in human progress, involving the sacrifice of a few thousands of an inferior race. … But the fact is that mankind, as a race, cannot choose to act solely as moral beings. They are governed by animal laws which urge them blindly forward upon tracks they scarce can choose for themselves."

In other words, he is justifying 'iniquity' (another word for sin) by appealing to the 'animal laws' of the evolutionary struggle for survival. Opposition can be dismissed as 'sentimental' — lacking understanding of such 'natural laws'.

There were isolated voices of protest. On p. 93, we read of a letter writer to an Australian newspaper in 1880, who, incensed by the treatment of his fellow man, stated:

> "This, in plain language, is how we deal with the aborigines: On occupying new territory the aboriginal inhabitants are treated exactly in the same way as the wild beasts or birds the settlers may find there. Their lives and their property, the nets, canoes, and weapons which represent as much labor to them as the stock and buildings of the white settler, are held by the Europeans as being at their absolute disposal. Their goods are taken, their children forcibly stolen, their women carried away, entirely at the caprice of white men. The least show of resistance is answered by a rifle bullet ... [those] who fancied the amusement have murdered, ravished, and robbed the blacks without let or hindrance. Not only have they been unchecked, but the Government of the colony has been always at hand to save them from the consequences of their crime."

But such voices were readily drowned out by the fashionable science of the day. Three pages further on, we read of someone else, also writing in an 1880 newspaper, who said:

> "Nothing that we can do will alter the inscrutable and withal immutable laws which direct our progress on this globe. By these laws the native races of Australia were doomed on the advent of the white man, and the only thing left for us to do is to assist in carrying them out [i.e. helping the 'laws' of evolution by hastening the Aborigines' doom—CW] with as little cruelty as possible ... We must rule the blacks by fear ... ."

Australian secular historian Joanna Cruickshank acknowledges, if somewhat reluctantly, not only the baneful effects of the Darwin-inspired 'scientific racism' on Australian Aboriginals, but the way in which belief in our common descent from Adam and Eve operated to temper such thinking. In a recent article[43] on the topic, she writes:

> "Supporters of Darwin have understandably often been reluctant to acknowledge how closely entangled Darwinism and social Darwinism were, preferring to distance Darwin from his theory's evil twin.

> "Yet those who debated the theory of evolution in the late nineteenth century were keenly aware of this connection .... Nowhere was this more obvious than in Australia."

She writes how by 1876, the library of a typical squatter (pastoralist) consisted of books by Shakespeare, John Stuart Mill, and Darwin. The pattern, widespread today, of church leaders anxious to compromise with this new 'scientific' ideology, was already evident. She writes how in 1869, a Reverend Bromby gave a public lecture defending Darwin's book, in which he

> "followed Darwin's logic in using the apparent dying out of Aboriginal people as evidence for evolution.

> "In response, the Anglican Bishop of Melbourne, Charles Perry, attacked both Bromby's evidence and his conclusions. Perry critiqued what he saw as the scientific inadequacies of Darwin's book.

> "In particular, however, Perry attacked the view that human beings could be divided by race—or any other category—into 'savage' and 'civilised' ... ."

Cruickshank explains that Bromby represented the 'progressive' wing of the Church of England. Betraying her pro-evolution bias, she calls him "open to scientific evidence" and "dismissive of biblical literalism."

She continues:

> "Perry, by contrast, was a staunch evangelical,

---

43. Cruickshank, J., Darwin, race and religion in Australia, ABC Religion and Ethics, www.abc.net.au, 11 Apr 2011, accessed 13 April 2011.

uncomfortable with the theological implications of Darwin's theory and horrified at what he saw as a threat to the biblical claim that all humanity was formed of 'one blood.'"

Cruickshank goes on to say that when legislation was passed

"enshrining the 'White Australia' policy and effectively denying Aboriginal people the vote, few voices were raised in protest. Progressives and conservatives alike saw the preservation of the more evolved white race as central to national identity.

"Those few protests against the policy came from unlikely quarters. The fledgling New South Wales Aborigines Mission, a small evangelical organization, pointed out that while most politicians claimed 'to be ultra-democratic, they are sadly conservative in democratic practice, and unChristian both in theory and in practice when they say that a native born Australian is not a man and a brother because his skin happens to be a few shades darker than their own.'

Finally, and very significantly for our purposes here, this secular historian states:

"In earlier periods, one of the few persistent barriers to social Darwinist theory in Australia was the Christian doctrine that all human beings were of 'one blood.'"

A gruesome trade

The body parts of Australian Aboriginal folk were keenly sought after. Following Darwin and his contemporaries, they were regarded by scientists and other evolutionary enthusiasts as 'living missing links'. The remains of some 10,000 dead Aboriginal people in all were shipped to British museums over the course of this frenzy to provide specimens for this 'new science'.[44]

David Monaghan, an Australian journalist, extensively

---

44. Darwin's bodysnatchers, *Sydney Morning Herald*, March 3, 1990, cited in *Creation* **12**(3):21, 1990. The original apparently stated that only 3,000 sets of remains were left after the bombing raids of World War II.

documented these—and far worse—effects of evolutionary belief. He spent 18 months researching his subject in London, culminating in an article in Australia's *Bulletin* magazine[45] and a TV documentary called *Darwin's Body-Snatchers.* This aired in Britain on October 8, 1990.

Along with museum curators from around the world, Monaghan says, some of the top names in British science were involved in this large-scale grave-robbing trade. These included anatomist Sir Richard Owen, anthropologist Sir Arthur Keith, and Charles Darwin himself. Darwin wrote asking for Tasmanian skulls when only four full-blooded native Tasmanians were left alive. (Ever the Victorian gentleman, his request came with a caveat; provided, that is, that it would not upset their feelings.)

American evolutionists, too, were strongly involved in this flourishing 'industry' of gathering specimens of 'sub-humans', according to Monaghan. The Smithsonian Institution in Washington holds the remains of 15,000 individuals of various groups of people.

Museums were not only interested in bones, but in fresh skins as well. These would provide interesting evolutionary displays when stuffed. Pickled Aboriginal brains were also in demand, to try to demonstrate that they were inferior to those of whites.

Good prices were being offered for such specimens. Monaghan shows, on the basis of written evidence from the time, that there is little doubt that many of the 'fresh' specimens were obtained by simply going out and killing the Aboriginal people. The way in which the requests for specimens were announced was often a poorly disguised invitation to do just that. A death-bed memoir from Korah Wills, who became mayor of Bowen, Queensland, in 1866, graphically described how he killed and dismembered a local tribesman in 1865 to provide a scientific specimen.

Monaghan's research indicated that Edward Ramsay, curator of the Australian Museum in Sydney for 20 years from 1874, was particularly heavily involved. He published a museum

---

45.   Monaghan, D, The body-snatchers, *The Bulletin,* 12 November 1991, pp. 30–38.

booklet which appeared to include his, my and your Aboriginal relatives under the designation of 'Australian animals'. It also gave instructions not only on how to rob graves, but also on how to plug up bullet wounds in freshly killed 'specimens'.

Many freelance collectors worked under Ramsay's guidance. Four weeks after he had requested skulls of Bungee (Russell River) blacks, a keen young science student sent him two, announcing that they, the last of their tribe, had just been shot. In the 1880s, Monaghan writes, Ramsay complained that laws recently passed in Queensland to stop the slaughter of Aboriginals were affecting his supply.

The Angel of Black Death

According to Monaghan's *Bulletin* article, that was the nickname given to a German evolutionist, Amalie Dietrich (pictured below). She came to Australia asking station[46] owners for their Aboriginal workers to be shot for specimens. She was particularly interested in skin for stuffing and mounting for her museum employers. Although evicted from at least one property, she shortly returned home with her specimens.

Amalie Dietrich
Public domain

Monaghan also recounts how a New South Wales missionary was a horrified witness to the slaughter by mounted police of a group of dozens of Aboriginal men, women and children. Forty-five heads were then boiled down and the ten best skulls were packed off for overseas.

Still in recent times

As much as one would like to think that such attitudes are long gone, remnants still linger, including in the scientific community itself. This is shown by a telling

---

46.   'Station' (e.g. cattle station, sheep station) is the Australian designation for what would be termed 'ranch' in the US. Many Aboriginal people worked on stations, often as stockmen (the equivalent of 'cowboys' or 'cowhands').

FEATURE

Racism—New Sin, or Old Sins?

To listen to many today speak of racism, one could almost think a new category of sin has been invented. But it really involves nothing new. It's driven by the same age-old sin problem that afflicts all of humanity. And the biblical categories of sin already in existence are more than adequate to cater for the various manifestations of what is collectively termed 'racism'. These include:

- Pride: imagining oneself or one's group to be in some way specially elevated above another, in the absence of any statement from God to that effect. The words of Christ Himself bear repeating here (Luke 18:10–14):

    "Two men went up into the temple to pray, one a Pharisee and the other a tax collector. The Pharisee, standing by himself, prayed thus: 'God, I thank you that I am not like other men, extortioners, unjust, adulterers, or even like this tax collector. I fast twice a week; I give tithes of all that I get.' But the tax collector, standing far off, would not even lift up his eyes to heaven, but beat his breast, saying, 'God, be merciful to me, a sinner!' I tell you, this man went down to his house justified, rather than the other. For everyone who exalts himself will be humbled, but the one who humbles himself will be exalted."

- Covetousness: wanting to exploit another group for economic gain—a breach of one of the Ten Commandments.
- Hatred: 1 John 3:15 even calls this murder in one's heart.*
- Injustice: The Bible consistently stands opposed to unjust dealings of even the slightest measure. The just dealings it demands—equality of treatment and opportunity—are not to be directly equated to many of today's notions of so-called 'social justice'—coerced equality of outcomes. Despite their promotion by sectors of the church, the latter often owe more to Karl Marx than to the Bible. But Scripture radically condemns the hugely unequal treatment that was meted out under apartheid to black Africans in such areas as education and health, for instance.

Note how some of the above list applies even where the actions of the group imagining itself to be superior are of a 'kindly', or 'paternalistic' nature, not involving any conscious cruelty, for example.

"The Bible consistently stands opposed to unjust dealings"

These are all in addition to the rejection of the implications of the 'big picture' of the history of mankind in the Bible. This is antibiblical, whether that rejection by any individual is tied to evolution directly, indirectly, or not at all. In order to be actively racist, one must reject, circumvent, or ignore the biblical teaching that all humans are descended from Adam and Eve, with its overwhelming implication that all people are thus equally created in God's image.

The additional fact that we are *closely* related, because we descended even more recently from Noah's family, makes racism even more indefensible. The issue is whether there is a willingness to bow to the teaching of Scripture, not just to mine it like a quarry to reinforce whatever we want to believe for other reasons.

*Of course, people can be racist in practice, or support racist policies that are unjust, without having any hatred as such of another individual or even of any people group.

extract from a secular writer in 2004 (emphasis added):

"It has been estimated that the remains of some 50,000 Aborigines are housed in medical and scientific institutions abroad. The Tasmanian Aboriginal remains in particular are there for two reasons. First, at the time of collection they were considered to be the most primitive link in the evolutionary chain, and therefore worthy of scientific consideration. Second, each skull fetched between five and ten shillings. ... in anthropological terms, while the remains maintain currency as a museum item, the notion that they are a scientific curiosity remains. Put simply, if it is now accepted that Tasmanian Aborigines are not the weakest evolutionary link, that they are simply another group of people with attendant rights to dignity and respect, there is no longer any reason to keep their remains for study. Institutions should acknowledge that by returning the remains. There are two reasons why this is not as straightforward as it appears. First, the British Museum Act of 1962 did not allow British government institutions to deaccess stored material. Second, *a number of scientists haven't accepted that Tasmanian Aborigines are not on the bottom of Social Darwinist scales,* and until they do, feet are being dragged."[47]

Darwinist views about the racial inferiority of Aboriginal Australians drastically influenced their treatment in other ways too. These views were backed up by alleged biological evidences, which were only much later seen for what they were—distortions based on bias. In 1908 an inspector from the Department of Aborigines in the West Kimberley region wrote that he was glad to have received an order to transport all half-castes away from their tribe to the mission. He said it was "the duty of the State" to give these children (who, by their evolutionary reasoning, were going to be intellectually superior to full-blooded Aboriginal ones) a "chance to lead a better life than their mothers". He wrote: "I would not hesitate for one moment to separate a half-caste from an Aboriginal mother, no matter how frantic her momentary grief".[48] Notice the use of the word 'momentary' to qualify 'grief'; such lesser-evolved beings, sub-human as they were, were to him clearly not capable of feeling real grief.

Many genuine Australian Christians and church institutions, though patronizing on occasion, seem to have tried to protect Aboriginal people from the full brunt of the many inhumanities sanctioned by evolutionary thinking. However, like today, most church leaders and institutions compromised in some form or another with this new Darwinian 'science'. Virtually no Christian voice in Australia did what was required—to affirm boldly the real history of mankind as given in the Bible. For the church to have stressed regarding Aboriginal people that we all go back

---

47.   Onsman, A., Truganini's funeral, *Island*, No. 96, 2004, www.islandmag.com/96/article.html. Truganini was the last surviving female full-blood Tasmanian.
48.   Ref. 45, p. 38.

only a few thousand years, to Noah's family, would have helped strongly refute both pre-Darwinian racism and the maxi-spurt it received from Darwin. It would also have anticipated the findings of modern genetics, as we shall see, that biologically we are all extremely closely related.

EUGENICS ACROSS THE WORLD

The late Stephen Jay Gould's acknowledgment of the huge impact of Darwinian thinking on racism has been repeatedly emphasized, both here and in other Genesis-defending works. However, "Darwin remained one of Gould's personal heroes."[49] Gould elsewhere tries to get his hero 'off the hook' as much as possible on racism, eugenics and 'racial hygiene'. Such brave attempts by evolutionary enthusiasts are as common as they are futile, given Darwin's own stated viewpoints. Peter Quinn, though an anticreationist,[50] writes:

> "Darwin played a prime role in bringing about a fateful confusion between cultural and racial differences, conferring new scientific authority and intellectual legitimacy on theories of human inferiority central to eugenics, the most destructive medical movement in history."[51]

No doubt. Darwin wrote, for instance:

> "With savages, the weak in body or mind are soon eliminated; and those that survive commonly exhibit a vigorous state of health. We civilised men, on the other hand, do our utmost to check the process of elimination; we build asylums for the imbecile, the maimed, and the sick; we institute poor-laws; and our medical men exert

---

49.   See www.notablebiographies.com, accessed 15 October 2010.
50.   In this book, 'creationist' is used to mean 'biblical creationist', i.e. someone who takes Genesis as written, a historical account. This necessarily involves the global Flood, creation of all things in six earth-rotation days about 6,000 years ago, and no bloodshed/suffering before Adam's Fall ruined a once-perfect world, etc.
51.   Quinn, P., The gentle Darwinians: What Darwin's champions won't mention, *Commonweal Magazine*, www.commonweal.org, 9 March 2007.

their utmost skill to save the life of every one to the last moment. There is reason to believe that vaccination has preserved thousands, who from a weak constitution would formerly have succumbed to small-pox. Thus the weak members of civilised societies propagate their kind. No one who has attended to the breeding of domestic animals will doubt that this must be highly injurious to the race of man. It is surprising how soon a want of care, or care wrongly directed, leads to the degeneration of a domestic race; but excepting in the case of man himself, hardly any one is so ignorant as to allow his worst animals to breed.

"The aid which we feel impelled to give to the helpless is mainly an incidental result of the instinct of sympathy, which was originally acquired as part of the social instincts, but subsequently rendered, in the manner previously indicated, more tender and more widely diffused. Nor could we check our sympathy, if so urged by hard reason, without deterioration in the noblest part of our nature. The surgeon may harden himself whilst performing an operation, for he knows that he is acting for the good of his patient; but if we were intentionally to neglect the weak and helpless, it could only be for a contingent benefit, with a certain and great present evil. Hence we must bear without complaining the undoubtedly bad effects of the weak surviving and propagating their kind; but there appears to be at least one check in steady action, namely the weaker and inferior members of society not marrying so freely as the sound; and this check might be indefinitely increased, though this is more to be hoped for than expected, by the weak in body or mind refraining from marriage."[52]

Small wonder, then, to see what BBC journalist Dennis Sewell, a Catholic evolutionist concerned with the impact of Darwinist

---

52. Ref. 36, pp. 168–169. See creation.com/darwin-and-eugenics for more documentation.

thinking on politics and society, wrote of the eugenics movement. He said that in the years leading up to the First World War, eugenics:

> "looked like a Darwin family business. ... Darwin's son Leonard replaced his cousin [Francis] Galton as chairman of the national Eugenics Society in 1911. In the same year an offshoot of the society was formed in Cambridge. Among its leading members were three more of Charles Darwin's sons, Horace, Francis and George."[53]

These eugenicist ideas were enthusiastically taken up in the United States in particular. Edwin Black is an award-winning investigative journalist who exposed many well-kept secrets with his book *War Against the Weak: Eugenics and America's Campaign to Create a Master Race.*[54] It documented America's huge selective breeding and forced sterilization programs in the period leading up to World War II. In a brief review article of the book in *Creation* magazine, my CMI[55] colleague Dr. Jonathan Sarfati described how eugenics was enthusiastically supported by such notables as President Woodrow Wilson, the Rockefeller Foundation, Margaret Sanger (founder of Planned Parenthood— see shortly) and influential Justice Oliver Wendell Holmes. He further wrote:

> "It was bankrolled by some of the richest people in America, including the Carnegie Institution, Rockefeller Foundation and the Harriman railroad fortune. The major textbook, *Hunter's Civic Biology*, blatantly taught white racial supremacy and eugenics. This was the one that the ACLU (the misnamed American Civil Liberties Union), in the infamous Scopes Trial of 1925, defended the 'right' to teach! The shocking results of the eugenics program included laws against so-called mixed-race marriages in

---

53. Sewell, D., *The Political Gene: How Darwin's Ideas Changed Politics*, Picador, London, p. 54, 2009.
54. Four Walls Eight Windows, New York/London, 2003.
55. *Creation Ministries International.*

27 states, human breeding programs, forced sterilization of over 60,000 US citizens and even euthanasia."[56]

German sterilization law: born in the USA

Many of these forced sterilizations were carried out under legislation modeled and prepared by a leading U.S. evolutionary biologist, Dr. Harry Laughlin. I wrote on this in 1997, explaining how Laughlin's law called for compulsory sterilization of not only the 'feeble-minded', but also the blind, drug addicts, sufferers from TB and syphilis, epileptics, paupers, the deaf and the homeless. These people were, it was claimed, obviously the victims of 'bad genes'. The law was *overtly* aimed at maintaining the 'racial purity of the white race' by preventing the further 'breeding' of those whose offspring would 'drag down' this race. I wrote:

> "As soon as Hitler (who campaigned on a platform of naked evolutionism—the survival of the fittest race) came to power in 1933, eugenics laws became one of his first acts. Not only was the Nazi program of forced sterilization for the 'unfit' lauded in the US—it was actually modeled after the law framed by Laughlin, who was awarded an honorary doctorate by Hitler's government. As the Nazis moved on to the euthanasia-murder of entire wards full of mental patients, 'scientific' admiration for their 'racial hygiene' policies was unabated. One U.S. evolutionist actually stated, 'The Germans are beating us at our own game'."[57]

Planned parenthood and the 'Negro Project'

It's not often known that Margaret Sanger (1879–1966), founder of the modern (and heavily pro-abortion) birth control movement now known as Planned Parenthood, was an avid eugenicist. Eugenics was a constant, even dominant, theme at birth control

---

56.   Sarfati, J., America's evolutionists: Hitler's inspiration? *Creation* **27**(2):49 2005, creation.com/weak.
57.   Wieland, C., The Lies of Lynchburg: How US evolutionists taught the Nazis, *Creation* **19**(4):22–23 1997, creation.com/Lynchburg. The article was based on the documentary *The Lynchburg Story*, produced by Bruce Eadie, made by *Worldview Pictures* in association with *Discovery Networks* and *Channel Four*, 1993.

conferences and in her publications. She believed her work was in harmony with the 'universal law of evolution'. She often quoted Darwin as an authority when discussing 'natural checks' of the population, such as war, which helped to reduce it.

She was undoubtedly a white supremacist, though toning this down later in her life. Sanger even addressed a meeting of the Ku Klux Klan. She maintained that "the brains of Australian Aborigines were only one step more evolved than chimpanzees and just under blacks, Jews and Italians."[58]

Her early birth control clinics were strategically located so as to target "immigrant Southern Europeans, Slavs, Latins, and Jews". Later, she focused on the communities of other 'dysgenic races'—such as Hispanics and, predominantly, African Americans, through what became known as the 'Negro Project'.

Margaret Sanger
Public domain

> "Sanger, in alliance with eugenicists, and through initiatives such as the Negro Project ... exploited black stereotypes in order to reduce the fertility of African Americans."[59]

Many of her programs were done under various covers and strategies to prevent the target populations becoming alarmed by awareness of her plans, though some realized it anyway.

Planned Parenthood itself reported that of the 132,314 abortions it performed in 1991 in the US, 42.7% were on African Americans and other minorities, even though these only made up 19.7% of the US population. Given its history, these figures give pause for thought—especially when the locations of its

58. Bergman, J., Birth control leader Margaret Sanger: Darwinist, racist and eugenicist, *Journal of Creation* **22**(3):62–67, 2008, creation.com/sanger. This article carries detailed documentation and references, and is relevant to all comments made about Sanger in this book.
59. Washington, H.A., *Medical Apartheid: The Dark History of Medical Experimentation on Black Americans from Colonial Times to the Present*, Doubleday, New York, p. 196, 2006.

clinics still demonstrate a very considerable bias for minority neighborhoods.[60]

THE DARWIN–HITLER CONNECTION— HOW REAL?

Eugenics, racial hygiene and the full evils of racist thinking reached their apogee in Nazism. Here, too, there have been valiant (one might even say desperate) attempts to weaken the Darwin–Nazi link. But the evidence is so overwhelming that these attempts invite comparisons with the ludicrousness of trying to deny the Holocaust itself. The prominent British evolutionist Sir Arthur Keith wrote:

> "The German Führer, as I have consistently maintained, is an evolutionist; he has consciously sought to make the practice of Germany conform to the theory of evolution."[61]

Christian biologist and sociologist Jerry Bergman, holder of nine degrees at last count, including two doctorates, wrote in an excellent paper in CMI's *Journal of Creation* (fully referenced in the original, accessible online): [62]

> "In the 1933 Nuremberg party rally, Hitler proclaimed that '*higher race subjects to itself a lower race ... a right which we see in nature and which can be regarded as the sole conceivable right,*' because it was founded on science."

Bergman also pointed out that

> "As early as 1925, Hitler outlined his conclusion in Chapter 4 of *Mein Kampf* that Darwinism was the *only* basis for a successful Germany and which the title of his most famous work—in English *My Struggle*—alluded to. As

60. www.ewtn.com/library/prolife/ppracism.txt, accessed 20 July 2011.
61. Keith, A., *Evolution and Ethics,* Putnam, NY, USA, p. 230, 1947.
62. Bergman, J., Darwinism and the Nazi race holocaust, *Journal of Creation* 13(2):101–111, November 1999. Accessible at creation.com/holocaust (with all the references given for the citations therein).

Clark concluded, Adolf Hitler:

> '... was captivated by evolutionary teaching—
> probably since the time he was a boy. Evolutionary
> ideas—quite undisguised—lie at the basis of all that
> is worst in Mein Kampf—and in his public speeches
> ... . Hitler reasoned ... that a higher race would
> always conquer a lower.'

"And Hickman adds that it is no coincidence that Hitler:

> '... was a firm believer and preacher of evolution.
> Whatever the deeper, profound, complexities of his
> psychosis, it is certain that [the concept of struggle
> was important because] ... his book, Mein Kampf,
> clearly set forth a number of evolutionary ideas,
> particularly those emphasizing struggle, survival
> of the fittest and the extermination of the weak to
> produce a better society.'

"Furthermore, the belief that evolution can be directed
by scientists to produce a 'superior race' was the *central
leitmotif* of Nazism," and many other sources existed
from which Nazism drew:

> '... its ideological fire-water. ... that concatenation of
> ideas and nightmares which made up the ... social
> policies of the Nazi state, and to a considerable
> extent its military and diplomatic policies as well,
> can be most clearly comprehended in the light of its
> vast racial program.'

"The Nazi view on Darwinian evolution and race was
consequently a major part of the fatal combination of
ideas and events which produced the holocaust and
World War II:

> 'One of the central planks in Nazi theory and doctrine
> was ... evolutionary theory [and] ... that all biology
> had evolved ... upward, and that ... less evolved
> types ... should be actively eradicated [and] ...
> that natural selection could and should be actively

aided, and therefore [the Nazis] instituted political measures to eradicate ... Jews, and ... blacks, whom they considered as "underdeveloped".'

"Terms such as 'superior race', 'lower human types', 'pollution of the race', and the word *evolution* itself (*Entwicklung*) were often used by Hitler and other Nazi leaders. His race views were not from fringe science as often claimed but rather Hitler's views were:

> '... *straightforward German social Darwinism of a type widely known and accepted throughout Germany and which, more importantly, was considered by most Germans, scientists included, to be scientifically true. More recent scholarship on national socialism and Hitler has begun to realize that ... [their application of Darwin's theory] was the specific characteristic of Nazism. National socialist "biopolicy," ... [was] a policy based on a mystical-biological belief in radical inequality, a monistic, antitranscendent moral nihilism based on the eternal struggle for existence and the survival of the fittest as the law of nature, and the consequent use of state power for a public policy of natural selection ... .'"*

Further support for the pre-Hitler prevalence of Darwinism and the near absence of biblical Christianity comes from a hostile witness: leading Darwinist, Ernst Mayr, (1904–2005):

> "Curiously, I cannot pinpoint the age at which I became an evolutionist. I received all of my education in Germany, where evolution was not really controversial. In the gymnasium (equivalent to a U.S. high school), my biology teacher took evolution for granted. So, I am quite certain, did my parents—who, to interest their three teenage sons, subscribed to a popular natural history journal that accepted evolution as a fact. Indeed, in Germany at that time there was no Protestant

fundamentalism. And after I had entered university, no one raised any questions about evolution, either in my medical curriculum or in my preparations for the Ph.D. Those who were unable to adopt creation as a plausible solution for biological diversity concluded that evolution was the only rational explanation for the living world."[63]

Growing up under the Nazis

My late mother, a gentle soul, was brought up in Germany in the Nazi era. She recalled to me her viewings of the various propaganda films on 'race hygiene'.

These were designed to convince people that it was only 'natural' and right to wipe out the severely mentally and physically handicapped, by talking about nature's elimination of the unfit. She stated how powerfully persuasive their 'scientific' arguments seemed at the time. They achieved their intended purpose—along with the bulk of the German populace, she felt little disquiet when wards full of medically and psychiatrically 'defective' people quietly disappeared while wartime drama was being played out on the world stage. It just didn't seem so important … . Later, of course, she was horrified in retrospect.

She also told me about seeing people marching on the streets, holding banners proclaiming, "We're sorry we have sinned against natural selection" (by allowing members of 'unfit' groups to survive and thrive in German

Adolf Hitler: His utterances repeatedly show him to have been a "firm believer and preacher of evolution." See text p. 67.
Public domain

---

63.   Mayr, E., 80 years of watching the evolutionary scenery, *Science* **305**:46–47, 2004.

A page from the 'evolution' section of Hunter's Civic Biology, the biology textbook used in schools at the time of the notorious 1925 Scopes trial about teaching evolution. The racist overtones in the highlighted section are obvious.

Public domain

society). Of course, the definition of the 'unfit' became flexible enough to include Jews, gypsies, homosexuals and more. One of the aforementioned Nazi propaganda films, *Opfer der Vergangenheit* (Victims of the Past), 1937, showed a disfigured handicapped person and declared:

"All weak living things will inevitably perish in nature. In the last few decades, mankind has sinned frightfully against the law of natural selection. We haven't just maintained life unworthy of life, we have even allowed it to multiply! The descendants of these sick people look … like this person here!"[64]

The portion of this film from which the above transcript comes is viewable, with English subtitles, within the article 'The Darwinian roots of the Nazi tree', at creation.com/weikart. The article is a review of a book by Richard Weikart, *From Darwin to Hitler*. Weikart (who is identified with the Intelligent Design Movement) is Professor of Modern European History at the University of California, Stanislaus. If any further documentation

64.   This clip is available within CMI's DVD *Evolution and the Holocaust* (2009).

were necessary to convince people of the direct Darwin–Nazi link, Weikart's book is definitive. To people like my mother, with firsthand experience, denial of such things was, and is, simply laughable.

∞

2 MODERN SCIENCE AND RACE

SCIENCE'S SEISMIC SHIFT

Today, molecular biology and genetics reveal that we are, indeed, all extremely closely related. Many scientists have actually gone on record as saying that, biologically, humanity consists of only one race. For example, one scientist stated, at the Advancement of Science Convention in Atlanta, Georgia, in 1997:

> "Race is a social construct derived mainly from perceptions conditioned by events of recorded history, and it has no basic biological reality."[1]

Researchers likewise argued, in an article in the *Journal of Counseling and Development* in 1998, that the term 'race' meant so little that it should be discarded.[2]

Avoiding political correctness

One has to be careful, of course, in such a complex and

---

1.   Hotz, R.L., Race has no basis in biology, researchers say, *Los Angeles Times* article reprinted in the *Cincinnati Enquirer*, p. A3, 20 February 1997.
2.   Cameron, S.C. and Wycoff, S.M., The destructive nature of the term race: growing beyond a false paradigm, *Journal of Counseling & Development* **76**:277–285, 1998.

emotionally charged subject, of the vagueness and vagaries of definitions. As welcome as any abandonment of racist attitudes is, one should also beware of being swept along in some knee-jerk quasi-politically-correct response to the excesses of the past. Terminology is important, since words have power. But sometimes using a different word is not the real issue, and can even deflect attention from it. The real issue is the underlying attitudes we bring to the table. (See feature 'Racial Slurs and Political Correctness in the Days of Empire' p. 244.)

What is important to note, and remarkable, is simply that scientists have said these sorts of things. Such statements, even if they were to turn out to be overstated (and they do require some clarification, both here and in Chapter 6, in the light of additional knowledge), were only possible because we *are* indeed so very closely related genetically.

In what follows, there is going to be a greater risk of oversimplification than in probably any other part of the book. This is because the more we find out about DNA and genetics, the more complex the whole subject becomes. Much depends on the nature of the data used for comparisons, as always. However, the 'big picture' of our overall genetic closeness, with the caveat in the preceding paragraph, is very clear. That part is not going to change in any significant way.

RACE AND DNA

Distinguished evolutionist Richard Lewontin, the Alexander Agassiz Professor Emeritus of Zoology at Harvard University, had this to say in 2006, on a web forum on race organized by the Social Science Research Council:

> "Over the last thirty five years a major change has taken place in our biological understanding of the concept of human 'race', largely as a consequence of an immense increase in our knowledge of human genetics. As a biological rather than a social construct, 'race' has ceased to be seen as a fundamental reality characterizing

the human species."[3]

There is a large amount of variation between any two people on the planet chosen at random—but it still involves only about 0.2% of the whole of our DNA. In other words, on average we are all 99.8% the same. Lewontin points out that of all the variation there is, by far the largest amount of this variation, some 85%, occurs *within* a particular local or ethnic group; what he calls "local national or linguistic populations, [e.g.] within the French, within the Kikuyu, within the Japanese".

Some 5% to 9% of the variation occurs *between* local populations *within* the classically defined human 'races'. For example, between Japanese and Koreans, or between French and Ukrainians. Or between Chinese who speak Hokkienese and other Chinese who speak Cantonese. The remaining "6% to 10% of the total human variation is between classically defined geographical races that we think of in an everyday sense as identified by skin color, hair form, and nose shape."

Thus, just 8% of 0.2%, or 0.016% of our DNA, generously estimated, causes what we think of as 'racial' differences. Others have put forward estimates of even less—commonly only 0.012%. Either figure is clearly trivial.

Lewontin's essay is worth reading for a discussion of further practical reasons as to why he claims that 'race' simply does not work as a predictor of anything useful in biology.[4] He also points out that the genetic differences between groups are in any case:

"in the process of breaking down because of the very large amount of migration and intergroup mating that was always true episodically in the history of the human species but is now more widespread than ever. The result is that individuals identified by themselves or others as

3.   Lewontin, R,, Confusions about human race, raceandgenomics.ssrc.org/Lewontin, 7 June 2006, accessed 3 October 2010.
4.   Things are further complicated by the fact that some genes do not sort independently of each other. Also, if one uses so-called 'microsatellites' in the non-coding DNA, one comes up with a different picture. But the overall message is little changed.

belonging to one 'race', based on the small number of visible characters used in classical race definitions, are likely to have ancestry that is a mixture of these groups, a fact that has considerable significance for the medical uses of race identification."[3]

When Lewontin first put this concept forward in the 1970s, he was criticized for just using comparisons of single genes. If one uses clusters of genes, it was pointed out, one can reliably sort people into the characteristic groups that we recognize as races. However, that is not surprising; Chapter 6 ("People groups—genes still matter") states the obvious fact that even though we are all related, we will be more closely related to some than to others. 'Race' as such is not a totally artificial concept (which is why I don't always put it in scare quotes). The problem today is the evolutionary connotations that have become built into the word, i.e., how we think about it.

But in any case, Lewontin's analysis is not invalidated by that comment about multiple-gene categorization. In 2007 seven researchers from various US universities published a paper in the journal *Genetics,* titled "Genetic Similarities Within and Between Human Populations". In it the authors concluded, regarding such criticisms:

> "The fact that, given enough genetic data, individuals can be correctly assigned to their populations of origin is compatible with the observation that most human genetic variation is found within populations, not between them. It is also compatible with our finding that, even when the most distinct populations are considered and hundreds of loci are used, individuals are frequently more similar to members of other populations than to members of their own population."[5]

In short, when it comes to genes that code for protein, there is more genetic variation *within* any particular group of people (for

---

5.　Witherspoon, D.J., *et al.,* Genetic similarities within and between human populations, *Genetics* **176**:351–359, 2007, doi:10.1534/genetics.106.067355.

example, from one Khoisan to another, or one Nordic-looking inhabitant of Sweden to another), than there is between the average Khoisan and the average Swede. So, rather than separate, or almost separate, groupings, one can view humanity as like a set of closely overlapping circles, genetically speaking.

Screening for disease

Lewontin argues that even for the purpose of medical and genetic screening (for inherited disease) the classical categories of 'race' have turned out to be not really much help. It would make much more sense to have people identify themselves on questionnaires by their ancestry rather than 'race'. Identification as 'Hispanic', for instance, is almost meaningless compared to where one's ancestors came from—say, Cuba (which had high percentages of West Africans, and thus a much higher frequency of the sickle cell gene), as opposed to Mexico (where there was major intermingling with Native American groups). In screening for the likelihood of genetic disease, it would be better to ask, for instance, whether one had any ancestors who were Ashkenazi Jewish (Tay-Sachs disease), or West African (sickle cell anemia), and so on.

'Junk' DNA—a caution

The above discussion refers to genes, i.e. stretches of DNA which code for the manufacture of individual proteins. However, some 98% of the DNA in the nuclei of our cells does not in fact consist of genes. This non-coding DNA was for a long time written off as being a useless leftover of evolution, and generally called 'junk DNA'. In fact, the 'junkiness' was needed to solve an evolutionary problem called 'Haldane's Dilemma': there would not be enough time to substitute so many different genes if they were functional; *ergo*, most of the genome was junk.

Over the last few years, however, substantial evidence has accumulated to indicate that this DNA is an important part of our cellular machinery, and the clues as to what it does keep coming. As long ago as 2003, one of the world's leading figures in genetics, John Mattick, Foundation Professor of Molecular

Biology and Director of the Centre for Molecular Biology and Biotechnology at the University of Queensland (Australia), was already predicting that

> "the failure to recognise the implications of the non-coding DNA will go down as the biggest mistake in the history of molecular biology".[6]

(It hardly needs stressing that this is a classic example of where the assumption of evolution, rather than God's intelligent design, inhibited the progress of science.)

It's become increasingly clear, for instance, that a lot of this former 'junk' plays a critical role in determining whether or not genes are active and how much of a particular protein gets produced. So, two people can have near-identical genes, but considerable differences in how these are expressed. Science has only scratched the surface of this fascinating area.

Incidentally, the complexity of how all of that programmed machinery makes us who we are is so stunning that, shortly before his death, the world's leading atheist philosopher at the time, Sir Anthony Flew, changed his mind.[7] He conceded that a designing intelligence had to be involved in the origin of such molecular marvels of nanotechnology as are being revealed today—especially since natural selection is of no help. It can't even operate until an organism exists that already has the machinery needed to make a copy of itself.

The discovery that non-coding DNA can reflect crucial differences that are not apparent in genes has obvious relevance to our subject. Because of the considerable evidence for our close relatedness already apparent in several fields, in addition to genetics, it is not conceivable that future elucidation of group differences in non-coding DNA will materially alter this. But in a debate on this subject, someone who relied on a simplistic mantra such as 'DNA shows virtually no difference between

---

6.   Genius of junk (DNA), *Catalyst*, 10 July 2003, www.abc.net.au/catalyst/stories/s898887.htm.
7.   Cosner, L., Former leading atheist argues for the existence of God, *Journal of Creation* **22**(3):21–24 2008, creation.com/flew.

races' could come unstuck. This is because in a crude numerical sense, non-coding DNA 'outnumbers' the coding part some 50 to 1. So any group differences that emerge in non-coding DNA could easily be spun to show that they are 'far greater' than the minimal differences in coding DNA.

Tissue matches for organ donors

Not many years before the Lewontin essay, an article in *Discover* magazine commented on this phenomenon of our genetic relatedness as follows:

> "This genetic unity [of all people on the planet] means, for instance, that white Americans, though ostensibly far removed from black Americans in phenotype [outward manifestation of one's genetic code], can sometimes be better tissue matches [for organ transplants] for them than are other black Americans."[8]

This is of course a practical issue, one that often involves life or death matters. It cuts through any debate about which genes to use in the analysis, or whether coding or non-coding DNA is more relevant. Those who are, like me, speakers with *Creation Ministries International* often highlight the case of two Australians (pictured below), from very different ethnic groups, who featured

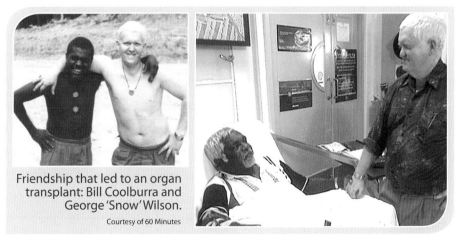

Friendship that led to an organ transplant: Bill Coolburra and George 'Snow' Wilson.
Courtesy of 60 Minutes

8.   Gutin, J., End of the Rainbow, *Discover*, November 1994, pp. 71–75.

in a 2002 article in CMI's *Creation* magazine.[9] Bill Coolburra and George 'Snow' Wilson are of Aboriginal and European extraction, respectively. They were 'best mates' (as Aussies refer to enduring friendships) since their service together in the Vietnam War. Bill was dying of kidney failure and needed a transplant. After six months in a fruitless wait for a good match, he accepted the offer of one of Snow's kidneys. It turned out to be a very good match, and Bill did very well after the operation.

The audience reaction we get from this tends to be surprise, sometimes even mild disbelief. This only goes to show that the false idea of radical biological differences between 'races' is still deeply ingrained today.

Note that even in modern theories of evolution, Bill and Snow are not supposed to have shared the same common ancestor for a very long time—tens of thousands of years, a huge number of generations if it were true. And they are supposed to have been evolving separately for most of the time since then. Even Lewontin says in his essay, referring to one particular form of genetic mapping, that the Australian Aboriginals are a "unique group". Yet once again, the biblical model directly fits the facts of the real world—and in a most practical sense (ask Bill Coolburra if he disagrees).

QUESTIONS OF COLOR

But what about those seemingly major differences in, for example, skin color? How could we all be that closely related with such different colors in the skin? And what about eyes? Some think, for example, that there must be a separately evolved chemical responsible for the color of blue eyes.

Actually, there is basically one main chemical responsible for the color of your skin. It's a browny-black pigment called *melanin*, which acts as a sunscreen. We all have the genetic information for producing a given *potential* amount of melanin

---

9. Wieland, C., Blood brothers, *Creation* **24**(3):54–55, 2002, creation.com/blood-brothers.

within our skin, in special cells called *melanocytes*.[10] In response to sunlight ('tanning') the amount will increase until that set potential is reached. If you have the information that specifies that a lot of melanin can be produced in your skin, people will call you 'black', but so-called 'black' people are really *brown*. Maybe dark brown, but if you hold a piece of black paper against your skin, the contrast will be clearly evident.

People call me 'white', but when talking on this to an audience, if wearing a white shirt I will generally point out that "my shirt is white, but I'm not white—can you tell the difference?" (See photo below.) It's so obvious, it's almost trite—but people can instantly see the difference. And it evokes a lot of smiles and soft chuckles—which indicates that for many, it's something that has not 'clicked' before. I'm actually very light *brown*, in fact, like other people of northern European extraction who are called 'white'. My genetic (DNA) information specifies a relatively low amount of melanin that can potentially be produced in my skin, no matter how much time I might spend cultivating a tan.

Like other whites my skin color is tinged with a bit of a pinkish hue. (Notice I didn't put whites in scare quotes that time, now that I've made the point—whites and blacks are well understood terms that convey something tangible in many contexts, e.g. a discussion of American society. In the US, such terms are freely used by both blacks and whites of each other and of themselves, mostly without offence.) The reason I'm pinkish is because I don't have enough of that sunscreen pigment, melanin, in my skin to stop the redness of the blood in all those microscopic blood vessels from showing through. So in a very real sense, though one talks of white, yellow, brown,

The author's 'white' skin cf. white shirt.
Emily Moes

---

10. Normally, that is. The genetic information for producing melanin can be damaged by mutation, giving rise to one of the several types of albinism. There are some albinos who can't produce any melanin at all.

FEATURE

Butterflies and Blue Eyes

iStockPhoto

The Ulysses butterfly, *Papilio ulysses*, from the rainforests of tropical far north Queensland, Australia, is renowned for the brilliant electric blue iridescent color of the upper surface of its wings. But, like the color of blue eyes, this color is an optical effect, although a different one. It's caused by very strong constructive inter-ference at blue wave-lengths, because the wing is a diffraction grating with the right spacing. Its 'true color' can be seen by looking almost level along the wings. That color is brown-black, because the pigment is melanin. It's the same pigment as in blue eyes, which, like this butterfly, also have no blue pigment in them. Brown eyes have more of this melanin. Also, the very deep black of the rims of the wings is another optical effect: the scales are shaped to trap light much more than any pigment could absorb.

red and black skin, the many different 'skin colors' are all just different shades of the same color.[11]

What about your hair color? Well, it's that same pigment, melanin. If you have the information that specifies that your body will produce a lot of melanin in your hair,[12] you will have brown or black hair. If you have only a little bit of melanin produced there—that means you have blond hair. (For red hair, see feature

---

11. Other factors can make a minor contribution—for example, variations in the amounts of the proteins elastin and carotene in the skin. Plus things like the thickness of the clear outer layer, and the depth and density of capillary networks. But all of us share all these factors—so here, too, it's just variations on the same theme.

12. The melanin is produced in the hair follicle, and deposited in the outer part (cortex) of the hair shafts.

page 92.)

Ah, but the eyes … ? Once again, it's just that same stuff, melanin. Put over-simply, if you have the information to pump out a lot of melanin in the iris of your eye, you will have dark brown eyes. The color is caused by melanin in the iris absorbing most of the light. If you have the information for just a little bit of melanin, you will have blue eyes. There is no 'blue paint' in blue eyes, just that same stuff—melanin. The blue color is an optical effect caused by having less melanin, in smaller granules causing scattering of the light.[13,14] This is the same sort of light-scattering effect that makes the sky blue, not any blue pigment.

It's a bit more complicated than this, and the old idea that there was only a simple recessive gene for blue color has been superseded.[15] But this is still a good working model for understanding the basics.

The twins that tell it all

It's things like the color of our hair, skin and eyes that have so much to do with 'racial' perceptions. The bottom line seems to be that when it comes to these matters of 'color', we're pretty much all different combinations of the same stuff. A graphic way of demonstrating this is the picture of the 'two-tone twins' on page 85 overleaf. These beautiful baby girls would definitely each be regarded as of a separate 'race'. Yet Remee (on the left) and Kian are *twins*.[16] They have the same parents, and shared the same womb. They were born in Nottingham, UK, in April 2005.[17]

One can tell from this, incidentally, that their parents must

---

13. Eye color is also affected by the way the pigment is distributed in the iris.
14. Light scattering is highly dependent on frequency (proportional to the fourth power), so blue light is scattered more strongly.
15. Eye color is actually determined by multiple genes. Some of the eye-color genes identified include *EYCL1* (for bluey-green color, on chromosome 19), *EYCL2* (brown) and *EYCL3* (blue/brown, on chromosome 15). Eye-color genetics is very complex, and almost no eye-color combination can be precluded from given colors in the parents.
16. Obviously not identical twins, but fraternal twins, coming from two separate fertilized eggs.
17. Laing, L., Twins in a million, *The Sunday Mail*, Brisbane, 12 March 2006, p. 3.

have had a very varied ancestry, i.e. they themselves must be a mixture of several different genetic strains. And it turns out that this is indeed the case. The twins' mother and father each had a parent of a different 'race'.[18]

Melanin is not there just as a coloring compound. It protects the skin from the harmful effects of ultraviolet (UV) light in the sun's rays. UV light not only causes sunburn and skin cancer, it has been shown to destroy folate (or folic acid), an important B group vitamin that also has a protective effect against the serious birth defect, spina bifida. So melanin protects folate. Melanin has also been shown to have a protective effect against tropical ulcers. This is not surprising, since melanin in insects is known to have an antiseptic effect. It may well be, as suggested by Australian biologist John Mackintosh[19] that this explains why there is extra melanin (causing darker skin) in areas that receive little sun exposure, such as the throat and nasal passages, and around the anus and genitals. All these are areas that have a high risk of attack by pathogenic (disease-causing) bacteria and fungi. Thus the darker skin of Africans is not only good for protecting against skin damage from the sun, but also against various skin diseases that are much more prevalent in hot, humid, tropical climes. Until fairly recently, Europeans could not venture too deeply into the continent because they were prone to catch diseases. This is why, as is stated in Chapter 4, they paid Africans to capture fellow Africans as slaves for them.

It's reasonable to ask: how could the patterns and varieties of color differences that we see in the world's people have arisen within the historical time-frame in Genesis? Over the years, I have many times had people tell me that they thought that each of Noah's sons must have had a different 'color' of skin. But not only is there no indication of that in the Bible, it would still leave unanswered the question of where that variety came from in the first place.

---

18. ABC News, One twin's white, the other's black—twins' parents both have white mothers, black fathers, abcnews.go.com, 19 Sept 2006, accessed 5 October 2010.
19. See for example cogweb.ucla.edu/ep/melanin.html.

In fact, it's not hard to show how a full range of skin colors (really, a full range of shades of brown) can potentially arise in *one* generation—and from only *one* set of parents, if they were able to have a large enough number of children. As the two-tone twins example suggests, the parents have to have the appropriate combination of genes. The following shaded section (overleaf) is a little technical, but if you've played with some simple genetics ideas in high school, it will be helpful to you. It is largely extracted from CMI's *The Creation Answers Book*.[20] The important point, as the heading shows, is that you can get all 'colors' in one generation.

RACE AND CREATION

All of this matches extremely well with an event the Bible describes as having happened not long after the Flood—the Tower of Babel incident. In Genesis Chapter 11, we read of the sudden (supernatural) creation of a number of different language groups (we'll see

Twins Remee and Kian (born April 2005) and their parents.
Barcroft Pacific

20.   Batten, D., (Ed.) Catchpoole, D., Sarfati, J., and Wieland, C., *The Creation Answers Book*, Creation Book Publishers, Powder Springs, GA, USA, 2009.

SEMI-TECHNICAL

All Colors in a Generation

Skin color is governed by more than one pair of genes. For simplicity, let's assume there are only two,[1] located at positions A and B on the chromosomes. One form of the gene, 'M', 'says' make lots of melanin; another form[2] of the gene, 'm', says only make a little melanin.

At position A we could have a pair such as M_AM_A, M_Am_A or m_Am_A, which would instruct the skin cells to make a lot, some, or little melanin. Similarly, at position B we could have the gene pairs M_BM_B, M_Bm_B or m_Bm_B instructing cells to make a lot, some or little melanin. Thus, very dark people could have $M_AM_AM_BM_B$ (see Figure 1). Since both the sperm and eggs of such people could only be M_AM_B (only one from each A or B pair goes to each sperm or egg), they could only produce children with the same combination of genes as themselves. So the children will all be very dark. Likewise, very light people, with $m_Am_Am_Bm_B$, could only produce children like themselves (see Figure 2). What combinations would result from brown-skinned parents with $M_Am_AM_Bm_B$ (the offspring of an $M_AM_AM_BM_B$ and $m_Am_Am_Bm_B$ union, for example; see Figure 3)? We can do this with a diagram called a Punnett square (see Figure 4). The left side shows the four different gene combinations possible in the sperm from the father, and the top gives the combinations possible in the eggs from the mother (remember that a parent can only pass on one of each pair of genes to each sperm or egg). We locate a particular sperm gene combination and follow the row across to the column below a particular egg gene combination (like finding a location

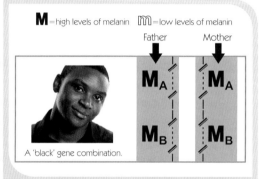

M = high levels of melanin   𝔪 = low levels of melanin

Father   Mother

M_A M_A

M_B M_B

A 'black' gene combination.

Figure 1. A 'black' gene combination.
iStockPhoto

---

1. This simplification is not done to help our case—the more genes there are, the easier it is to have a huge range of 'different' colors. The principle involved can be understood by using two as an example.
2. Variant forms of a gene are called 'alleles'.

on a street map). The intersection gives the genetic makeup of the offspring from that particular sperm and egg union. For example, an $M_A m_B$ sperm and an $m_A M_B$ egg would produce a child with $M_A m_A M_B m_B$, the same as the parents. The other possibilities mean that five levels of melanin (shades of color) can result in the offspring of such a marriage, as roughly indicated by the level of shading in the diagram. If three gene pairs were involved, seven levels of melanin would be possible. Thus a range of ' colors', from very light to very dark, can result in only one generation, beginning with this particular type of mid-brown parents.

Still referring to the diagrams here, we can explain how we can have not just variety occurring rapidly, but also how we can have groups with 'stable' colors. For example, when a typical West African marries another West African, all their children have the same coloration as their parents. And the same for light-skinned northern Europeans. Here is how: if people with $M_A M_A M_B M_B$, who are 'pure' black (in the sense of having no genes for lightness at all), were to migrate to a place where their offspring could not marry people of lighter color, all their descendants would be black—a pure 'black line' would result. If 'white' people ($m_A m_A m_B m_B$) were to migrate to a place where their offspring could not marry darker people, a 'pure' (in the same sense) 'white line' would result—they would have lost the genes needed to produce a large amount of melanin and so could not produce 'black' children. It is thus easily possible, beginning with two middle-brown parents, to get not only all the 'colors', but also people groups with stable shades of skin color. Today, we see a considerable number of different groups that each have this sort of 'stable' skin tone.

But what about the people groups like we have today that are permanently of a middle brown shade? Again, this

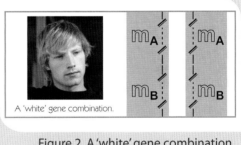

A 'white' gene combination.

Figure 2. A 'white' gene combination.
iStockPhoto

A 'brown' gene combination.

Figure 3. A 'brown' gene combination.
iStockPhoto

SEMI-TECHNICAL continued...

is easily explained. If those with genes $M_A M_A m_B m_B$ or $m_A m_A M_B M_B$ no longer intermarry with others, they will be able to produce only mid-brown offspring. (You can work this out with your own Punnett square.) If either of these lines were to interbreed again

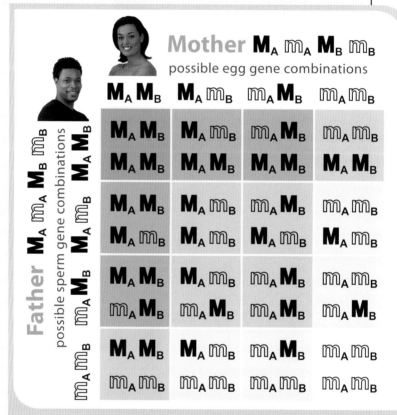

Figure 4. Punnett square showing the possible offspring from brown parents with MAmAMBmB genes.

with the other, the process would be reversed. In a short time their descendants would show a whole range of colors, often in the same family—just like our two-tone twins.

If all people were to intermarry freely, and then break into random groups that kept to themselves, a whole new set of gene combinations could emerge. It may be possible to have almond eyes with black skin, blue eyes with black frizzy short hair, etc.

> Even today, within a particular people group, you will often see a feature normally associated with another people group. For instance, you might see a European with a broad flat nose, and so on.
>
> We need to remember, of course, that the way in which genes express themselves is much more complex than this simplified picture. For example, sometimes certain genes are linked together.

later how these relate to the language families of today). Because people within a particular extended family group could no longer understand those from other groups, the resultant confusion and likely alienation had the effect of dispersing people from a central location. (On a face-value reading of Genesis, the breakup was along extended family lines, which makes sense, so that closely related people could understand each other.[21])

The population of the world at that time would have been modest, but significant, since there had been around 200 years since the Flood.[22] Till then, people had been able to freely intermarry, as they were all in the same geographic area. That group was broken up into a number of smaller groups, who could only marry within their group from then on, due to this migration/dispersion. God brought this about to enforce His command to the early post-Flood population to spread out over the face of the earth. There is no indication that it had anything to do with creating 'races', but that would have been a side effect. This is because each dispersed group would have carried a different

---

21. This would probably have included those related by marriage, because it is unlikely that God would have wanted husbands and wives to no longer be able to understand each other, or their children.

22. Deduced from the likely time when Peleg lived, as it was in his days that the earth (*eretz*) was divided, i.e. the Babel division. *Eretz* can mean 1) The physical 'earth' 2) Land or nation, as in *eretz Yisrael*, the land of Israel; or 3) The earth's people, just as in English 'let all the earth know'. The surrounding context here clearly favors the 3rd option: a few verses on, we read, 'Now the whole earth (*eretz*) had one language and one speech' (Genesis 11:1). Chapter and verse numbers are NOT inspired; without them, no one would miss that the "earth" that was divided was the "earth" that spoke one language. See also creation.com/peleg2.

subset of the gene pool of the original population.

When explaining this briefly to lay audiences I've found an analogy involving a game of bridge useful, despite its limitations. Imagine that each player represents one of the dispersed subgroups, and the 'hand' that is dealt is the gene pool of that subgroup at the time of the breakup. The number of clubs that get dealt into each hand represents the genes for more melanin in the skin—more clubs means that the group will have more genes for darker brown skin, fewer clubs will mean lighter skin.

Most of the time in bridge, all players receive some clubs—some more than others. But at the end of each game, the deck is shuffled again. This reshuffling represents the fact that in the population pre-Babel, whenever there was someone in a family who was on the 'extremes' of either darkness or lightness, they were free to marry someone with any other combination of genes. There was only one language and culture, and all were in the same geographic area. So, the whole population would have tended to hover around that average middle-brown.

Now imagine instead that the game is broken up, so that every player takes their hand and leaves the table—they all scatter far away from each other, losing all contact. The deck can no longer be reshuffled, and so each player 'is stuck with the hand they've been dealt'. In the same way, following the Babel breakup, a particular language group that already had a preponderance of genes for lighter or darker skin would only have its own group as potential marriage partners. In other words, it would from then on have no choice, genetically, other than to 'play the hand it's been dealt'.

There are two factors that would act to fine-tune the skin coloring in each such group. One would be the tendency for 'outliers' to be less likely to find a mate. Consider a group that had mostly (but not exclusively) darker brown skin. If the occasional combination of genes in an individual were such that a person was born with considerably lighter skin than the rest, that person would likely be seen as 'unusual' and thus less desirable as a marriage partner. In such ways a group could tend to enhance the already existing norm—it could be said to 'purify' itself in its own estimation.

Selection and skin

The other factor is natural selection (NS) acting on these human populations. This is an obvious and easily understood phenomenon. The scientist who first described NS, and whose ideas some think Darwin may have plagiarized, was a Christian creationist called Edward Blyth. Many assume, without further thought, that 'natural selection equals evolution'. By 'evolution' they mean a process capable of turning microbes into microbiologists, something that requires the progressive addition of huge amounts of complex, functional, new genetic information, or specified complexity. But of course NS, in eliminating the unfit, gets rid of genes; it *culls* genetic information. On its own, therefore, it is not a creative process.[23] Neo-Darwinian theory requires mutations—random accidental copying errors—to add the information from which NS is then able to 'choose'. However, observed mutations, even where they are seen to confer an advantage (such as the loss of wings of beetles on windy islands, in which the defect makes it less likely to be blown out to sea), have simply shown themselves incapable of this.[24]

To see how NS would affect the distribution of skin colors in people, consider two groups, one with a preponderance of genes for light skin, the other for dark skin. If they both headed in the direction of high-sunlight-intensity tropical regions, those in the group with more melanin in their skin would be at an advantage. The ones in the lighter-skinned group would suffer more skin cancer, folate deficiency (including spina bifida) and tropical ulcers (and likely other tropical skin diseases, as discussed earlier), and would not do as well in that area. Or they would tend to move away again, back to less sunny zones—if only due

---

23. See Wieland, C., Muddy waters: clarifying the confusion about natural selection, *Creation* **23**(3):26–29 2001, creation.com/muddy.
24. Wieland, C., Beetle Bloopers, *Creation* **19**(3):30, 2003, creation.com/beetle.

FEATURE

Redheads—How?

The gene for red hair arose some time after the Fall (Genesis 3), through mutation. Melanin has two components: eumelanin, which is brown-black, and pheomelanin, which is reddish-brown. Redheads have inherited two copies of a mutated gene which means that they mostly produce pheomelanin, and not much eumelanin. In addition to red hair, they have pale skin that burns easily, lighter eye colors than normal, and a tendency to skin freckles. About 1–2% of people worldwide are redheads. It is more than twice as common in low sunlight regions, such as northern Europe. It is particularly common in Scotland, where some 13% have red hair and 40% carry the gene for it. This distribution is probably due to natural selection; in intense sunlight areas like equatorial Africa there would be strong selection against such a mutation, since it makes both sunburn and skin cancer much more likely. Also, in low-light regions, having less natural sunscreen (eumelanin) gives redheads a positive advantage, since having sunlight penetrate the skin means adequate vitamin D production.

iStockPhoto

to the discomfort of frequent sunburn and skin infections. In this environment, black is beautiful—desirable marriage partners come to be dark-skinned people because they are seen as being healthier, better able to work and bear and rear healthy children. Within the darker-skinned group, any that inherited more genes for lightness than the average in their group would then be less likely to pass on their genes as they would tend to miss out in the marriage stakes. So a somewhat intelligent selection involving human choice now operates to enhance the already existing skin tones.

This is really a form of 'sexual selection': the genes are passed on because their carriers were preferred by the opposite sex in mate choice. This is a reality, even though it fails for the very phenomenon that Darwin concocted the theory to explain: the mathematically complex peacock tail.[25] Peahens turn out not to care about the brilliance of the tail, but rather about mating calls.[26,27,28]

It's important to note that neither NS nor human selection creates the colors; they were there already in the genetic information. Selection merely fine-tunes them, e.g. relative to the environment, causing a degree of local adaptation. So in equatorial regions, one is much more likely to find darker-skinned people groups.

In contrast, a dark-skinned group that migrated too far into the high latitudes, where the light intensity is low, would not get enough sunlight to penetrate their skin to make sufficient vitamin D. This is needed for healthy bones; a deficiency in this vitamin causes rickets and has also been linked to certain cancers. In this environment, white becomes beautiful in the marriage stakes. So this helps explain why, historically, lighter-skinned people groups occupied the high latitudes such as far northern Europe.

But one would not expect selection to operate 'perfectly', and so it's not surprising that we find exceptions to these general rules. Again from *The Creation Answers Book*:

"The Inuit (Eskimo) have brown skin, yet live where there is not much sun. Presumably they all have a genetic makeup such as $M_AM_Am_Bm_B$, which would not be able to produce lighter or darker skin. The Inuit fish diet provides plenty of vitamin D. On the other hand, native South Americans living on the equator do not have black skin. These examples confirm that natural selection

25.   Burgess, S., The beauty of the peacock tail and the problems with the theory of sexual selection, *J. Creation* **15**(2):94–102, 2001, creation.com/peacock. Stuart Burgess is Professor of Design and Nature and Head of Department, Mechanical Engineering, University of Bristol (UK), and a world expert on biomimetics.

26.   Takahashi, M. *et al.*, Peahens do not prefer peacocks with more elaborate trains, *Anim. Behav.* 2007, doi:10.1016/j.anbehav.2007.10.004.

27.   Viegas, J., Female peacocks not impressed by male feathers, *Discovery News*, March 26, 2008, dsc.discovery.com/news/2008/03/26/peacock-feathers-females.html.

28.   Catchpoole, D., Peacock tail tale failure, creation.com/tale, 2008.

does not create new information—if the genetic makeup of a group of people does not allow variation in color toward that color desirable for that environment, natural selection cannot create such variation."[20]

All native American groups are descendants of Asians who migrated across the Bering strait land bridge, so had the same genetic 'deck'. This explains why the polar-dwelling Inuit and the equatorial-dwelling Incas have olive complexions, neither very light nor very dark.

Of course, the same sorts of things we have outlined regarding skin pigmentation would apply to any other factors controlled by genes—the shape of one's nose, the shape of one's eyes, and so on. These are things that we also see as 'racial' features. For such factors, too, generally no group has anything 'unique' not shared by any other group. For example, the Asian or almond eye differs from a typical Caucasian or round eye in having a tiny ligament that pulls the eyelid down a little (see diagram below). All babies are born with the ligament, but non-Asians usually lose it before 6 months of age. Some retain the ligament and thus have almond-shaped eyes like Asians, and some Asians lose the ligament and so have round eyes like most Caucasians.

Our first parents looked like ... ?

Incidentally, Adam and Eve could not have been, as they are often drawn, blue-eyed, pale-skinned and blond. If they had been, they could not have given rise to all the variety in the coloring/shading of their offspring today. In all probability, they had middle brown skin, brown hair and brown eyes. Like the parents of Remee and Kian, the 'two-tone twins', they could have then had a huge range of variety in their offspring.

Similarly, Noah and his family may have been of

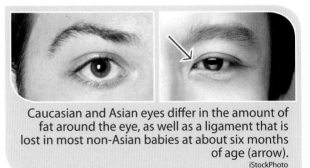

Caucasian and Asian eyes differ in the amount of fat around the eye, as well as a ligament that is lost in most non-Asian babies at about six months of age (arrow).
iStockPhoto

a 'balanced' genetic makeup in regard to skin color—enough melanin to protect adequately against UV in most climates, yet not enough to give rise to vitamin D deficiency. They may, however, have had a range of skin shades, as is seen in some families today, particularly in southern India. Either way, the post-Flood population at Babel would have had a range, but with 'extremes' of light and dark being relatively rare.

It is also possible, though not definite, that blue eye color arose by mutation of a brown-eyed gene —a loss of information, causing reduction in melanin production in the iris. Such a mutation would then have occurred soon after Babel in the ancestor of much of Europe's population. This makes it even easier, if anything, to explain eye color and its distribution, and of course even more certain that our first parents were brown-eyed.[29]

Interracial marriage

Given all the misconceptions surrounding race, especially the hangover notions from an earlier generation of committed evolutionists, it's no wonder that there are still taboos within various circles against so-called 'interracial marriage'. But these have no basis in either science or the Bible. The Bible does counsel believers not to marry unbelievers (2 Corinthians 6:14). And in Old Testament times, the Israelites were not to marry outsiders. But they *were* allowed to if the outsiders converted to faith in the God of Abraham, Isaac and Jacob. This shows that the issue was religious, not racial.

Of course, in marrying someone from a different *culture,* there are wisdom issues to consider. Cultural differences can arise even when two people are of the same 'race', e.g. an English person marrying a Russian. Even those speaking the same language, such as Americans and Australians, are often surprised at how great the cultural differences can be.[30] Cultural differences can greatly

---

29.   It has been suggested that pale skin itself may be the result of a 'loss' mutation from an initially dark-skinned population. This is not precluded within biblical history either.

30.   Well, sort of the same language. ☺

enrich both person's lives, but they can also bring a unique set of problems. Couples wise enough to seek counseling[31] on various matters prior to betrothal should consider such things, too. It helps to be able to anticipate the sorts of problems that may arise, and bring the issues out into the open. The intention is to try to minimize problems should the marriage proceed.

Notice that it was the 'interracial' marriages of the two sets of grandparents of our two-tone twins that provided the genetic richness in their children, permitting a greater variety in their children's children. I was listening once to my long-time compatriot and CMI speaker Peter Sparrow,[32] giving a talk on creation that also covered this issue of race and genetics. With his trademark wide grin and booming voice, Peter made a statement which even startled me (it certainly seemed to shock many in the audience). What he said was (emphasis his): "Adam and Eve were the ultimate *mongrels!*"

Dog breeding and 'racial purity'

When you think about it, though, his statement is absolutely right. The problem is that we have been conditioned to think of genetically depleted populations as 'pure' when in fact it is the 'mongrel' combinations in both animals and humans that have the greater genetic richness, more like the originals that God created. A good example is in domestic dog breeds. Starting from a 'mongrel' dog population, breeders have been able to select out many different 'pure' breeds. Notice that this artificial selection is actually a very good analogy of natural selection. Dogs that are 'unfit' are those that do not meet the breeder's criteria. It's only the 'fit'—those meeting the selection criteria—whose genes are

---

31. An experienced pastor with a mix of godliness and common sense is a great start.
32. Well known in Australian rural and outback areas for the 17 years that he, a science teacher, and his wife Cathy, a registered nurse, spent mostly on the road ministering on creation while living in the now-retired *Creation Bus*. See creation. com/the-creation-bus-and-us. Peter was already speaking out on creation as a university student in the mid 1970s, which brought us into contact. In 1977, we were both on the committee of the first creation organization in our country, the Creation Science Association of South Australia (later merged with what is now CMI).

permitted to pass to the next generation.

The figure below shows a simplified example of natural selection for fur length in dogs. Only one gene with two forms, long (L) and short (S), has been assumed for simplicity. In reality of course it will be more complex than that. But it helps us to see how a new variety can arise as selection actually *eliminates* genes. This sort of change may lead to greater variety, but less variability (the new population is now unable to adapt to hot climates).

A simple way of understanding it as it applies to domestic dog breeds is as follows. Imagine breeders wanting a small, cute dog to sit on someone's lap. So from each generation they choose the smallest and cutest. Eventually, they will have maximized the concentration of genes for those characters in one line—achieving something like, say, the Chihuahua. Notice how this new breed is now 'adapted' to its environment (its environment is one in which its maximal chance of passing on its genes is to look the way certain humans want it to look). But in the process, the genes for

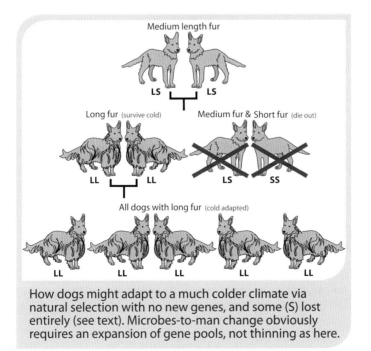

How dogs might adapt to a much colder climate via natural selection with no new genes, and some (S) lost entirely (see text). Microbes-to-man change obviously requires an expansion of gene pools, not thinning as here.

other characters, like large size, have been 'crowded out'.[33] Thus, if all dogs in the world apart from Chihuahuas were to cease to exist, you could never again breed something big and strong like a Great Dane. The genes needed to do that are simply no longer there in the Chihuahua population as a whole.

All the selection in the world is useless unless there is the right 'raw material' (the right genetic information) to choose from in the first place. So the 'pure' breeds are in fact thinned-out and genetically depleted populations. They are more specialized, yes, but also less able to vary and adapt further. The real richness and variety is in that mongrel population. That's why, if you wanted to start again and breed a Great Dane (say they had all died out), you would need to see if there were dogs still around that were like that original mongrel population from which the 'pure' lines had been bred. Such pure lines in the world of show-breeding are, incidentally, also much more likely to suffer from accumulated mutational defects, especially from inbreeding.[34]

Here, I can't help thinking of all of those vast numbers of people (fortunately much rarer today) who, inspired by evolution (or by others who have been), put so much effort and passion into preserving their particular 'pure race'. Many have even willingly died (and killed) for this 'cause'. I can well remember my late uncle Hans-Joachim (who was in the German infantry throughout World War II) giving his observations of the pitched tank battles of the Battle of the Bulge, that last desperate attempt by the German High Command to roll back the D-Day advance. What especially stuck with me was his description of the suicidal bravado, born of fanatical idealism, of the teenage Hitler Youth volunteers who comprised many of the tank crews there. They charged into the jaws of death, convinced that they were not only fighting for *Führer und Vaterland*, but to preserve their 'pure race'. Once one sees it for what it is, one's genetically depleted

33. Because there is only a given number of positions for genes to occupy on the dog's chromosomes, so more of some means less of others.
34. Cosner, L., "A parade of mutants"—pedigree dogs and artificial selection, *Creation* **32**(3):28–32, 2010, creation.com/pedigree.

race, it doesn't sound like a cause worth wasting any breath on, let alone dying for.

But, enough of World War II—back to dog breeding. What's interesting is this: we've already seen that as you go forwards in time with selection operating, there are more varieties with time, each adapted to different environments. These daughter populations get increasingly specialized, but with decreased genetic variety, and so they have a decreased ability to adapt to a different environment. Such a process is clearly downhill; the very opposite of microbes-to-man evolution, which requires gene pools (gene variety) to be expanded over time, not thinned out. Extrapolated forwards, such a process leads to extinction, not evolutionary progress.

Now mentally trace this *backwards* from the present time. The many 'pure' lines merge into the single mongrel dog population from which it was bred. As you go backwards, the amount of variability *increases* as the number of distinct populations (varieties) *decreases*. But this is only one of several different mongrel dog populations; these, in turn, as you go backwards, merge into the wolf population from which domestic dogs were originally bred.[35] Again, we see less distinct varieties, but more variability (i.e. *potential* to vary) as you go backwards.

Now what's really interesting is this: go back still further, and wolves themselves, and other canids like Asiatic wild dogs and coyotes (which can still interbreed with wolves) merge together still more, with a greatly increased variety, until you have the population that represents the original Genesis kind. So Noah did not have to take wolves, coyotes, Asiatic wild dogs, etc. onto the Ark. Just a pair of a 'dog kind' which had all that variability. And which, by this same straightforward process—going forwards

---

35.   It's likely that this came about as some wolves that were genetically predisposed to tameness approached closer to human settlements—thus they were more likely to be tamed and bred from. Researchers have noticed that if you breed various types of wild dog, even foxes, choosing the tamer and tamer varieties, you eventually get floppy ears and wagging tails. The tameness seems to be linked to genes for these features that are common in domestic dogs.

All modern domestic dogs are descended from the wolf (*Canis lupus*) via a process of specialization which narrows gene pools. Wolves can still interbreed with coyotes, since both descended from the same biblical kind.
sxc.hu

in time now—could break up into these daughter populations under the influence of selection with rapidly changing post-Flood environments. (I think it's great to see Genesis history come alive in this realm of biology.)

Each of these daughter populations represents additional varieties. Each of those varieties is usually more specialized, more adapted to local conditions but it has less variability, less potential to vary, and thus less information. Note that this is the opposite of what is supposed to take place with the evolutionary hypothesis, which has to have an overall[36] net *increase* in information with time. That is, gene pools should be expanding, not getting thinned out. It's time, though, to get back to our focus on the human family, in the next chapter.

∞

---

36.   Evolutionists would expect gene pools varying in all manner of directions within their view of history, but what is being claimed here is that this downhill change should not be slated as demonstrating the sort of change that people associate with the word 'evolution'.

3 PREJUDICE AND PRIVILEGE

Anything that involves people is going to be complex, and I certainly don't want to make this whole issue of racial prejudice more simple than it is. It's been stressed already that Darwinian evolution is not the cause of racism so much as it is a justification, and a major booster, for it. The motivation for racial prejudice can simply be that excessive, even rapacious, self-centeredness, to the detriment of others, that is unfortunately a widespread part of the human condition. (The Bible indicates it's part of our sin nature.)

Associated with this is a tendency for prejudice against readily identifiable groups of people that seem to threaten our self-interest. This is so even where 'race' characteristics do not feature heavily. As a university student in the late 1960s, I went fruit-picking during the summer holidays in South Australia's Riverland fruit-growing region. At the time, many Italian immigrant families had been moving into the region and buying up fruit blocks (orchards) that had been in families for generations.

Economic achievement—and threat

Several of these Italian families at a time would move onto one block initially, and operate it jointly. They would work hard, and live frugally—growing their own vegetables and making their own bread, exotic smallgoods, preserves, etc. This would enable them to quickly save up the deposit to buy another such orchard. Even after they had several between them, the cooperation continued, enabling them to share operating expenses. For example, the same tractor used on the first block was able to service all the rest as well. This was a clear economic advantage over the traditional model of 'one block, one tractor' that surrounding orchards utilized.

There was more than one collective of families doing this, and ownership of more and more blocks was transferring to them. The ones I came across were mostly from central to northern Italy, and looked much the same as many of the Anglo-Australian 'blockies', as the fruit farmers were called. What identified all of them as 'outsiders' to the locals was mostly language and culture, particularly their economic habits—not any perceived biological differences.

The resentment this group inspired was huge, and derogatory comments about the Italians were legion. The main factor triggering the prejudice, in addition to sheer jealousy at their rapid advancement, seemed to be the perceived socio-economic threat. Most people could only see farms that had been worked for generations by the fathers and grandfathers of 'Australians' now being 'lost', swallowed up by the voracious hordes from overseas. No thought was ever given to the fact that the orchardists who sold them the blocks were not compelled to do so, and that these newcomers were not doing anything that the old-school blockies were not free to emulate.

These days in Australia, the Italian immigrants of the post-war period have mostly become prosperous, and their children are often doctors, lawyers and accountants. The same thing happened to the numerous post-war Greek immigrants,[1] renowned for their long hours slaving over vats of hot oil in takeaway fish-and-chip/

---

1.   Melbourne, Australia's second-largest city, was for some time known as the city with the second-largest number of Greek inhabitants after Athens.

hamburger shops.[2]

Each of these immigrant groups is now almost universally seen as part of mainstream Australia. The prejudice each of them experienced is now mostly transferred to the more recently arrived Vietnamese. Most arrived here as penniless refugees from the Vietnam War era, so-called 'boat people'. They show the same pattern of hard work and frugality as their Mediterranean predecessors. The prejudice they experience is generally tinged with overtones of biological race, because of their easily visible group characteristics. And, by the way, they now seem to own most of the fish-and-chip shops.

The same sort of thing has been seen in US neighborhoods that are prominently African-American. Koreans, working hard and living frugally, have moved in to own the fruit shops, and experienced prejudice as a result from their black neighbors. Here, too, the target group looks dramatically different from those doing the resenting.

Following the money

Another factor worth mentioning is that it simply suits people to think that they are in some privileged group, and hence others are lesser to them. Which skin tone is seen as being either more or less privileged has varied, depending on the cultural context. Among the English aristocracy in earlier times, ultra-pale skin was definitely a mark of privilege. After all, only those who did not have enough money had to go out and labor in the fields. So, pale and insipid was the sought-after 'look'. This pattern seems to have prevailed in agricultural societies for a very long time. In the Old Testament book Song of Solomon we read:

> "Do not stare at me because I am dark, because I am darkened by the sun. My mother's sons were angry with me and made me take care of the vineyards" (1:6).

---

2.   A while back, going to one of these rather than the (then) newly established McDonald's outlets meant you were 'going to a Slippery Nick's'. This affectionate term combined references to both the fat that made them much tastier than a 'Macca's' and to a common Greek first name.

As England industrialized, however, the situation changed. The 'peasant classes' no longer toiled on farms, but were stuck indoors all day in grimy factories. They were now the sickly-looking pale ones. The privileged classes could afford regular long holidays in the south of Spain or France, unlike the average worker. So people's drive to identify with privilege is now still being expressed, only in reverse. Tanned skin is now the desirable look in the UK, with millions spent on tanning clinics and lotions.

In countries like Thailand, Cambodia and so on, the opposite still applies, and for similar reasons to earlier times in England. Desirable looks, as epitomized by models in fashion magazines or in advertizing of glamor products, always involve ultra-pale skin. Many women in those countries have naturally bronzed skin tones that English girls would pay much to achieve. But they express frequent dissatisfaction, even dismay, at their dark 'farmer skin'. Lotions promising a whiter skin are on display in every pharmacy and supermarket, and millions are spent each year on such products, despite their dubious effectiveness.

The Hinduism/Brahmanism of India was imported and imposed onto India's earlier population from outside invaders who happened to have lighter skin tones on average. It's probably no coincidence that the upper caste of Hindu society, the Brahmins, are mostly lighter-skinned. The lowest caste, the so-called 'untouchables', who can still occasionally be killed for daring to touch a Brahmin, are predominantly the darker-skinned descendants of the vanquished people group. The whole horrible caste system seems designed to keep an entire group of people in a permanently servile state. Did I say 'horrible system'? Indeed so. 'Political correctness' should not deter us from 'speaking the truth in love' (Ephesians 4:15).[3]

Racism—across the board
Racist prejudice, including that inspired and/or justified by

---

3. All too often, this verse is used as a mere garnishing of speech—or as an excuse to say something nasty with syrupy-sweet background 'noise'. Its citation here is meant to reflect an *agape* concern for those members of our one human family who remain horribly oppressed under such systems and their derivatives.

evolution, is not just a 'white *vs* black' issue, either. In the years leading up to World War II, the Japanese public were frequently assured that they were a superior race, destined to rule over all others. This supremacism had its roots in their Shinto religion, with them purportedly being direct descendants of the Gods. Darwinian ideology was easily added to the mix: Europeans have longer arms and hairier chests, so they are self-evidently closer to the apes than the more advanced Japanese. But their racial supremacy doctrine also applied to very similar-looking Asian peoples, such as the Chinese and Koreans, who were appallingly brutalized.

It can even be black *vs* black. If only because of the superb film *Hotel Rwanda*, most Westerners are aware of the horrendous genocidal violence inflicted on the Tutsi people of Rwanda by their Hutu countrymen. A secular documentary[4] made in the late 1990s identified evolutionary racism as at least one major factor involved in the background to this tragedy. Rwanda was officially taken over by Belgium in 1917. There followed a program of intense missionary activity by Belgian Roman Catholics, which established a number of worthwhile social projects. However, one of the legacies of this Belgian state/church alliance was a declaration that one of the tribal groups involved (Tutsis) was superior to the others, which were 'less evolved'.

Such ideas have the potential to change the behavior of one group of people towards another, generating bitter and lasting hatred. According to the documentary, this Darwinist concept became "official colonial ideology". One group became the oppressor, the other the oppressed, with the latter later seeking to exact a gruesome revenge. And these differences were regarded as biological/racial, regardless of their shared skin color.

The point here is that any group of people, given the right circumstances, opportunity and 'cultural justification', is just as capable of racist denigration and oppression of other people groups as any other. If a black American, for example, sees

---

4.   *Rwanda: A nation gone mad*, shown on SBS television in Australia, 16 January 1997.

FEATURE

Dark Deeds—King Leopold and the 'Belgian Congo'

The 'black on black' racism featured in the main text is not an attempt to whitewash European colonialist* and racist atrocities. These received a huge impetus in the second half of the 19th century, when social Darwinism was in full flight. One such atrocity was the near-wiping-out of Namibia's Herero people by the German colonialist rulers.[†] A review of the book *The Kaiser's Holocaust: Germany's Forgotten Genocide and the Colonial Roots of Nazism* pointed out:

> "Darwin's On the Origin of Species, with its brutally materialist account of nature as bleak survivalism, was made to serve as justification for the extermination of Namibian tribes and, later, for Hitler's biological anti-Semitism."[‡]

Another particularly dark chapter in that period was when Belgium's King Leopold II

Two youths during Leopold's reign, c. 1904. "The right hand of Yoka, standing, was cut off by soldiers wanting to claim him as killed. The hands of Mola, seated, were destroyed by gangrene after being tied too tightly by soldiers." Alice Harris / Anti-Slavery International.
Public domain

used his own funds to set up a country in Africa, with himself as absolute ruler, to enrich himself further. This started out as the Congo Free State, later the Belgian Congo, then Zaire and now the Democratic Republic of the Congo.

His harsh regime was directly and indirectly responsible for the deaths of millions of people. Many of its atrocities will never be known—just before the handover to Belgium's civilian government, palace officials took several days to incinerate virtually all the official records. However, a mass of these horrors are documented in Adam Hochschild's prize-winning 1998 book *King Leopold's Ghost*. The practice of cutting off of hands with a machete is widely associated in Western minds with African brutality to other Africans. It was, however, a common form of punishment for the natives under Leopold's reign of terror, and is believed by many social commentators to be the likely reason this tragic practice has now become commonplace in African conflicts.

Belgium's King Leopold II (1835–1909), later revealed as one of history's bloodiest tyrants.
Public domain

A paper on the Stanford University website, by Professor Bruce Lusignan, states that more than 10 million Congolese were massacred under Leopold, "on the scale of the Jewish Holocaust". The paper also says that this and other consequences of "entrenched European racism" were justified by "a theory of cultural Darwinism premised upon the idea of 'might makes right' and the 'ends justify the means.'" [§]

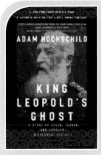

This prize-winning 1998 exposé helped to belatedly bring Leopold's reign of terror to the attention of the modern world.

How much harder would it have been for such brutal and greedy tyrants if European public opinion had widely held to the truth of the close relatedness of us all.

*Not all aspects of colonialism were bad for countries colonized; often the reverse. Individuals are complex—much more so their interactions as whole societies.

†See Ambler, M., *Creation* **27**(3):52–55, 2002, creation.com/herero-genocide.

‡Ian Thompson, review of *The Kaiser's Holocaust: Germany's Forgotten Genocide and the Colonial Roots of Nazism,* by David Olusoga and Casper Erichsen, Faber and Faber, 2010, in *Telegraph* (UK). p. 54, Picador, London, 2009.

§Lusignan, B, The Congo: From Leopold to Lumumba, downloaded from www.stanford.edu 13 October 2010.

white Americans as somehow uniquely evil in this area, or more prone to racism than their own group, that belief itself is clearly also racist in its turn. It sets up one's own group as intrinsically superior, if only in a moral sense.

That's why it's important to repeatedly emphasize the truth of Genesis history and what it means for *all* such ideas—they are simply untenable. Our true history should remind Christians in particular of two great facts. One is our fallen nature, so prone to thinking and acting wrongly towards others. The other is the immensely close relatedness of all members of our *one human family*.

∞

4. SLAVERY AND WHITE GUILT

In the USA, it's the issue of slavery that can most easily lead people to think that white people are uniquely prone to racism, and particularly so against blacks. It's easy to understand why African Americans pondering this dark chapter of history and the suffering of their people might think this way. This can lead on to the idea of 'white guilt', that today's whites, perhaps because they share this propensity, in some way bear a group responsibility for the sins of that time.

Also, the enslavement of Africans to work on American plantations commenced well before Darwin's book. Thus, even for African-American Christians, the racism and guilt of whites will tend to dominate thinking on race more than the fact that it involved a rejection of the biblical history of mankind.

DID RACISM DRIVE SLAVERY?

But just because something is widely believed, and even if understandably so, it does not make it true. CMI's Dr. Jonathan Sarfati has written extensively on the topic of slavery, on creation.com. One article in particular gave an excellent, detailed

FEATURE

One Drop of Blood: Black or White?

In several Western societies, one is regarded as 'black' (or in Australia, Aboriginal) even if the majority contribution to one's ancestry was 'white'. In the slavery era in the US, this was known as the 'one-drop rule'. At the time, it implied inferiority, with the 'lower' group's 'blood' regarded as if it were a 'contaminant'. It was enshrined in law in Virginia's 1924 Racial Integrity Act, passed on the same day as the state's eugenics act to sterilize people by force (see 'Eugenics across the world' in Chapter 1). If a white person married someone who had even 'one drop' of African 'blood' (ancestry), their marriage was a criminal offense.

However, in Brazil the one-drop rule almost applies in reverse. According to Jose Neinstein, executive director of the Brazilian-American Cultural Institute, for people living in the USA, "If you are not quite white, then you are black." But in his native country of Brazil, "If you are not quite black, then you are white."* Many Brazilians who regard themselves as white back home find that when they come to the US, people see them in the opposite way. This highlights the somewhat arbitrary and culturally determined nature of our notions of race and skin color.

Economic factors may complicate the mix. In Australia today, even very modest Aboriginal ancestry might qualify one for various benefits set aside for indigenous people. A group of very light-skinned public figures identifying as Aboriginal recently launched a court action against a journalist and newspaper for naming them in this context.

To highlight further the silliness of our 'racial' divisions, a report on the trial stated that one of them was, as a child, "shunted from the white area of her segregated school playground after her clearly Aboriginal father came to school one day. Then, when the white parents complained that the school was allowing a white kid to be lumped in with the blacks, she was moved back again."[†]

*Fears, D., People of color who never felt they were black: racial label surprises many latino immigrants, The Washington Post, p. A01, 26 December 2002.

†Quinn, K., Between black and white, April 5, 2011, www.theage.com.au.

and thoroughly documented overview.[1] It was written for the 2007 bicentennial honoring William Wilberforce, the evangelical who spearheaded the campaign to abolish slavery. Some of its points are as follows:

Slavery has been widespread across the world for most of human history. And for most of this time, it was *not* a racial issue. Most slaves did not differ racially from their masters. Sarfati writes (acknowledging the research of conservative black US economist Dr. Thomas Sowell, who will feature more in these pages to come):

> "For example, Europeans enslaved Europeans—indeed, it was a European people group, the Slavs, that was such a common victim of slavers that the very word comes from this group (although in the Slavonic languages, *slava* means glory). Also, Asians enslaved Asians, and Africans enslaved Africans—black slaves were usually first captured by other blacks because the Europeans were susceptible to African diseases if they ventured into the interior.

> "And in many cases, Caucasians were enslaved by non-Caucasians: the dark-skinned Muslim Moors enslaved 'white' Europeans during their occupation of the Iberian peninsula (what they called 'al Andalus') from 711 to 1492.

> "Later, from the 16th century, the Muslim Barbary States of North Africa encouraged pirates who had a flourishing white slave trade. In the first half of the 17th century, 20,000 captives were said to be imprisoned in Algiers alone. The Europeans paid blood money to these rogue states until US President Thomas Jefferson sent the American Navy[2] to bomb the pirate ships and ports in 1805."

---

1.   Sarfati, J., Antislavery activist William Wilberforce: Christian hero, 20 February 2007, creation.com/wilberforce.
2.   Hence the line "To the shores of Tripoli" from the Marine Hymn.

In short, enslaving others and/or keeping them as slaves depended on having the means and opportunity. Rather than racism being the cause of slavery in the antebellum American South, it was mostly the other way around—it was slavery that exacerbated racism.

Slavery and biblical compromises

Some interesting evidence for the statement in the preceding sentence comes from the different social outcomes concerning racism in the US and Brazil, which also had African slaves. In the United States during the era of slavery, there was an emphasis that was largely lacking in Brazil: that all people, being descended from Adam, are created in God's image and are intrinsically equal, as the Declaration of Independence made plain. So there was a pressure to concoct contrived schemes to make the enslaved group less human—but not in Brazil. This is one important reason why, after slavery was abolished, Brazil had far fewer social problems involving black–white racism than the US (see also feature p. 110 'One Drop of Blood ...'). It also explains why such nonsense as the idea of pre-Adamite races, and the 'curse of Ham led to black skin' (feature p. 44) arose and/or were prevalent in the white culture of the USA and southern Africa, not that of the UK or Brazil.[3] Like today's theistic evolution compromises, these ideas were not primarily driven by what the Bible said, but by the outside ideas prevalent in the society, which were read *into* the Bible.

iStockPhoto

---

3.   See also the book by secular researcher Sylvester A. Johnson, *The myth of Ham in nineteenth-century American Christianity*, Palgrave Macmillan, 2004.

Black slavery flourishing today

Black people are still being enslaved today, tragically—and not by whites. In an article called 'Black Slavery is Alive in 2001',[4] African-American economist Dr. Walter Williams (1936–) writes:

> "Slavery in the Sudan is in part a result of a 15-year war by the Muslim north against the black Christian and animist south. Arab militias, armed by the Khartoum government, raid villages, mostly those of the Dinka tribe. They shoot the men and enslave the women and children. Women and children are kept as personal property or they're taken north and auctioned off."

The price in 2001 of a woman or child in the Sudan was US$90 each. Williams also reports that in 1994, there were an estimated 90,000 black Africans living as slaves of Berbers in Mauritania. He documents horrible atrocities that have been suffered by them. He cites the American Anti-Slavery Group as saying,

> "Most distressing is the silence of the American media whose reports counted for so much in the battle to end apartheid in South Africa."

Williams writes:

> "In fact, it's fairly safe to say that most of today's most flagrant human rights abuses occur in Africa. But unfortunately they get little attention—maybe it's because Africans instead of Europeans are the perpetrators; Europeans are held accountable to civilized standards of behavior, while Africans aren't."

If only people were *truly* 'colorblind' about race, from understanding our close relatedness in the *one human family*, rather than just following fashionable antiracist causes. In this case, such trendy selectivity in the intelligentsia's antiracism is to the *detriment* of black Africans: both to the victims and, more subtly, to the perpetrators in implying that they should be held to lower ethical standards.

---

4. Available at www.capitalismmagazine.com, 4 January, 2001, accessed 10 October 2010.

CHRISTIANITY AND THE SLAVE TRADE

Slavery in the United States was not just a southern institution. Slave keeping was common in all the colonies at one time.

> "In the 1600s, writes Yale's David Brion Davis, a towering figure among historians, slave labor was far more central to the making of New York than to the making of Virginia. As late as 1830, there were 2,254 slaves in New Jersey."[5]

Because the US was generally considered to be a Christian society, many assume that slavery was a widely church-sanctified institution in the past. However, the church in the main has always *opposed* slavery, but was too often ignored.

It was no accident that the leaders of the abolitionist movement were evangelicals like William Wilberforce (1759–1833), discussed further in our later section on religion and culture. He fought against slavery in Britain tirelessly for 50 years, his motive completely derived from biblical morality—and he was criticized by the pro-slavers for bringing religion into politics!

Pro-slavers in the antebellum US similarly decried those who would use the Bible's teaching of human equality to dare to oppose the huge economic benefits that they thought slavery would bring—especially with the opportunities provided by westward expansion.

Civil War mythology

A persistent myth has it that America's Civil War was mostly fought over 'states' rights', or 'large government with heavy taxation', and that slavery was merely an incidental matter, interwoven with such other issues. John Toures, Associate Professor of Political History at Georgia's LaGrange College, recently set out to test that hypothesis by locating the declarations of secession for the four states available to him—South Carolina, Georgia, Mississippi, and Texas. Not only was there a virtual absence of mention of things like tariffs, taxation, etc. but he

---

5.   Von Drehle, D., The way we weren't, *Time*, 18 April 2011, pp. 24–31.

found that:

> "The word 'slave' appears 82 times in these four state declarations. The states even refer to themselves as 'Slave-Holding States.' I always thought that was a Northern term. On the other hand, the words 'State's rights,' 'states' rights' or 'states rights' do not appear in any of these four secession declarations. The word 'rights' appears 14 times and 'right' appears 32 times, but many of these references involve 'the right to own slaves.' ... if you read the declarations, they are chock full of excuses for the necessity of slavery that would make the most politically incorrect person today cringe."[6]

Princeton Professor James McPherson's book *Battle Cry of Freedom* is regarded as the authoritative one-volume history of the war. He says of this war: "Everything stemmed from the slavery issue."[7]

As inconsistent as it was with some of their own practices,[8] the founders of the United States, heavily influenced by the Bible, had written this in the 1776 Declaration of Independence:

> "We hold these truths to be self-evident, that all men are created equal, that they are endowed by their Creator with certain unalienable Rights, that among these are Life, Liberty and the pursuit of Happiness."

Yet barely a century later, the Vice President of the Confederate States of America, Alexander Stephens, in his famous 1861 Cornerstone Speech in Savannah, Georgia, felt emboldened to be able to directly rebut that statement:

> "Our new government is founded upon exactly the opposite idea; its foundations are laid, its cornerstone rests, upon the great truth that the negro is not equal to the white man; that slavery, subordination to the superior

6.   Toures, J., Was the Confederacy really about slavery?, www.southernpoliticalreport.com, 15 April 2010, accessed 15 May 2011.
7.   Ref. 5, p. 24.
8.   The principal drafter Thomas Jefferson, a deist, owned hundreds of slaves in his lifetime, despite being an opponent of slavery in principle.

race, is his natural and normal condition."[9]

In the minds of the vast majority of the population of its time, the Declaration's source of authority for this "self-evident" truth of equality, and that which was being overtly appealed to, was itself "self-evident"—the Creator, who had made all people from one couple. So what alternative authority source, if not 'science', would have been in mind for Confederate Vice President Stephens to be able to confidently and defiantly declare to millions that the polar opposite was in fact a "great truth"?

Though the speech was only two years after the publication of Darwin's *Origin*, we saw earlier that pre-existent evolutionary and other antibiblical 'scientific' notions rejecting Genesis history had been gathering speed for some time. The *Origin* merely gave them a huge kick along. So despite Darwin's own abolitionist sentiment, it should be no surprise that ideas of innate biological inferiority as 'great truth' could have handily fueled the fires of the pro-slavery camp across the Atlantic. Like Darwin's own book in its first edition, Stephens' speech contained a later passing reference by way of a sop to the notion of a creator. This was despite the speech's earlier overt rejection of what the (actual) Creator had made plain—that we are all *one human family*.

Before leaving that era of history, note that as far as the men in uniform are concerned, this is not about villains and heroes. Large numbers of those in grey never owned a slave, and were not filled with zeal for slavery as a cause. Similarly, large numbers of their counterparts in blue were not fighting because of any passion for liberating slaves.

Bible teachings *contra* slavery

As Wilberforce and his followers realized, the Dominion Mandate in Genesis 1:28 gives human beings dominion over plants and animals, but *not* over fellow human beings. They knew, too, that slaves were created in the image of God. And they were aware that in 1 Timothy 1:10, Paul lists 'slave traders'

9.   Alexander H. Stephens, Cornerstone speech, 21 March 1861, from www.teachingamericanhistory.org.

(ἀνδραποδιστής *andrapodistēs*, literally 'men-stealers') with murderers, adulterers, perverts, liars and other evil people. The same Apostle Paul also encouraged Philemon to free his escaped slave Onesimus (Philemon 16), and ordered masters to treat their slaves in the same way as they were treated, and not to threaten them (Ephesians 6:9). Consistently applied, that would see slavery disappear.

By contrast, as we saw, pagan philosophers like Aristotle believed that some people were 'natural slaves'. And the anti-Christian philosophers of the so-called Enlightenment, such as David Hume and Voltaire, believed in the idea of a natural inferiority of dark-skinned people.

In 2003, Princeton University Press published sociologist Rodney Stark's book *For the Glory of God: How monotheism led to reformations, science, witch-hunts and the end of slavery*. He thoroughly documents that Christianity was indeed *the* force that undermined slavery. His Chapter 4 is devoted to the church's consistent teachings against slavery—even in the 7th century, Christians were publicly opposed to slavery. Sarfati writes:

> "The bishop and apologist Anselm (c. 1033–1109) forbade enslavement of Christians, and since just about everyone was considered a nominal Christian, this practically ended slavery [in Western Europe, where the church had hegemony]. Then the famous theologian and apologist Thomas Aquinas (c. 1225–1274) denounced the practice. Several popes supported this from 1435, and Pope Paul III (1468–1549) gave three major pronouncements against slavery in 1537, e.g. *Sublimus Dei*—On the Enslavement and Evangelization of Indians in the New World."

In addition, according to Australian theologian Peter Barnes:

> "The greatest preacher in the early Church, John Chrysostom, urged Christians to buy slaves in order to release them. By the Middle Ages, slavery had virtually died out in Europe, only to be revived with

the discoveries of the New World in the 15th and 16th centuries."[10]

Stark's work cannot be lightly dismissed. He is Distinguished Professor of Social Sciences at Baylor University. Stark felt compelled to defend against perceptions that 'religious bias' was distorting his work by writing:

"I am not and have never been a Roman Catholic. When I note virtues that many historians have misrepresented or ignored in their writings about Catholicism, I deny acting as an apologist. Indeed, sincere Catholics will find much to be uncomfortable about when reading some of the chapters that follow, and I have written some unpleasant things about Protestants, Jews, Muslims, heretics, skeptics, and pagans too. It is, of course, easy to find fault. Sad to say, in today's intellectual climate it takes much greater courage to praise. I hope that I measured up.

"Finally, because this is a work of social science, not philosophy, I have taken pains neither to imply nor to deny the existence of God. This is a matter beyond the scope of science. Consequently, my personal religious views are of concern only to me."[11]

Paul's teachings on slavery, and condemning slave-trading, were not some New Testament re-invention. The Law of Moses explicitly forbids kidnapping and selling others into slavery, 'Whoever steals a man and sells him, and anyone found in possession of him, shall be put to death' (Exodus 21:16). Moses is of course well known as the one whom God used in His miraculous deliverance of the Israelite nation from bondage in Egypt, commemorated in the celebration of the Passover, a

---

10. Barnes, P., If the Foundations are destroyed—what we owe to the Christian faith, *Evangelical Times*, February 2011, p. 31.
11. See press.princeton.edu/chapters/i7501.html—Stark grew up in a Lutheran home. Though not a biblical creationist, he has expressed sympathy for the aims of the Intelligent Design (ID) movement. He described himself once as being neither an atheist nor a man of faith, then some time later as "an independent Christian".

forerunner of God's coming Deliverer, Jesus Christ.

Southern Baptists and slavery

Much has been made of the fact that the largest affiliation of Protestant Churches in the world, the Southern Baptist Convention (SBC), originally split off from other Baptist churches in America in the 1830s over the issue of missions and also the southerners' support for slavery. It's interesting that this split was framed in terms of race, more than slavery *per se*—the race debate followed the practice, not the other way around. Northern Baptists made it plain that God would not condone treating one race as superior to another. Southern Baptists at the time said that God intended races to be separate. Several of the arguments employed in support of this contention were identical to what we will later see were used in relation to apartheid. A key point in the light of this book's main thesis is that the northern Baptist leaders not only framed their opposition on biblical grounds, they apparently did so with an eye on the 'big picture' of Genesis history.

The episode also highlights once more the importance of being ever vigilant of the dangers of *reading into Scripture something that suits the society within which one finds oneself*, despite that something being antiscriptural to the core. That is as true of the desire to read evolution and/or long ages into the Bible as it was true of the situation with the early SBC, and with apartheid and its predecessor policies.

Thankfully, the SBC long ago repudiated that position, and has stood strongly on the authority of Scripture in all areas. Under its current leadership, it is especially concerned to do so in regard to the complete veracity of the Genesis record—including the fact that we are all extremely closely related. In all our diversity, we are, each one of us, members of this *one human family*.

Are some Bible passages *pro* slavery?

The accusation that the Bible endorses slavery is a perennial favorite of anti-Christian writing. Especially, one could add, of the less sophisticated variety, who ignore all the information above

FEATURE

Toothpaste *vs* Dignity

Front and center in any discussion on race and the Bible is the dignity of the individual. This is something that comes not from what someone does, but who they are as God's image-bearer. Because of our sin nature, individuals can and do act in ways that defile aspects of this image. But individual flaws do not alter the fact that all descendants of Adam are entitled to an intrinsic or *a priori* assignment of that basic human dignity.

One of the antibiblical outworkings of racism is to do the opposite, i.e. to make *a priori* assumptions or characterizations about others that serve to degrade and violate that aspect of God's image. The toothpaste packaging shown here (still on sale in Thailand in 1988, and made by a company that was acquired by Colgate-Palmolive in 1985—the brand was later changed to 'Darlie') is one example. It is obviously offensive, and most of us would readily agree. But do we do that on the basis of a truly biblical ethos, like Wilberforce in his struggle against the slave trade, or are we mostly just following the cultural fashion of our times, with a Bible verse or two hastily thrown in as an afterthought?

To be swept along by the shifting winds of the day is fine when they sometimes blow in the right direction for a while. But it also means that we would likely have condoned many things we now condemn, had we lived in a different time. What is needed in every generation are Christians who will take the lead in application of the Bible to culture, rather than belatedly playing catch-up to the world.

about the Bible's prohibitions on slavery. In the same Wilberforce bicentennial article as before, Sarfati writes that regarding these other mentions of slavery in the Bible, such critics:

"are guilty of gross decontextualising of the Bible, in presuming that the word in the Bible refers to the antebellum American South. In reality, it had a wide range of meanings. E.g. in the biblical culture, the Prime Minister's cabinet members would be called his 'slaves'. The New World slavery that most people think of was *expressly forbidden* in the Bible, because it resulted from kidnapping, and because converted slaves were not freed as per Philemon and Anselm (above). A helpful apologetics site[12] explains more:

'Scholars do not agree on a definition of "slavery". *The term has been used at various times for a wide range of institutions, including plantation slavery, forced labor, the drudgery of factories and sweatshops, child labor, semivoluntary prostitution, bride-price marriage, child adoption for payment, and paid-for surrogate motherhood.* Somewhere within this range, the literal meaning of "slavery" shifts into metaphorical meaning, but it is not entirely clear at what point. A similar problem arises when we look at other cultures. The reason is that the term "Slavery" is evocative rather than analytical, calling to mind a loose bundle of diagnostic features. …

'The word '*ebed* [עבד], however, denoted not only actual slaves occupied in production or in the household but also persons in subordinate positions (mainly subordinate with regard to the king and his higher officials). Thus the term '*ebed* is sometimes translated as "servant". Besides, the term was used as a sign of servility in reference to oneself when addressing persons of higher rank. Finally, the same term was also used in the figurative meaning "the slave (or servant) of God". Thus, the patriarchs Abraham, Isaac, and Jacob, prophets, David, Solomon and other kings are regularly called slaves of Yahweh (Exod 32:13; Lev 25:55; 1 Sam 3:9; Ezra 9:11, etc.). Similarly, all the subjects of Israel and Judah are called slaves of their kings, including even wives, sons, and brothers of the latter (1 Sam 17:8; 29:3; 2 Sam 19:5, etc.; cf. also Gen 27:37; 32:4). …

'For example, courtiers of an Aramean ruler or the soldiers of the Babylonian king Nebuchadnezzar II were considered slaves of their monarchs (2 Kgs 6:11; 24:10–11). It is natural that kings of Judah depending on more powerful rulers of neighboring countries were considered their slaves. Thus, Ahaz is referred to as a slave of the Assyrian king Tiglath-pileser III (2 Kgs 16:7). In modern translations of the Bible '*ebed* / *doulos* [δοῦλος] and several other similar terms are rendered "slave" as well as "servant", "attendant", etc. Such translations, however, might create some confusion and give the incorrect impression that special terms for the designation of servants and slaves are attested in the Bible…

'However, selecting the proper meaning from such a broad metaphorical application of the term designating a general dependence rarely presents great difficulty. For example, Abimelech, king of Gerar, called up his slaves and told them his dream (Gen 20:8). Apparently, these "slaves" were royal courtiers and officials.'

---

12.   www.tektonics.org.

The article by Sarfati continues:

> "Then why is there no command in the Bible to free the slaves immediately? Because the commands in the Bible already documented would subtly undermine the institution far better than a slave rebellion. E.g. the prohibition on trading in slaves would drastically localize it."

Sarfati asks readers to compare the application of Paul's teachings with the tragic end to the rebellion of Spartacus (c. 120–70 BC), or in modern times, compare Martin Luther King's peaceful (and Bible-based) protests with secular revolutionaries willing to use violence.

In summary, far from slavery being a Western Christian invention, slavery:

- was widespread throughout history;

- was almost never based on racial considerations but motivated by opportunity and greed;

- with a handful of notable exceptions involving compromised biblical exposition, was consistently opposed by the Christian church on biblical grounds, despite much opposition from secular interests;

- was only abolished due to the intervention of the Christian West, including British 'imperialist' warships being sent to attack slavers and slave ports and liberate the slaves of other nations.

∞

5 MODERN EVOLUTIONISTS *CONTRA* RACISM

An issue of obvious relevance in all this is that today's foremost promoters of evolution are almost invariably opposed to racism in any shape or form. Why is this, and does it mean the whole issue is now passé?

There's no doubt that the biological discoveries over the last few decades about our closely shared humanity have played some part. Much of this information has come in leaps and bounds in recent years (for example, the genetic data). But it's probably fair to say that there has long been a gradual accumulation of such knowledge. And the simple facts listed earlier about melanin and so on have been known for a very long time. Even in Darwin's day, speculation about racial differences, fueled by evolutionary assumptions and willing prejudice, kept coming up against uncomfortable facts—our inter-fertility, for one thing.

But that alone would not easily account for the way in which racism has most definitely been untrendy, for several decades now, among intellectuals, academia and the media (collectively referred to from here on as 'the intelligentsia'[1]). These are the very

---

1. The traditional definition of intelligentsia does not normally include the media, but nowadays there is such a close interplay between them and the media that the line is often blurred.

same sectors that were mostly eugenicist—often aggressively so—in the interwar period.

Americans might readily assume that the civil rights movement in their country caused the change. But much of the intelligentsia had already switched sides well before Martin Luther King expounded his dream.

The fact that racism has mostly become un-cool, and not just among the intelligentsia, is one of the pluses of the modern world. The explosion in mass entertainment, for all the associated downside, has definitely played a positive part. The list of media influences would be too long to detail even if it were compilable. It goes well beyond the spoofing of the racist attitudes of the fictional Archie Bunker[2] and Eddie Booth[3] in the 1970s.

One notable example is the Cosby Show of the 1980s and early 1990s. It's hard to imagine that something as entertaining, warmly human and typical of many American families of all 'races' would not have had a major impact. Even the most diehard white supremacist would have required considerable effort to keep regarding their African-American counterpart as some sort of less evolved animal. Here, too, however, the 'side-switching' of the intelligentsia had already largely taken place in the early post-war years.

There is in fact an easily identifiable factor that could well explain why this same segment of society, that prior to World War II was so into racism and eugenics, now sees these as abhorrent. And there is a reason, I think, why the timing of the big turning point for them was just after the Allied conquest of Nazi Germany in World War II.

Shock treatment for the planet's people

I believe that this sea-change in attitude was largely triggered by the revelation to the world of the stark horrors of the Nazi death camps. This was something on a scale and of a nature

---

2.   A bigoted blue-collar American worker in the hit sitcom *All in the Family*.
3.   A racist white socialist, usually outwitted by his conservative black immigrant neighbor, in the comedy *Love Thy Neighbour*.

unprecedented in history, and indeed, in all of modern human experience. There was from that point on a dramatic plummet in the popularity of expressing, or being known to hold, overtly racist and eugenicist ideas, particularly among intellectuals and in public discourse. Anything with the vaguest hint of Nazi overtones was suspect. Regardless of what one's personal views or deep-seated feelings on the subject might still have been, it was no longer acceptable to voice racist or eugenicist opinions openly in civil company. Whatever remained of the eugenics movement soon dissipated or was forced underground.

It's likely that it also set back the cause of the acceptance of evolution itself, among the American public in particular—despite the Scopes trial of the 1920s. Harvard Professor Richard Lewontin, whose essay on race featured earlier, said that prior to the mid 1950s, evolution "was barely mentioned in school textbooks".[4] But, he stated, shortly after the launching by the Soviet Union of *Sputnik 1* (the first manmade satellite[5] in space), "the study of evolution was suddenly in all the schools". Presumably concerned about the nation losing its scientific and technological edge after having been beaten to the punch by the Russians, the US government mandated urgently for more science to be taught in schools.

What does evolution have to do with the space race? Not much.[6] But remember that the difficulty of having evolution mentioned in textbooks would have been a source of frustration for many academics at the time—for ideological as well as professional reasons. Evolution is a key plank of justification for humanism, a religion in which man 'sets the rules', not God. For such academics, having a bureaucracy clamoring for 'more science, more science in schools' would have been like an open invitation. Biology is obviously a part of science, and it would have been easy to argue that evolution was a vital part of biology.

4.   Lewontin, R., in Godfrey, L.G. (Ed.), *Scientists Confront Creationism*, W.W. Norton and Co., NY, 1983, p. xxv.
5.   *Sputnik* (Спутник) is Russian for 'satellite'.
6.   Note that the moon landing was planned by scientists educated *before* the major evolutionary push in the schools.

So even though this push from the top was doubtless intended to apply to the hard sciences, like physics, it would have been simple to slip a lot of evolution into textbooks as a not-asked-for part of the bargain. (Like handing over some bathwater along with the baby, if you'll pardon the reversed metaphor.)

Such a dose of shock and horror as Auschwitz, Buchenwald, Dachau, and Treblinka, among others, administered to the world could certainly change the *popularity* of certain ideas suddenly. But it was not going to magically erase the deeply ingrained prejudices of the bulk of people, as the following anecdote affirms. (Its real effect would be mostly on the following generations, via the radical change in intellectual climate and its effects on literature, media and so forth.)

Immediately after the war, my father, a citizen of the then-occupied Germany, was easily able to get work with the US Occupation Forces. This was initially as an interpreter; due to having been born and raised in what was then called Palestine, he already spoke fluent English, in addition to German and Arabic.

By way of a 'race-relevant' aside, he entered the country of his citizenship, then Nazi Germany, for the first time in 1942.[7] His mannerisms, absorbed from the Jews and Arabs he was surrounded by, coupled with his black hair and tanned skin, made him a frequent object of racial suspicion. Especially since he came from *Palästina*, as Germans then called the ancient homeland of Jewish people. Many Germans, especially if they wanted to have a job in the civil service, were required to have an *Ahnenpass*—'ancestor passport', depicted in the feature on p. 128 —to show that for at least four generations back, they had no 'non-Aryan'—especially Jewish—ancestry. He told me that in spite of his *Ahnenpass* meeting all the criteria, he even had to have his skull dimensions measured, just to make sure. (This was supposed to reveal if he was a closet Semite.)

I remember him telling me how even some high-ranking officers in the US Army occasionally let their guard down in his

---

7.   This was via the exchange of interned German civilians such as himself from Palestine for captured Allied POWs.

presence with caustic and derogatory remarks about (their term) the 'niggers' among their forces there (they were largely racially segregated)—and also on other occasions the 'kikes' (Jews). It must have felt strange to a German reeling under the impact of the recently exposed racist mega-atrocities committed by his own government. Think of it—seeing frank racism, segregation, and especially antisemitism right at home among the Nazi-conquering liberators of the death camps.

Nevertheless, the utterly shocking spectacle of what level of inhumanities man was capable of inflicting on his fellow man was so starkly on display, and so clearly linked to Darwin's ideas, that the overall effect was dramatic. The many eugenicists outside of Germany that had been praising Nazi racial hygiene policies right up to the breakout of war fell instantly silent. This included academics in the sciences in particular. It was as if they had all suddenly slunk into the shadows, ashamed.

The truth that's seldom told

There has since been a virtual conspiracy of media silence about the Nazi–evolution connection. This is not surprising given evolution's key role in secular worldviews such as atheism and humanism. These ideas can only have any semblance of credibility if things all made themselves (evolved).

For example, an article that appeared in *Time* magazine a few decades back was pondering why so many medical doctors willingly took part in the ghastly Nazi machinations of the time, including horrific medical experiments.[8] The item was commenting on a book by an American Jewish psychiatrist who had interviewed many such doctors on the subject. What sorts of beliefs motivated these men and women and helped still their consciences?

The writer seems to flail around helplessly searching for an answer as to why the bulk of these educated and reasonable-seeming people so willingly participated in such ghastly doings.

8.   Doctors of the Death Camps, *Time*, 25 June 1979, accessed at www.time.com, 31 September 2010.

FEATURE

The Ancestor Passport and the Swastika

The cover of the *Ahnenpass* ('ancestor passport') of each of the author's parents, plus p. 20 of his mother's, showing how details were entered for a particular ancestor. Many Germans in the Nazi period were required to complete this to help confirm their 'Aryan lineage'.

The *Ahnenpass* was only one form of the Aryan Certificate (*Ariernachweiss*)—membership in the Nazi Party required even more extensive racial profiling to evidence 'racial purity'. Germany's policies of 'racial hygiene' were in fact widely praised by the pre-war intelligentsia, especially in the US.

In the 'scientific racism' of the time, the designation 'Aryan' roughly corresponded to those sharing the Indo-European language group. The swastika (in German called the *Hakenkreuz*, or hooked cross) is an ancient Indian symbol. It was adopted by the Nazi party as a symbol of 'Aryanism', with its hooks pointing clockwise. It is still widely used (hooks in either direction) in Indian-derived religions. Shown here from 2011 are (left) the border on a plastic fruit wrapper at Bangkok airport, and a sign on a Zen Buddhist Temple in a Singapore street.

It is as if the clue is staring him in the face as he starts talking about the Nazi "racial ideology" and the "eugenics movement that gained unfortunate respectability in some scientific circles in Europe and America during the '30s". (Note how he can only bring himself to say 'some', as if it had not been as wildly popular in scientific circles as it was.) He even reports how the doctor who ranked third in the Nazi hierarchy told him why he had joined the Party. It was because someone had fired his imagination by arguing that "Nazism is applied biology". Of course, this could only be a reference to evolution. Nevertheless, the 'e-word' is conspicuous by its total absence from the article.

The (eu)genie that won't stay in the bottle

Despite this general hush about eugenics, the evolutionary underpinnings of the practice are so strong that from time to time eugenicist impulses, mostly carefully couched, have surfaced in the scientific literature. In the early post-war years, some still tried to utilize the term, though giving it a more sanitized gloss. Thus, in 1948, McGraw-Hill published the fourth edition of a textbook called *Heredity*. Used by medical students into the 1950s, the book, by A. Franklin Shull, Professor of Zoology at the University of Michigan, still had an entire chapter titled "Eugenics".

A good deal of it would today pass muster as simple 'genetic counseling', to help families carrying known inherited diseases determine the risks of passing them on. Shull cannot, however, resist comment about the need for 'public policy' (p. 246) in situations where individuals are likely to resist simple encouragement not to reproduce. He says: "Society as a whole must decide." But then he seems to raise the stakes by adding: "The call for social control is especially obvious with respect to feeble-mindedness because the afflicted persons are not only incapable of sound judgment but are also particularly prolific." A few lines earlier, however, he has already made plain his view that those who are not capable of such "sound judgments" are not just the mentally afflicted.

As his eugenic itch grows stronger, he goes on to bemoan the "public burden" of defective people, among whom he includes epileptics, paupers and petty criminals. Shull flirts with discussions of what sort of public programs could attain the desired outcome, conceding that "to carry out any plan, there must be public support". His lobbying efforts in the book for such support are, though obvious, much more carefully worded than their usual pre-war counterparts. He seems continually conscious of a public that on the one hand needs the 'enlightenment' his scientific insights can bring on this noble topic, but on the other hand is now quite skittish, and must not be alienated. Shull even tries to put a positive spin on sterilization operations, claiming that it has been "reported" that they give physical and mental benefits to the recipients.

Not content with preventing 'inferior' people from breeding, Shull also has a section headed "Increasing the Superior". He discusses the notion of actively breeding from people whose traits are decreed to be of greater benefit to humanity and are thus a "superior class"—no different in principle from Hitler's attempt to breed a super-race.

The textbook also states plainly that those in laboring and farming occupations are going to be on average of a lower eugenic class of individual than those in the professions (like himself). Among the problems/questions listed at the end of the chapter for students to contemplate is this one: "What factors must be considered in determining how many children must be born to a pair of parents in order to maintain the class to which they belong?"

A subsequent chapter (p. 270) headed "Race and Immigration" provides the then-standard classification of people into "the Negroid, the Mongoloid and the Caucasian races". While this chapter, too, bears the marks of post-war nervousness about racial issues, he mentions the "cephalic index" (the ratio of skull measurements). While conceding as a weakness that this ratio could be affected by diet, he states that in the absence of dietary variation, "head shape is a very serviceable racial mark". No doubt that's what the Nazi officials who had my father's head measurements taken thought, too.

Again being very careful, Shull discusses things like the potential downsides of "miscegenation" (interracial marriage) and the desirability of admitting immigrants from various racial groups and countries. He often gets his points across by referring to the opinions of others, thus avoiding being too offensive himself. But he makes his own preferences plain, by stating that permitting immigration by people of the "same European stocks … could only be beneficial". Southeastern Europeans, Italians in particular, do not fare well in the chapter.

Another clear example of eugenics again rearing its ugly head appeared in *Scientific American* in November 1955— particularly notable because the same publication reprinted it in 2010, without criticizing any of its content.[9] The writer was the renowned evolutionist H.J. Muller (1890–1967), famous for his pre-war work on genetics, especially mutations in fruitflies. He was awarded the Nobel Prize in 1946 for his work linking mutations to X-rays.

Muller concedes that "in more than 99 percent of cases the mutation of a gene produces some kind of harmful effect, some disturbance of function". This is an interesting track record, incidentally, for a process that is supposed to have produced the intricately programmed functions of living things.[10] He states that "although each of us may be handicapped very little by any one of our detrimental genes, the sum of all of them causes a noticeable amount of disability, which is usually felt more as we grow older."[11]

Muller points out that in our modern civilization there is a "tremendous saving of human lives", many of which represent persons who "under more primitive conditions would have died as a result of genetic disabilities". Moreover, he says, such "genetically less capable survivors apparently do not have a much lower rate of multiplication than the more capable. *In fact, there are certain oppositely working tendencies*" (emphasis mine). Note how, despite the very careful wording, there is more than a hint of the common pre-WWII lament that 'genetically inferior' people are 'outbreeding' the 'superior' types.

Muller says that the danger from this increasing accumulation of inferior genes is that they will lead to problems for humanity that are worse than the effects of the radioactive fallout that concerned the people of his day. He calls for "basic education

9.   Muller, H.J., Radiation and human mutation, reprinted in 2010 in a special commemorative edition of *Scientific American*, 'Nobel-prize-winning authors volume II'.
10.   Selection can only choose from something that is there; it needs the genetic novelty that, in evolutionary theory, ultimately only mutation can provide. So it has no creative function of itself.
11.   Ref. 9, p. 44.

of the public and publicists" so that they might "reshape their deep-rooted attitudes and practices". The "alternate policy" he advocates, "hopeful it will be adopted", is that those "relatively heavily loaded with genetic defects would consider it their obligation… to refrain from transmitting their genes, except when they also possessed genes of such unusual value that the gain for the descendants was likely to outweigh the loss". Despite the carefully sanitized way in which Muller presents his proposal, the same old eugenic urge seems to be just under the surface.

There actually *is* a substantial biological problem posed by the increasing genetic burden of mutations accumulated in each generation since the Fall. Research in recent years shows that it's much worse than Muller realized, and points strongly to biblical (recent) creation—see 'The declining genes in our human family', p. 144. Given the naturalistic belief system of most evolutionists, it's not hard to see why they are repeatedly drawn to such innocuous-sounding 'rational solutions' as Muller's.

However, Muller admits that the effects of an individual mutation may be so subtle as to be barely noticeable, if at all. So which group in society would get to determine who, in fact, was "heavily loaded with genetic defects"? And who would adjudicate on the genes that needed preserving due to their "unusual value"?

Also, presuming that most individuals whose DNA is judged to be unworthy will not be so obliging as to voluntarily "refrain from transmitting their genes", such a policy would be pointless without some sort of compulsion … .

It seems the world has been to this movie before, and any rerun will not likely have a happier ending.

∞

6 PEOPLE GROUPS— GENES STILL MATTER

Does all this mean there are no significant genetic differences between the people groups commonly known as races? Definitely (and perhaps one should add 'obviously') not.

There are firstly the observable physical differences between groups. For example, Masai will on the average be much taller than Khoisan. These clearly reflect differences in the DNA code, i.e. genes. We're not talking qualitative differences here; it's not as if some people have genes for radically different biological structures or functions. It's just that some people will have more or less of particular characteristics (like melanin in the skin), and those differing proportions can, for a small number of characteristics as we've seen, be clustered in association with the groups identified as races.

DIFFERENCES REFLECTED IN GENES

Is it a coincidence that African Americans are more likely to excel in athletics, on average, than their European-American counterparts? Almost certainly not; there are very likely genetic differences in muscularity, again on the average. Maybe cardiovascular capacity, too. But all of us have muscles; it's just that some are more muscular than others. It has more to do with the 'average' distribution of characters in that population being such that one can talk about a genetic predisposition for certain traits.

There will of course be many very athletic and muscular individuals in non-African groups. And many less-than-athletic types among African Americans. It's just that on the whole … well, just check out the US's basketball 'Dream Team' when the next Olympics comes along. One doesn't have to be a prophet to predict a preponderance of African Americans over European-Americans, just as for previous Olympics.

Certain inherited diseases are much more common among some groups than others. For example, having at least one gene for the disease called sickle cell anemia is relatively common among African Americans, but almost unheard of in folk of northern European extraction. The reason is not hard to fathom, once one realizes that the people concerned came from areas of Africa where malaria was endemic (see section on sickle cell anemia and malaria, p. 138).

Passing on your defects

Inherited diseases, incidentally, are those caused by mutations, i.e. copying mistakes in genes. Reproduction involves passing on a copy of one half of your DNA. It's a different half each time, and there is also considerable recombination. This is why siblings, who inherit half of their DNA information from their mother and the other half from their father, don't all look alike.

Once there is a particular defect in a code being copied, and then *that copy* is copied, and so on, the defect will keep getting passed on. That's why mutation-caused diseases are inheritable. It's also why mutations are *accumulating* in all lines of organisms as time goes on—as another defect arises, it gets added to the existing defects already being copied, generation after generation. And natural selection, as will be mentioned shortly, can't get rid of these defects fast enough to stop them accumulating.

That's why each one of us is carrying thousands of these inherited mistakes, of which many have the potential to cause serious problems if they are inherited from both parents (see later in the section on Cain's wife).

Some mutation-caused diseases are found virtually exclusively in particular ethnic groups. For example, Tay–Sachs disease, caused by an inherited mutational defect, is very commonly found among Jewish people—specifically, within that group predominantly made up of Jews from Europe and Russia, called Ashkenazi Jews.[1,2]

In short, certain patterns of genes are more commonly found in one group as opposed to another. Plus, in our discussion of the criticisms levied at Lewontin on race, we have already seen that people can be classified into their recognizable groups once you have enough clusters of genes to compare. (This is not surprising, because any heritable variation in external characteristics, no matter how trivial it might be, must reflect variations in the underlying genetic code.)

Genetic screening takes ethnicity or race into account. So, increasingly, does research on the response of people to various medical treatments. That is not something in opposition to everyone's genetic closeness to each other, but something that makes perfect sense—if we apply common sense, as follows.

Some relatives closer than others

The main message of this book is to stress the implications of the fact that we human beings are all closely related—astonishingly

---

1.   To be distinguished from Sephardi Jews, generally defined as those descended from the Jewish inhabitants of Spain and Portugal before their expulsion in the late 1400s. In modern Israel, it includes Jews who follow a Sephardi liturgy, and includes many of Middle Eastern or African descent.
2.   There is actually more than one type of mutation that causes the clinical syndrome, which is a rare disease. It manifests when the child is a few months old, commencing a process of mental and physical decline until death occurs at a few years of age. The same mutation as in the Ashkenazi is not infrequently carried by the Cajun population of Louisiana. French Canadians of south-eastern Quebec are carriers about as commonly as Ashkenazi Jews—but it's not the same mutation, even though both they and the Cajuns have French ancestry.

SEMI-TECHNICAL

Sickle Cell Anemia and Malaria

Natural selection in malaria-prone regions will favor those who carry a mutated (damaged) gene from one parent for a defective form of hemoglobin (the molecule that gives red blood cells their color, and carries oxygen). This is because they are less likely to die in childhood from cerebral malaria caused by *Plasmodium falciparum*.

Those who happen to inherit one such damaged gene from *each* parent will have fullblown sickle cell anemia. This is a very serious and often fatal illness. Without modern medical care, transfusions and so on, reaching any sort of respectable old age is very unlikely for sufferers. This is because the red cell carrying only this defective form of hemoglobin (HbS) is distorted into a 'sickle' shape because of it, and destroyed by the spleen.

The reason that a carrier (someone with only the one defective gene) has a degree of immunity is that when the malaria parasite invades a red blood cell, it will often disturb the conditions around the hemoglobin sufficient to activate the sickling. The misshapen blood cell is then destroyed by the spleen, along with the parasite.

Normal red blood cell (rbc) and 'sickled' rbc.
iStockPhoto

Myths about sickling and malaria

1. 'Carriers are immune from malaria.'
   - Not so—especially as adults. The protection is mostly against death in childhood from one form of malaria.
2. 'Those with *two* sickle cell genes will be even more resistant to malaria than carriers, with their *one* such gene'.
   - In fact, they are more vulnerable to malaria and to dying from it.

3. 'Carriers are otherwise healthy and normal.'
   - There is a significant association of a large number of disease conditions with the carrier state.*

All in all, this mutation is hardly an example of an evolutionary improvement, as it is sometimes touted. Mutation has resulted in a defective form of a healthily functioning protein, hemoglobin. Natural selection in malaria-prone regions has generated a 'tradeoff', so that a much higher proportion of the population than otherwise will suffer from this devastating blood disease.

Dr. Felix Konotey-Ahulu

There is nothing in this that remotely suggests a mechanism for adding the complex functional information that would be needed to turn microbes into microbiologists. In fact, it is a good example of the way in which many mutations that benefit survival do so not by adding new information but by way of a 'scorched earth' policy. I.e. destroying things that the enemy could otherwise use (like when retreating defenders destroy bridges and burn crops). Similarly, in dealing with the malaria parasite, a blood cell is sacrificed for each organism destroyed.

Ironically for those who try to cling to sickle cell anemia as an example of 'evolution in action', the world's leading authority on this disease, distinguished Ghanaian medical scientist and geneticist Dr. Felix Konotey-Ahulu (pictured), is a convinced biblical creationist.[†]

*Tsaras, G. et al., Complications associated with sickle cell trait: a brief narrative review, Am. J. Med. **122**(6):507–512, 2009.

†See the interview with Dr. Konotey-Ahulu, titled Exposing Evolution's Icon, Creation **29**(1):16–19, 2006, creation.com/sickle2.

so, given the *a priori* expectations of an evolution-minded world. But clearly there are differing degrees of relatedness. You are more closely related to someone in your own 'inner' family (brother, sister, mother, father) than you are to someone in your extended family (cousins, nephews, nieces, and aunts and uncles other than by marriage). They, in turn, are more closely related to you than I would be. In the same way, members of a tribe descended from a small number of people are going to be more closely related to each other than to 'out-groups'. Thus, Aboriginal Australians[3] will be more closely related to each other than they are to someone of European ethnicity. The Adnyamathanha people of southern Australia's deserts will be more related to each other than they are to the Gugu Yalanji people from the rainforests of Australia's tropical northeast.

But a Gugu Yalanji and an Adnyamathanha person are probably more closely related to each other than they are to the average European. This is because creationists and evolutionists alike think that today's Aboriginal groups probably arose from a very small number of modest-sized 'founder' populations—for example, tribal groups progressively migrating down via the chain of islands to Australia's north. Upon reaching this island continent, they gradually dispersed further, coming to occupy quite different environments. We would disagree on the dates of when that took place, of course.

The only husbands and wives available to such an isolated population are going to be each other. Any pattern of gene frequencies in such a founder population will be reflected in similar patterns among all of those interrelated descendants.

We have already seen some of this in the discussion on skin color and Babel (p. 85ff.), of how a large group was broken up suddenly into smaller groups, which from then on were only able to marry within that smaller group. We mentioned how the differences in preponderance of certain genes, e.g. dark and light skin, would be reflected in differences between the groups. Some of these would be fixed or in the process of becoming so. Once

---

3.　'Aborigines' is an unpopular term among Aboriginal Australians, who today generally prefer to be referred to as simply 'indigenous Australians'. However, this also refers to the quite ethnically different group of people that inhabited the Torres Strait Islands off Far North Queensland before European settlement, so to avoid confusion I have used 'Aboriginal' where applicable.

those groups intermarry again, the cards are reshuffled, as it were.

In the case of the 'two-tone twins', the parents obviously had such a 'reshuffled' ancestry, so their descendants will once again have a great deal of variety in their genetic makeup. This will permit a whole lot of new combinations to arise. It again shows the ludicrousness of making a big deal about something as ephemeral as so-called 'racial' differences, such as skin color.

Also, one individual may happen to have a genetic mutation such that her descendants will either suffer from a disease or carry the gene to greater or lesser degrees of probability.[4] That's why it's not surprising that some types of mutations are more commonly found in some groups or 'races' than others. In fact, unless the same mutation had occurred in another person somewhere else, a particular mutation would be a 'marker' diagnostic of the group of people that descended from that individual. However, because of the relatively high rate of mutations overall, particular mutations might have happened more than once in human history.

But transplants ...?

I mentioned earlier, in reference to the black–white transplant between the two Aussies, Bill and Snow, that if you needed to receive an organ transplant, the best match available to you could well turn out to be someone from a totally different people group. Despite this, however, if you don't have an identical twin, you will *generally* be more likely to find a suitable donor among those closely related to you—if their organ in question is available to you. That's no surprise, and the more closely related, the more likely the match, obviously. Therefore, *generally speaking*, you will be more likely to find a good match from someone of your own ethnicity—for the simple reason that they will likely be more closely related to you than someone who is not.

The Bill and Snow situation surprises so many people (it sometimes stuns them, actually) because of their cultural assumptions about large alleged biological differences between

---

4.   Depending on how often carriers of the gene marry other carriers in subsequent generations.

FEATURE

The Word 'Race'—In or Out?

The Bible refers to tribes and nations, but does not refer to people groups as different races. In one sense, as stated, there is only 'the human race'. But in another sense, the word does have a proper connotation, in terms of our greater relatedness to one group than another. And most people who either use it or hear it know what is meant in the context. In fact, what would be the point of claiming that someone engages in discrimination on the basis of race, if there were no such thing as race?

The problem is of course that the word itself has become loaded with all of those biblically and biologically incorrect connotations we've been discussing. Nevertheless, it's not certain that taking a quasi- 'politically correct' route and avoiding it altogether is really helpful, and it may be somewhat artificial, too. That's why you'll notice, as stated earlier, that the words 'race(s)' and 'racial' are sometimes in scare quotes, but often are not.

iStockPhoto

It is far more important to stress the 'Genesis solution' to racism—the true and close relatedness of all of humanity, because we are all descendants of that one couple and, later, Noah's family. We're all *one human family*, and always have been, evolutionists and eugenicists notwithstanding.

such racial groups. These beliefs are often so deeply ingrained that it seems impossible that an organ transplant could ever work with such 'obviously different' ethnicities.

What I'm trying to highlight here is that, just as people in each of those extended family groups migrating from Babel were more closely related to each other than to those in other groups, this will be the same for all ethnic groups and tribes. This closer relatedness will be reflected in their genetic makeup, which in turn will be demonstrated by their physical and biological characteristics.

Given all these well-known facts and the speed with which variety can arise by such isolating mechanisms, the fact that we are all still so biologically close is a striking testimony to how recent our origin is, despite the popularity of 'millions of years'. For even more definitive evidence of this recency, see feature 'The Declining Genes in our Human Family' p. 144.

The reason for a group remaining genetically distinct, more closely related to each other than to the rest of humanity, does not have to be geographical isolation, such as in the post-Babel founder populations, or the early Australian Aboriginal people. Cultural/religious factors can also be the cause of marriages taking place mostly within the related group—for example, the Ashkenazi Jews. Another example is found in the Amish people. These live in small communities scattered throughout eighteen US states and southern Canada, with populations ranging from 1,000 or less up to 50,000 or so—some 100,000 in total.

Because marriage outside their community is forbidden, they are particularly closely related to each other. Unfortunately, it also means that they have an extremely high rate of inherited diseases, including some very serious ones. Some are so rare they don't even have a name yet. All this has led to the Amish being a source of useful research information for those studying patterns of inheritance.

THE (NON-) ENIGMA OF CAIN'S WIFE

The topic of inherited defects and close intermarriage brings up the issue some readers might think I've been avoiding. Namely, if all people came from Adam and Eve, doesn't this mean that in the first few generations, brothers, sisters, nephews, nieces—all kinds of close relatives—would have had to marry each other?

Correct. But the Bible is adamant that we all started off from that one couple. All people alive on Earth are the descendants

FEATURE

The Declining Genes in our Human Family

Dr. John Sanford

D r. John Sanford (at right) is renowned as a pioneer in the field of genetic engineering. He is a former evolutionist and professor at Cornell University, where he maintains the title of Courtesy Professor. The scientific evidence in his own field of genetics was instrumental in convincing him of recent, six-day Genesis creation. His landmark book *Genetic Entropy and the Mystery of the Genome** shows that mutations have thrust all multicellular life on a fast track to extinction. It also shows that in humans, mutations are accumulating so quickly in our DNA that the human genome is already perilously close to 'error catastrophe'.

More specifically, the human genome cannot possibly have been around for even hundreds of thousands, let alone millions, of years. Selection slows the decline, but even intense selection has no hope of getting rid of most of the mutations. This is because most of them, though deleterious overall, are individually very close to 'neutral' in their effects, meaning that selection cannot weed them out (see H. J. Muller's relevant comment decades earlier, p. 132; the known rates of mutation are *many* times what Muller thought).

Dr. Sanford has also collaborated with other creationists (notably geophysicist Dr. John Baumgardner—pictured page right—who developed the world's leading supercomputer model of plate tectonics) in the development of a rigorous computer simulation of mutation and selection, named *Mendel's Accountant*. Doctors Sanford and Baumgardner both spoke at a major CMI conference on Philip Island, Australia, in January 2009. They explained why they believe that the proposed evolutionary mechanism has now been comprehensively falsified. A stunning presentation by Dr. Sanford on this whole subject of our declining genes is available on DVD.*

In an interview for *Creation* magazine, Sanford said:

"Even with intense selection, evolution is going the wrong way—toward extinction! ... The bottom line is that Darwinian theory fails on every level ... all higher genomes must clearly degenerate. This is exactly what we would expect in light of Scripture—with the Fall—and is consistent with the declining life expectancies after the Flood that the Bible records. The problem of genetic entropy (genomes are all degenerating), is powerful evidence that life and mankind must be young."[†]

A recent paper on mutations in humans, by the University of Indiana's Mike Lynch in the *Proceedings of the National Academy of Sciences* (USA), adds weight to Dr. Sanford's comments. Though doubtless there will be attempts to reconcile the findings with the evolutionary paradigm, Lynch states that mutation imposes "a substantial burden on fitness through the production of predominantly deleterious alleles, a matter of concern from a human-health perspective" and that "a substantial reduction in human fitness can be expected over the next few centuries in industrialized societies unless novel means of genetic intervention are developed." He also estimated that:

Dr. John Baumgardner

"... it is likely that an average newborn acquires a total of 50 to 100 new mutations at the diploid level, a small subset of which must be deleterious."

This is vastly more than previously thought, and serves to further strengthen Sanford's conclusions.[‡]

*See creation.com/store

†Batten, D., Plant geneticist: "Darwinian evolution is impossible" (interview with Dr. John Sanford), *Creation* **30**(4):45–47, 2008, creation.com/sanford.

‡Lynch, M., Rate, molecular spectrum and consequences of human mutation, *Proceedings of the National Academy of Sciences*, 19 January 2010, accessed at www.pnas.org, 13 October 2010.

of Adam—and so is Eve. She was not made directly from raw materials (dust) like Adam, but from his body. So because Eve was, like the rest of us, a physical descendant of Adam's, he truly is the federal head of all humanity. But there is more to it than that. The prophet Isaiah spoke of the coming Messiah as literally the 'Kinsman-Redeemer' (Isaiah 59:20), i.e. one who is *related by blood* to those he redeems. The same Hebrew word גֹּאֵל (*gôēl*) is used to describe Boaz in relation to Ruth. Hebrews 2:11–18 also explains how Jesus took upon Himself the nature of a man to save mankind, but not angels—nor hypothetical aliens, for that matter. This is a clinching argument against intelligent life on other planets, incidentally. Jesus never took on Vulcan or Romulan nature, for example; He now sits at the right hand of God the Father, as the Advocate for His kinsmen whom He redeemed.[5]

In the incarnation, Jesus entered Adam's line to literally become our relative, to be a part of this *one human family*. Eve's physical descent from Adam is thus crucial to the possibility of her salvation. If all people are not descended from Adam, this vital kinsman-redeemer concept is undermined. Or, conversely, there are people around today who are not able to be saved, as He is not their relative. Both are biblically unviable.

So that would seem to leave Christians on the horns of an unsolvable dilemma. The puzzle can be stated like this:

EITHER: Adam and Eve weren't the only people at the beginning. But then the Bible is unreliable, and also only some humans can be saved, not all.

OR: Adam and Eve were the only two people around.

But that has to mean brothers marrying sisters. And it is widely believed that this can't be, because of two apparently huge problems.

Apparent problem 1—biological

Close intermarriage like that is known to give rise to serious

---

5.   See also Bates. G., *Alien Intrusion* (book) and creation.com/did-god-create-life-on-other-planets.

defects in the offspring.

Apparent problem 2—moral

God has given a law to mankind which forbids marrying even one's half-sister or half-brother.

Genetic backup copies

The biological problem comes from the fact that, as stated earlier, we all carry substantial numbers of seriously defective genes. These have accumulated from those copying mistakes, generation after generation, in our ancestors. Our genes are like sentences of code. They are stretches of our DNA 'recipe' that specify making some particular protein—e.g. insulin for regulating blood sugar, or hemoglobin for carrying oxygen in the blood. Genes come in pairs—one inherited from your mother and one from your father. And it's a good thing they do, because if you inherit a defective copy of the gene for making insulin from one parent, you still have the normal instructions for making it on the gene from the other parent. It's like a 'backup copy' arrangement. But if you were to inherit the same defective gene from both parents, then you would have no set of normal instructions for making insulin.

Many of these inherited defects work that way, so that there is a noticeable problem only if *both copies* are defective.[6] That's why we don't usually show the substantial numbers of mistakes (defective or mutated genes) we carry. When you marry someone outside your close family, you and your spouse each have hundreds (some estimates have it at 800 or so) of these inherited mistakes capable of causing serious disease or deformity. But they're usually not the same ones. So there's generally no problem, as there are thousands of 'OK' genes. But if someone were to marry

---

6. The technical term for such genes is 'recessive', which means that they are kind of 'hidden' until one sees their effects when they're paired up with each other. Where the mutation in question causes a disease, people having only one copy of a recessive gene do not get the disease. But since they can contribute that gene to the next generation, they are called carriers of the disease in question. (Note: all inherited diseases are caused by mutations, but not all mutations by any means cause inherited diseases. Most are either neutral, or the defects they introduce are too mild in isolation to cause recognizable clinical syndromes.)

a sibling, they would both have the same parents. So the chances are really high that several of these same mistakes will 'pair up' (see diagram at right). Even marrying a half-sister or half-brother would be a substantial risk of genetic problems.

But notice from before how these mistakes accumulate more and more as you go forwards in time, as another copying mistake is added to the previous ones being copied. So as we go back in time, there are fewer and fewer mistakes, until we get to the first couple, Adam and Eve, who had *no* mistakes. After the Fall, with God in a sense pulling back somewhat from His previous superintendence of a perfect world, such things as defects could start to happen each time there was reproduction. But it would take time—many centuries, in fact—before the numbers of mistakes would be high enough for close intermarriage to be a substantial genetic risk. (By the way, remember that we're talking here about real marriages, lawful before God, not some sort of child abuse.)

And there is biblical support for that. Abraham lived many centuries after creation—a good many years after the Flood, even. Yet he was still able to marry his *half-sister*, Sarah. And there is no hint of any deformity in the offspring. That child was Isaac, who became an ancestor of our Lord Jesus Christ. Nor is there any condemnation of Abraham's marriage to Sarah. There is no suggestion that it was anything other than a blessed union, which eventually gave rise to the promised Messiah.

Why not? Why didn't God at least rebuke Abraham for having broken His law? Simple—because Abraham did not break any law in marrying Sarah. That particular law was given at the time of Moses, hundreds of years after Abraham. Close marriage was originally *essential* in fulfilling God's purposes in starting humanity off with just one couple. But in a fallen world in which defects are accumulating, it makes sense for Him to draw the curtain on it at some stage.

New times, new law

Incidentally, I don't believe that this is a case of God changing His standards, as some have suggested. I've often used the following analogy. Imagine a shepherd looking after his flock on an open meadow. There are no wild animals around, and the only danger to the sheep is at one end of the meadow, where it forms the edge of cliffs from which they could fall down. So the shepherd builds a fence, but only around the cliffs. That fence represents a law, a 'Thou shalt not'. There is no need to fence the rest of the meadow.

Some time later, a pack of wolves (it's dingoes for audiences in Australia ☺) moves into the district. Now there is a new danger

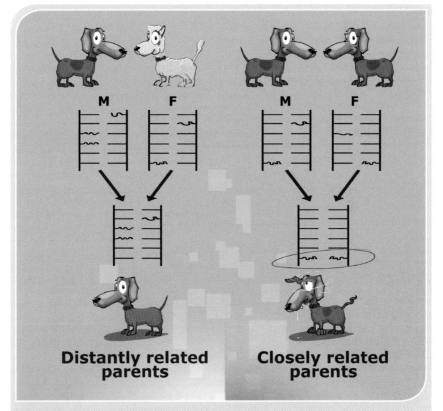

Distantly related parents

Closely related parents

INBREEDING AND GENETIC DEFECTS

These dogs inherit one stretch of DNA from each parent. The straight horizontal lines represent genes still undamaged by mutation; squiggly lines represent mutated genes. The dog on the bottom left is the offspring of two distantly related parents, so the mother's DNA has different defects from the father's. Every one of her defective genes is masked by the backup copy from the father, and vice versa. But the unfortunate dog on the bottom right is the offspring of close relatives. Because the father and mother have many of the same mutations, this dog has inherited a pair of the same mutant genes. This is relevant to 'Cain's wife' (main text).

SEMI-TECHNICAL

Was Eve a Partial Clone of Adam?

It is theologically very significant (see main text) that Eve was, like the rest of us, a physical descendant of Adam. That's why she was not created separately from basic elements ('dust') like Adam was, but from the flesh and bone of Adam's rib.* So some have suggested that she shared the same DNA.

In that proposal, God 'cloned' all of Adam's DNA, with an added twist that meant she would be a different gender. Women have two copies of the X chromosome, whereas men have an X and a Y chromosome. It is the 'Y' which specifies maleness, so the suggestion is that God merely deleted that, and duplicated Adam's X chromosome to end up with Eve's XX pattern.

This idea does have significant consequences, however. For any position ('locus') on the chromosome, any individual can only carry a maximum of two different types (or 'alleles') of the gene. This is due to the fact that we carry two copies of each chromosome. The more alleles for a given gene, the more the potential variety there is in any population from reshuffling and recombination of existing genes; all without any 'evolution'.

In the case of Adam and Eve starting the whole of humanity, that means that for any locus, the maximum originally created variability, i.e. the *maximum* number of alleles (different forms of the same gene), is four (two on each of the couple). Let's use the gene for a hypothetical protein, and call that gene 'Z'. That means it could originally have existed only in four different forms, or variants of Z. Call these Z_A, Z_B, Z_C, and Z_D, where Adam might have $Z_A + Z_B$ so Eve would have to have $Z_C + Z_D$ to get all the types in that first couple. If there are any more than four then it means that some of them arose by mutation.

Specifically, if the number of alleles is 'N' then the minimum number that had to arise by mutation after the Fall is 'N – 4' (Some such mutations, even though they would appear random, might also have arisen by 'directed' mutation if there turns out to be an algorithm in the genome to do this. 'Designed variability' exists in the human immune system, for instance.)

Having mutation generate additional 'versions' (alleles) does not mean that mutation has created new functional structures. Many proteins have sections on their long chain of 'letters' (amino acids) that are deeply involved in the molecule's function. So having one 'typo' (one amino acid substituted by the wrong one) in such places on the molecule leads to disastrous consequences. An example is sickle cell anemia, where one amino acid in the wrong spot causes this major disease. But there are often other sections on such a protein that are nowhere near as crucial to its intended function. Thus, the sequence of these 'letters' in such sections can tolerate quite a bit of random 'typographical' error without causing any problems.

Now if the 'clone' idea were right, that would restrict the maximum number of alleles at any locus to *two*, which places an additional explanatory burden on the postulate of mutations for all the rest.

Interestingly, some of the evidence coming in indicates that variation in most genes in humans is extremely limited, tending to support the 'clone' idea after all. There seem to be only two original blood groups, for instance—A and B; the most common of the O variants is obviously a 'broken' copy of the A allele.[†] So it is likely to have been a mutation early in human history. This, incidentally, would make Eve even more definitively a physical descendant of Adam.

The Bible does not speak directly for or against the 'clone' theory, and there is still much more to learn about human genetics. So one would not want to come down definitively on one side or the other of this notion, but rather to 'hang loose' on it for the moment.

*Note that when the periosteum (a membrane that surrounds every bone) is left intact, ribs routinely regenerate; Adam did not have to walk around with a defective ribcage. One of my own ribs re-grew several times following surgery. See the booklet *Adam's Rib: Creation and the Human Body* at creation.com/store.

†There are other rare blood groups that have arisen relatively recently through mutations causing the *loss* of surface antigens on blood cells.

to the sheep; if they stray beyond the sight of the shepherd, they risk being killed and eaten. So a new set of rules is called for, a new 'thou shalt not', and the shepherd now puts a fence around the entire meadow.

SEMI-TECHNICAL

Origin of the Blood Types

One aspect of the wide variety of humans is all the different blood types. The following explanation covers the main **A**, **B** and **O** blood types.

The **A** and **B** blood groups are caused by different antigens (substances which provoke immune responses) on the surface of the red blood cells. Their production is under the control of the DNA. The antigens develop from a red blood cell surface precursor called H substance, which is common to **A**, **B** and **O**. Type **A** results from the placement of N-acetylgalactosamine by the enzyme type **A** transferase on the H substance. Type **B** results from attachment of galactose to H by Type **B** transferase.

Type **O** is very likely the result of a simple point mutation that greatly reduced or destroyed the ability of Type **A** transferase to attach N-acetylgalactosamine to H substance. Note that this is an example of **loss** of information, so is irrelevant to particles-to-people evolution. This ineffective Type **A** transferase is called circulating protein. The ineffectiveness of type **O**'s circulating protein depends on the point in the DNA where the mutation occurred, because some type **O**s attach more N-acetylgalactosamine to H than others. This sometimes causes discrepancies between blood banks. The mutations probably happened early in human history, since **O** is the most common blood group. Unattached H substance itself is an antigen which results in the rare blood type Bombay or O_h.

There is one gene in humans that controls the **ABO** blood type. There are three versions of the gene, or alleles: **A**, **B**, or **O**. Since the gene is always present as a pair of alleles, with one inherited from each parent, the possible genetic make-up of any individual is **AA**, **BB**, **AB**, **AO**, **BO**, or **OO**. The **O** allele is recessive to the **A** or **B**, meaning that in the presence of the **A** or **B** allele, the blood type is determined by the **A** or **B** allele. That is, an **AO** person has **A**-type blood; a **BO** person has **B**-type blood, whereas only an **OO** person has **O**-type blood. Anyone with **O**-type blood is called a universal donor because their blood lacks the **A** or **B** antigens, so **O**-type blood can be given to a person with blood of type **A**, **B** or **AB**. If, for example, **A**-type blood is given to a person with **B**-type blood, an allergic reaction can result in death of the recipient.

For a husband and wife to pass on all alleles to their children, they need to, between them, have the **A**, **B**, and **O** alleles. So Adam and Eve could have had any of the following genetic make-ups: **AO** and **BO**, **AB** and **OO**, **AB** and **AO**, **AB** and **BO**, **AA** and **BO** or **BB** and **AO**; that is, any combination where both parents have all three alleles between them. Another possibility is that the **O** gene arose later by mutation as discussed above. If so, the parents would only need to have **A** and **B** between them, so they could both be **AB**, or **AA** and **AB**, **BB** and **AB** or **AA** and **BB**.

If Adam and Eve were genetically **AO** and **BO**, for example, their children could have had **AB**, **AO**, **BO** or **OO** genetic make-up, giving **AB**, **A**, **B**, or **O** blood types. Indeed, about 25% of their children would have been of each type (see the Punnett square above).

	A	O
B	AB	BO
O	AO	OO

The above was extracted from Sarfati, J., Countering the Critics: Blood types and their origin, *Journal of Creation* **11**(1):31–32, 1997, creation.com/blood-groups. As Dr. Sarfati states elsewhere in this article, "It is a mistake to assume [as many do—CW] that there is no use for the blood types. There are immunological relationships between **A, B** and H antigens and those of bacteria and vegetable matter and how our bodies respond to invading micro-organisms without destroying self."

It's interesting to note that Native Americans are almost 98% blood group **O**. This extraordinarily high percentage suggests strong selection pressures favoring this gene. It has been postulated that the gene confers some resistance to syphilis, which decimated Amerindian populations with the advent of Europeans. Recall the earlier section (p. 138) on sickle cell anemia and malaria; this is often called an example of 'balancing selection'. The sickle cell gene is selected for because of malaria resistance, but its disease-causing downside means it is also selected against. So the level of sickle cell genes in the population strikes a 'balance' between these opposing selection pressures. With blood type **O**, no such downside is known, so the selection will all go in one direction, allowing much higher levels of the gene to be attained in that population.

The shepherd's standards have not changed; his loving care for the flock is the same as always. But times have changed, and a new law is called for in order to express that loving care.

Incidentally, you can still marry a relative today. In fact, you have no choice, if you want to marry a human being—because we *are* all related. So, if you didn't marry a relative, you would not be marrying a human being! Because of those accumulating effects of the Curse, it is both biblically wrong and biologically disastrous to marry a *really close* relative, like a sibling or half-sibling. And it's against the law in most places, too, for good reason.

All in all, we can see that the biblical and biological considerations in this matter are not a problem for the idea of our descent from Adam and Eve. In fact, they are strongly consistent with it.

Interracial marriage was discussed earlier (p. 95) and we saw that it was not a biblical or biological problem. We also saw from the case of our two-tone twins that it increases the potential genetic variety in the offspring. But we can now see that it's a biological positive in another way, too. Simply put, if you marry someone from a different ethnic group, you're marrying someone who is less closely related to you than those from your own group. So you are even less likely to have the same harmful mutations coming together in your children.

∞

7 THE EVER-CHANGING STORY OF 'HUMAN EVOLUTION'

I mentioned how human evolution theories had to be changed to cope with the genetic evidence of our relatedness. A big part of this change in modern times is one that many would have heard of. It's the 'out of Africa' story of human evolution, also associated with 'African Eve'.

OUT OF AFRICA—REPEATEDLY

I've had people ask me, puzzled, why this is a big deal for evolutionists. Haven't they been saying since Darwin that people are 'out of Africa', because that's where they first evolved from apes? True, but here's the change that's happened, and it could really be called 'out of Africa—twice'. Evolutionists still believe that people (or at least the genus *Homo*) evolved from apes in Africa, but that was the first time, they say, over a million or so years ago, that people left Africa. They claim that these early 'almost-people' (in their view) spread out over the earth. Some of them became the Neandertals (see shortly), and then there was Peking Man in China, Java Man in Indonesia, and so on. All of these were upright, tool-making populations with distinct cultures.

But meanwhile, the story goes, back in Africa, some of these early people were evolving into what are now modern humans, with much less robust (i.e. with 'gracile') bony features. Then, they postulate (for reasons we will see later) that their population went through a genetic bottleneck, i.e. shrank to a fairly small number. All or some of this small group then left Africa (again) and spread out across the earth. This was a long time—more than a million years—after the first African exodus. The date for this second-wave migration varies greatly, but seems to be settling on some 200,000 years ago. This group of newcomers eventually replaced all the other human groups that were living in places like Europe and Asia—either by outcompeting them, or by wiping them out in some sort of prehistoric ethnic cleansing. Notice, by the way, how this now makes it easier for evolutionists to 'explain' why we are all so closely related.

African Eve

I referred to African Eve, aka Mitochondrial Eve, as part of this 'out of Africa' story. Here's what that's about. Most of our DNA is inherited equally from our mother and father. But there is a small bit of our DNA that is different. It's in the mitochondria,[1] little energy factories inside the cell. This mitochondrial DNA, or mtDNA, is virtually never inherited from one's father, just from one's mother. (Before the egg is fertilized, the egg cell already contains mitochondria, so the existing 'maternal' mitochondria are just duplicated with no input from Dad.[2]) Mutations also occur in the mtDNA. By comparing the mtDNA from different people (i.e. by comparing the patterns of these mistakes), we can make reasoned guesses as to maternal lines of descent.

Many important things can be learned from such studies, even though most researchers will always try to shoehorn the results into some sort of evolutionary framework. From this work came

---

1.   Singular = mitochondrion.
2.   The mitochondria from the sperm are actively destroyed in humans. Paternal mtDNA inheritance happens regularly in some species, but is thought to be rare or non-existent in humans, despite a paper in the year 2000 suggesting some degree of recombination in mtDNA.

the idea of this 'Eve', because it's possible to trace all of the mitochondrial lines back to one woman. The claim is that she is 'the mother of us all', and that some of her descendants were part of a small group that came 'out of Africa'. Before going on, we need to understand that this relates to lines of maternal descent only, and that this 'Eve' could have been living alongside Suzie, Judy, Rebecca, etc. All of these other women theoretically living with her could have contributed genes to later generations, but their *mitochondrial* lines have died out (their line of female descendants ceased somewhere).

To explain, consider the analogy of *surnames*. In Western culture, these are only passed on via the father, so it's the converse of mtDNA, which only passes on via the mother. Notice that surnames can die out in a given population. My paternal grandfather, Carl G. Wieland, had six children. The only one of his three sons to have any male offspring was my father. I was an only son, so I'm the only one in that generation of the family to have inherited the surname. But apart from my two wonderful daughters, I had no other children. That means that the surname in that paternal line has died out due to a lack of male offspring. Similarly, mtDNA 'bloodlines' can die out; individual maternal lines reach dead ends if there are no female descendants. In time, there may be only a few mitochondrial ancestors identifiable, even though many of the women whose mitochondrial lines have been extinguished contributed genes to our nuclear DNA via their male descendants.

So this research is not *necessarily* saying that there was only one woman from whom all came. But as Dr. Robert Carter (pictured), who is a speaker-scientist for CMI in the US and whose qualifications are in marine biology and genetics, states:

> "Evolutionists expected modern humans to be descended
> from many female lineages. When they only found one,
> they invoked a 'population bottleneck' as an explanation.
> That is, the number of people living in Africa supposedly
> shrank sharply to as few as 1,000–10,000 people—and

we only just escaped becoming extinct. They reason that, while many females lived during this bottleneck period, only one lineage persisted, with the others going extinct through random chance.[3] The parallels to the Bible are glaringly obvious. Genesis tells us clearly that humanity went through a population bottleneck (the Flood, where only 8 people survived), with one ultimate female ancestress (Eve).[4]"5

In short, the findings are totally consistent with us being descended from the biblical Eve.

Another plank of this theory is that there is more genetic diversity in African populations than those in other parts of the world. This gives statistical support to the idea that modern humans spread out from Africa, rather than Ararat, in contrast to what the Bible would indicate. But Professor Sir Alec Jeffreys, who discovered DNA fingerprinting, has published new research in September 2010 that places serious doubt on the assumptions used for these 'out of Africa' conclusions.

Dr. Robert Carter

To explain his research: It's been known for a long time that the key factor in diversity is the reshuffling of our genes with each generation, a process called recombination. But this has long been believed to be totally random, a necessary assumption for the claim that greater genetic diversity in Africa means African origins. For the last 20 years, Jeffreys has been investigating unusual and highly variable bits

3.   Carter, R.W., The Neutral Model of evolution and recent African origins, *J. Creation* **23**(1):70–77, 2009.
4.   See Wieland, C., Mitochondrial Eve and biblical Eve are looking good: criticism of young age is premature, *J. Creation* **19**(1):57–59, 2005.
5.   Carter, R., cited in Sarfati, J., Corals, genes and creation, *Creation* **33**(1):53–55, 2011, creation.com/carter-interview.

of DNA called 'minisatellites' in people. He found that these were changing and "picking up mutations at an extraordinary rate" relative to other DNA.

Now, Jeffreys and his team from the Department of Genetics at the University of Leicester, UK, have shown that a gene called PRDM9 influences and controls the development of little areas on the DNA that are like 'hotspots'. At these hotspots recombination takes place much faster than elsewhere.[6] There is, oddly, a minisatellite in PRDM9 that affects the way it drives "all kinds of human DNA diversity, including variation at minisatellites themselves."

This is complex stuff. But the bottom line seems to be that once there is genetic control, with something that modifies the control, variation is no longer statistically truly random. So the whole 'out of Africa' thing looks like having to go back to the drawing board. This new research raises the prospect of an explanation from these hotspots for the greater diversity in African populations.

Incidentally, CMI's Dr. Carter is also involved in research in collaboration with Dr. John Sanford (feature p. 144). The research involves human mtDNA in populations around the world, looking at the patterns of migration in and among various people groups.

Some exciting things are emerging. For instance, mtDNA seems to be showing three main mitochondrial lineages spread out on all continents. Secular researchers are aware of this pattern but seem oblivious to its ramifications. It matches what we might expect from biblical history. Genesis 9:18–19 strongly implies that after the Flood, Noah and his wife had no more children (for one thing, he was already 600 years old[7] when the Flood started). Thus, the world was solely repopulated from Noah's three sons and his three daughters-in-law. Referring to these three women and their mitochondrial lineages, Dr. Carter said in a recent interview for *Creation* magazine:

6. Jeffreys, A. *et al.*, Role of key genetic catalyst for human diversity discovered, www.sciencedaily.com, 6 September 2010, accessed 10 October 2010.
7. For an explanation of long lifespans and the post-Flood decline, see Wieland, C., Living for 900 years, *Creation* **20**(4):10–13, 1998, creation.com/900.

FEATURE

People Getting Taller

Looking at the suits of armor in medieval collections, it's clear that we are significantly bigger in most respects than previous generations. This is a continuing trend; the average woman today is taller than the average male soldier in World War I. So are we evolving greater height in some Darwinian sense? Evolutionists themselves agree that this trend reflects environmental factors, not genetic ones, so it has nothing to do with evolution. It's come about through improvements in such things as nutrition and childhood disease control. Some of the fossils of humans living prior to the Middle Ages seem to have overall been more strapping specimens than later people. If the same conditions of poor health and nutrition as in medieval times were to return, children would again not grow to be as tall.

One sometimes hears speculation that Adam was extremely tall. Some of the more extreme claims I have heard (unfortunately, from a tiny minority of well-meaning creation-defenders) have him as anything up to 20 ft (6 m) tall (!). Apart from the lack of any biblical basis for this, there is the problem of scale. Say you were to scale a human being up from 6 to 18 feet, i.e. triple every linear dimension.* The volume of the person (hence their weight) would not triple, it would go up by a factor of 27 (3^3)! So a person weighing 130 lbs (60 kg) would now weigh 1¾ US tons (1½ tonnes)! However, sturdiness of bones and strength

Lifesize wax sculpture of the late Robert Wadlow, 272 cm (8ft 11.1 in) tall, alongside CMI's Dr. Jonathan Sarfati, who at 182 cm (6 ft) tall is actually of above-average height, at the Ripley's Believe it or Not museum, Gold Coast, Australia, 2006 (see text at right).

of muscles is proportional to the cross-sectional area. This would not have increased 27 times, only 9 (3^2) times. That means that in order to support this new crushing weight, or to move as easily, it would not be enough that this person's legs were three times the diameter as previously; they would have to be *much* thicker than that.

That's the reason why elephants, though only modestly bigger than a draft-horse in linear dimensions, have leg bones that are *very much* thicker in proportion to those of horses. From this consideration alone (and there are others) a 20-ft (3-m) high person would have to be substantially 'redesigned'. But we are the biological descendants of Adam and Eve, i.e. we have inherited our DNA information from them, in addition to our collection of mutations acquired since the Fall. Hence the design of their bodies could not have been radically different from ours. So on that basis, Adam could not have been that tall.

The tallest people reliably documented in modern times are around or just under 9 ft (2.7 m)—the modern record is Robert Wadlow (1918–1940), who stood 2.72 m or 8 ft 11.1 inches tall (see photo left). That's roughly the same as the tallest person in the Bible for whom the actual height is given, the giant Goliath.[†]

*It's a reasonable approximation to regard the body as a sphere and the cross-section of the legs as the area of a circle. Whereas the area of a circle increases proportional to the radius *squared*, the volume of a sphere increases by the radius *cubed*.

†The bedstead of King Og (Deuteronomy 3:11) was over 13 feet (4 m) long, if the 18-inch cubit is used. But his height is not mentioned. King's beds are often deliberately oversized to express opulence and grandeur. Very palatial hotel suites not uncommonly have beds that are some 30–50% longer than their expected occupant's height. So the size of a king's bed is not a reliable measure of his precise height. There is no biblical reason to assume that he was significantly taller than the giant Goliath.

"Even though they were direct descendants of Eve, each of them would have carried their own particular mutations, picked up in the generations prior to the Flood. After the Flood, their descendants spread out across the world from Babel."[8]

Dr. Carter is the presenter in a fascinating DVD which is called *The three 'daughters' of Noah*, and is about these sorts of

8.   Carter, R., cited in ref. 5.

developments. Stay tuned![9]

APEMAN CLAIMS

To do a detailed analysis of the fossil evidence alleged for 'human evolution' is beyond the scope of this book. But to leave it without any comment at all seems inappropriate, since it's this particular aspect of evolution, that mankind supposedly descended from ape-like creatures, that has led to so much race-related anguish.

Fortunately, it's not that difficult to deal with. This is because for several decades now, with few exceptions (one is the tiny fossil human from Indonesia—see feature 'Hobbit Wars' p. 164), a consistent pattern has emerged, as we will see. I'm referring to the 'hominids', as a collective name for fossil creatures that are supposed to be ancestral to all of us, and transitional between us and the alleged common ancestor of both apes and humans.[10]

It's as if with each such hominid fossil find, there are more and more pixels switching on but the picture on the screen was already obvious in outline some time ago. Each of the pixels just fills in some details, without changing the big picture. That is, all of the finds just keep on more or less naturally falling into one of only a very small handful of major groups—three, in fact.

So, by doing an overview assessment of them all, as will follow, the reader will very likely be able to apply it to any future hominid claims. This is because such finds will have a high probability of falling into one of these three groups. The purpose is to equip readers with the tools to be able to work out where to mentally 'slot in' the next such discovery that is proclaimed as a 'human ancestor'.

Most of these hominid specimens are found in deposits which were very likely formed after the Flood. When something is found

---

9.   An important way of keeping up with cutting-edge stuff in all creation-related fields is of course through getting *Journal of Creation* posted to your home. Subscribing (see creation.com/journal-of-creation) also helps creationist research.
10.   Strictly speaking, the term is also often applied to those believed to be from a group regarded as a 'side-branch', rather than directly ancestral, where the group is believed to be significant in helping flesh out the story of human evolution.

in a cave, for example, it means that it was post-Flood. For one thing, this is because the walls of the cave are often made of strata containing marine fossils formed during the Flood.

In the discussion that follows, you'll note that I've left out the Cro-Magnon finds, the classical cave people that drew beautiful works of art on cave walls. This is because everyone agrees that they were anatomically modern humans, just like us.

Neandertals

The first specimen of 'Neanderthal Man' (today often spelt 'Neandertal') unearthed in modern times was in 1856, in Germany's Neander valley. In German, *tal* means valley, and it was named after Joachim Neander (Neumann) (1650–1680), writer of the famous hymn, *Praise to the Lord, the Almighty, the King of Creation* (German title: *Lobe den Herren, den mächtigen König der Ehren*). In old German it was spelt *thal*, hence the variation in spelling—but there is no difference in pronunciation. The rules for nomenclature mean that the original spelling stays for the scientific name. This is either *Homo sapiens neanderthalensis* or *Homo neanderthalensis*, depending on whether the namer believes they were a 'subspecies' of modern man or a separate species altogether.

Neandertals have more robust skeletons than most people living today. Everything about them is consistent with regarding them as post-Flood/post-Babel descendants of Adam, members of our *one human family*. We have seen how certain physical characteristics and genetic patterns predominate in some groups of our relatives as opposed to others. The Neandertals had a distinctive combination of bony features, and bone structure is controlled to a large extent by genes (in addition to factors such as physical load[11]). Although most people today don't have prominent brow ridges (as most Neandertals did for instance), some do.

Evolutionist Donald Johanson was the discoverer of the

---

11.   See Wieland, C., Bridges and bones, girders and groans, *Creation* **12**(2):20–24, 1990, creation.com/bones.

FEATURE

Hobbit Wars

Fossil evidence of a midget human type, less than 1 m (c. 3 ft) tall and with a grapefruit-sized brain, was found in 2003 on the Indonesian island of Flores. At the time of writing (mid-2011) arguments still rage among evolutionists as to its significance. One camp claims it's a separately evolved hominid species, *Homo floresiensis*, another that it's a pathological modern type of human. Each side has recently brought out salvos claiming to be 'definitive'. The latest will likely not be the last shot fired, and is from a team led by an evolutionist Professor Emeritus of Anatomy at the University of Western Australia, Charles Oxnard.* It purports to conclusively confirm their previous finding that the 'Hobbit' specimens are consistent with a type of dwarf cretinism associated with iodine deficiency (which is endemic in the region). Oxnard, previously awarded the Charles R. Darwin Award for Lifetime Achievement in Physical Anthropology, says that this notion "would not occur to evolutionary biologists because evolutionary biologists would be looking for things to do with evolution".[†]

Cast of reconstructed skull of the 'Hobbit'.
CC-BY-SA 2.0 Ryan Somma

*Oxnard, C., *et al.*, Post-cranial skeletons of hypothyroid cretins show a similar anatomical mosaic as Homo floresiensis, *PLoS ONE* **5**(9) 2010, DOI:10.1371/journal.pone.0013018.

†Weber, D., Hobbit was a cretin, not a new human, abc.net.au, 28 September 2010, accessed, 18 November 2010.

famous 'Lucy' fossil. In *Lucy's Child*, the book he co-authored with James Shreeve, we read concerning Darwin's chief defender, friend and apostle, Thomas Huxley:

"From a collection of modern human skulls Huxley was able to select a series with features leading 'by insensible gradations' from an average modern specimen to the Neandertal skull. In other words, it wasn't qualitatively different from present-day *Homo sapiens*."[12]

Though many in his day would have liked to use this to show that Neandertals evolved into modern humans, Huxley himself did not, regarding them instead as fully human. However, nowadays most evolutionists do not believe that Neandertals were a direct ancestor of modern people, but rather a side branch. Huxley's skulls make perfect sense if one sees Neandertals as part of the range of bony variation in our *one human family*.

Neandertals also had teeth of a type called taurodont or 'bull' teeth. Some people today have taurodont teeth. These appear to be linked to genes for a longer average lifespan, which is interesting because they are also thought to be more resistant to wear than non-taurodont ones.[13] The genetic makeup of Neandertals may be closer to that of the bulk of the pre-Flood population, with its much longer lifespans.[14]

Interestingly, the average size of their braincase was *larger* than that of people today. To be fair, it needs to be stated that size is not as important as organization of brains. Endocasts (imprints of the inside of the skull) have been interpreted as showing a difference between the patterns of brain development shortly after birth between Neandertals and 'moderns'.[15] Studies on living humans and other creatures do show some connection between endocast patterns and brain structure. But at the risk of stating the obvious, it's impossible to establish brain wiring with any certainty from empty fossil skulls. To highlight this, a while back, researchers were claiming that australopithecines must have been able to talk, based on the brain wiring deduced from certain

12.   Johanson, D. and Shreeve, J., *Lucy's Child*, William Morrow and Company, New York, p. 49, 1989.
13.   Wieland, C., The teeth of the patriarchs, *Creation* 33(1):38–39, 2011, creation.com/patriarch-teeth.
14.   Wieland, C., Living for 900 years, *Creation* 20(4):10–13, 1998, creation.com/900.
15.   Gunz, P. *et al.*, Brain development after birth differs between Neanderthals and modern humans, *Current Biology* 20(21): R921– R922, 9 November 2010, doi:10.1016/j.cub.2010.10.018.

skull imprints—until they found that chimp and gorilla skulls had similar imprints.

The things that signify true humanity and which have been found in association with Neandertal remains include:

- Stone tools
- The controlled use of fire (including heating birch bark peelings in the absence of air to make special pitch to haft wooden shafts onto stone tools)[16]
- Perfectly balanced and finely crafted wooden hunting javelins
- Jewelry[17]
- Evidence of body decoration and cosmetics[18]
- Cooking utensils and the use of herbs in food
- Burying their dead with ornaments
- Musical instruments
- Symbolic thinking[19]
- High-tech 'superglue'[20]
- A complex structure built 1 mile (1½ km) deep under the ground, where no daylight penetrates, suggests they had the technology and know-how to transport sustained

16. Neanderthals were nifty at controlling fire: study, www.physorg.com, 14 March 2011, accessed 15 March 2011.
17. The evidence for this has been challenged by a recent redating on one site leading to a claim that the ornaments were later intrusions. But Francesco D'Errico of the University of Bordeaux, France, an authority on Neandertal artefacts, has challenged the dating and remains, convinced of the evidences for jewellery from other Neandertal sites.
18. Carter, R.W., The Painted Neandertal: Ancient cosmetics are upsetting evolutionary stories, creation.com/the-painted-neandertal, 20 May 2010; João Zilhão *et al.*, Symbolic use of marine shells and mineral pigments by Iberian Neandertals, *Proceedings of the National Academy of Sciences* (USA) published online before print, 11 January 2010.
19. J. Sarfati, Neandertals were fully human in thinking: Symbolic items show human cognition and symbolic thinking, creation.com/nean-thought, 30 August 2006. João Zilhão and 5 others, Analysis of Aurignacian interstratifications at the Châtelperronian-type site and implications for the behavioral modernity of Neandertals, *PNAS* **103**(33):12643–12648, 15 August 2006 | 10.1073/pnas.0605128103.
20. Viegas, J., Neanderthals Made High-tech Superglue, *Discovery News* (16 January 2002); Neanderthals 'Used Glue to Make Tools', news.bbc.co.uk.

fire as a source of light that far down. Try it sometime!

- The capacity for compassion shown by caring for the disabled. There is bony evidence of people severely and permanently handicapped by injury, yet living for many years after the injury.
- Evidence that they had dwellings made of timber draped with animal skins. For a long time it was believed they only lived in caves. However, the simple fact that many of their remains are found in caves does not mean they were exclusive cave-dwellers. In fact, they probably were nomadic hunters, so caves were likely of significance to them for their permanence of location. They likely returned to them periodically for ceremonial reasons. Also, in many instances, to bury their dead, as people were doing in the time of Abraham (Genesis 23:9).

Also, despite the popular image of Neandertals as exclusively hunter-carnivores, recent analysis of remains on their teeth shows them to have regularly eaten both raw and cooked vegetable matter.[21]

There were long-standing claims that Neandertals could not speak—but the discovery of a hyoid bone (associated with the larynx or voice-box) just like ours has made that difficult to sustain. And now that Neandertal DNA has been sequenced,[22] there is also strong genetic evidence that they had full speech capacity.[23]

For a long time, lone voices in evolutionary circles were pointing out evidence from fossils that Neandertals and 'moderns' must have interbred at times. But this did not suit the prevailing vision, for a number of reasons. For one thing, it violated the

21.   Henry, A., Brooks, A. and Piperno, D., Microfossils in calculus demonstrate consumption of plants and cooked foods in Neanderthal diets (Shanidar III, Iraq; Spy I and II, Belgium), www.pnas.org, 12 November 2010.
22.   Carter, R.W., Neandertal genome like ours (There may be Neandertals at your next family reunion!), creation.com/neandertal-genome-like-ours, 1 June 2010; based on Green, R.E. *et al.*, A draft sequence of the Neandertal genome, *Science* **328**:710–722, 2010.
23.   Borger, P. and Truman, R., The FOXP2 gene supports Neandertals being fully human, *J. Creation* **22**(2):13–14, 2008, creation.com/foxp2.

'out of Africa' doctrine. Neandertals were not supposed to have contributed to the inheritance of people today. They were supposed to have become extinct, not 'lived on' in modern people. Also, Neandertals supposedly lived 'hundreds of thousands' of years ago. So it would have suited most evolutionists (and in fact, so-called 'long-age creationists', aka 'progressive creationists'), for them to have been *very* far removed from today's people, genetically—preferably, a separate species.

But now that their DNA has been sequenced, we can say a number of things. First, the mere fact that DNA is still recoverable suggests that the fossils are unlikely to be anywhere near as old as they are stated to be. DNA is a very fragile molecule that 'falls apart' readily.[24] Second, as is now generally conceded by evolutionists themselves, Neandertal DNA has passed through to modern populations. In other words, Neandertals can't be a separate species, even though evolutionists have claimed that they split off from the line that led to modern humans 500,000 years ago. And biblically that means that they are definitely the same created kind as people. You might live next door to the local animal population, but you don't go having kids with them, who grow up to have more kids, and so on.

Homo erectus

This group includes Java Man, Peking Man, and Turkana Boy. I also include in this category specimens that have been called by a different species name, but are actually near-identical, e.g. *Homo ergaster*. All these are actually very similar to Neandertals in their skull features. From the neck down, it's been said, they would have looked like an Olympic athlete of today. Their brain size was *on average* smaller than that of today's human, whereas the opposite was true for Neandertals. But the *erectus* brain size is still within the modern human range.[25] Of the features indicating

---

24. If you're not already aware of the exciting evidence of *soft tissue found in dinosaur bones*, including transparent blood vessels, soft and stretchy ligaments, red cell structures with their nuclei visible, and identifiable proteins, check out Wieland, C., Squirming at the Squishosaur, creation.com/squishosaur—follow the links, too.
25. Woodmorappe, J., How different is the cranial vault thickness of *Homo erectus* from modern man? *J. Creation* **14**(1):10–13, 2000.

humanity listed for Neandertals, a good number, though by no means all, have been found associated with *erectus*, too. In fact, if it weren't for the smaller braincase, they could almost be seen as simply a Neandertal variant.

Paleoanthropological evidence from the Indonesian island of Flores, of Hobbit fame, indicates (to the surprise of evolutionists) that the *erectus* people must have had complex seafaring skills.[26] They were able to reach, and hunt on, an island that was only accessible across significant stretches of open ocean.

There is no reason I know of not to regard these, too, as one more group of post-Babel descendants of Adam, then Noah. Later in this book, there is mention of the particular stone technology they had, including evidence of considerable sophistication. In fact, it's not unreasonable to regard these first two groups as almost forming one group; let's call them 'archaic humans'. Humans, yes, but with some bony distinguishing features, prominent among these being robusticity in their skulls. Some modern humans also have significantly more of this robusticity than others.

The remains of some 40 Aboriginal people were excavated in the late 1960s and 1970s at Kow Swamp in northern Victoria. The work was done by Dr. Alan Thorne, of the Australian National University.[27] The skulls were so robust that Thorne was initially sure that they were *Homo erectus*. But the problem was that the 'dates' came in at 9,500 to 13,000 years ago, so they couldn't be *erectus*. This is because the northern New South Wales site of Lake Mungo had revealed Aboriginal skulls which were gracile, like modern Aboriginal ones, not robust like these—and they 'dated' to 40,000 years ago! So Thorne changed his mind. But what that shows is that being 'robust' is not something associated only with 'earlier' people, because in this case, the *erectus* features

---

26.   *New Scientist* **157**(2125):6, 1998, based on Morwood *et al.*, Fission-track ages of stone tools and fossils on the East Indonesian island of Flores, *Nature* **392**(6672):173–176, 1998.
27.   Major, J., Kow Swamp remains are re-dated to more than 20,000 years old, UniNews (a University of Melbourne publication) **13**(3), 8–22 March 2004, accessed at uninews.unimelb.edu.au/news/1255 on 9 October 2010.

came *after* the 'modern' ones. Grappling for answers, subsequent researchers have frantically tried to 're-date' the Kow Swamp find, and have in fact managed to nearly double the dates, to 20,000 years—but that's still not enough to solve the problem. So they have come up with quite reasonable explanations of why robusticity re-emerged, such as the harsh conditions of the Ice Age, genetic isolation and so on. But those are also quite acceptable explanations of how robusticity (in Neandertals, among others) came about in the biblical understanding as well![28]

All of this makes it not surprising to hear that some evolutionary paleoanthropologists, such as Milford Wolpoff from the University of Michigan, have been saying for some time that one should really no longer see either of these two groups, Neandertals and *erectus*, as species separate from us. They should all be renamed *Homo sapiens*, as we are—then described as they are, robust or gracile, modern or archaic.

They were saying this on the basis of fossil evidence *before* there was the Neandertal DNA evidence available, incidentally. But then, Wolpoff and others have long supported a different view of human evolution, the 'multi-regional hypothesis'.[29] They oppose the 'out of Africa' idea. They point to many reasons to believe that there is a genetic continuity between us and these groups who were supposedly 'wiped out' by the African emigrants 200,000 years ago. And the recent sequencing of the Neandertal genome (the total nuclear DNA sequence) gives strong support to that view, as indicated.

I suggest that both contending evolutionary camps in this are each right about some things. There *is* a genetic continuity between us and these fossil humans, as both the fossil and nuclear DNA evidence shows. And we *are* all closely related, much closer in time, coming from one small population bottleneck (the Flood)—as the mtDNA evidence shows. Here, the biblical

---

28.   See the Q&A section of creation.com for lots of fascinating information about the Ice Age caused by (and hot on the heels of) the Flood.

29.   See Line, P., Inconvenient Neandertaloids, *Journal of Creation* **21**(1):15–19, 2007, creation.com/inconvenient-neandertaloids.

model would seem to provide the best of both worlds.

Australopiths

This last group includes virtually all the rest of the specimens that have been strongly put forward by leading evolutionist spokespersons at some point in recent times—as being either our ancestors, or highly significant in demonstrating human evolution.

It incorporates the australopithecines (of the genus *Australopithecus*). These include the famous 'ape-woman' Lucy (*A. afarensis*), the Taung skull, Nutcracker Man, Mr./Mrs. Ples, and more.

It also includes *Ardipithecus*.[30] I've lumped the habilines (i.e. *Homo habilis*) in here too, because it is widely conceded that *habilis* is a 'phantom taxon'; some bony fragments labeled as that should be reassigned to *erectus*, and others to *Australopithecus*.

What follows is a run through the reasons why the australopiths do not qualify as the human ancestors many of them (e.g. Lucy) are claimed to be.

Their limb bones were highly suited to life in the trees—not the open savannah, as textbooks depict. Curved hand and foot bones, long arms and more indicate this.[31]

As evidenced by CAT[32] scans of the fossil skulls (which show the orientation of the organ of balance), they did *not* walk habitually upright in the human manner.[33] Lucy's kin have also been shown to have had a locking wrist mechanism typical of knuckle-walkers.[34]

The 'upright walking' claims are largely based on a set of bipedal footprints in volcanic ash, the famous 'Laetoli prints'.

30. Some evolutionists have said that it does not merit a separate genus, and is really *Australopithecus*; all the more reason to include it in the same grouping here.
31. Stern, J., and Susman, R., *Am. J. of Phys. Anthropology* **60**(3):279–317, 1983.
32. Computerized Axial Tomography—a way of using plain x-rays to view 'slices' through a three-dimensional specimen.
33. F. Spoor, B. Wood and F. Zonneveld, Implications of early hominid .morphology for evolution of human bipedal locomotion, *Nature* **369**(6482):645–648, 1994.
34. Richmond, B.G. and Strait, D.S., Evidence that humans evolved from a knuckle-walking ancestor, *Nature* 404:382, 2000.

FEATURE

Skull 1470—Exception to the Rule?

Argument has raged, in both evolutionist and creationist circles, about the proper assignment of the fossil skull labeled KNMR 1470. Often called *Homo rudolfensis*, it was reconstructed from a large number of fragments. Evolutionists sometimes point to this assignment difficulty as evidence of its 'transitional' status. However, it is more likely to reflect the many ways in which the fragments can be, and have been, reconstructed in papers published in secular journals. These have ranged from giving it a flat, more human-like face, to a markedly protruding one, similar to apes. In addition, the published brain capacity from such reconstructions has varied from as high as 752 cc (humans today average about 1300 cc) to as low as 526 ('+/- 49') cc. The latter figure, which generated angry reactions from many evolutionists, was by Timothy Bromage, an anthropologist at New York State University.* He said that his team's reconstruction was based on principles of mammalian architecture which were not previously known. Whether due to pressure or not, Bromage later revised his estimate upwards to 700 cc. Such flexibility makes it seem more than reasonable to assign Skull 1470 to the australopith category (see main text).

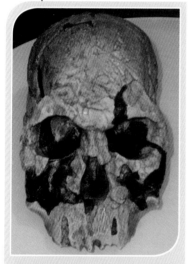

One reconstruction of KNM ER 1470.
CC-BY-SA 3.0 Durova

*See, e.g., Bromage, T., Faces from the past, *New Scientist* **133**(1803):32–35, 1992.

But, as Dr. Russell Tuttle of the University of Chicago showed, they are indistinguishable from the prints of modern humans who walk habitually barefoot.[35] The only reason they are assigned to Lucy and her kin is because of the 'dating' of the ash. This is more

---

35. Tuttle, R., *Am. J. of Phys. Anthropology* **78**(2):316, 1989. See also his article in *Natural History*, March 1990, pp. 60–65.

than '3 million years', and modern humans are not supposed to have been around that early. So by the circularity that is quite common in evolutionary reasoning, the prints have to have been made by the ancestors of humans—which then shows that the ancestors of humans walked upright. Go figure.

Importantly, these creatures were, overall, *not* anatomically intermediate between humans and apes. This was based on a detailed objective analysis of multiple coordinates on the bony skeletons of australopiths. The work was carried out over several years by a team led by evolutionist and anatomist Charles Oxnard. He has been Professor of Human Anatomy at the University of California at Santa Barbara, and is still Professor Emeritus at the University of Western Australia. The approach uses a computerized technique, known as multivariate analysis, that tries to remove the subjective element from anatomical comparisons. The total anatomical coordinates of the three groups—modern apes, modern people, and australopiths—are plotted in a 3-D morphometric space, as it's called. Evolutionary expectations for the results are clear. People would be expected to cluster in a blob around one position in this space, apes around another, and australopiths somewhere in-between. That's not what Oxnard's team found at all. They concluded that this was a unique group of extinct primates with an anatomy that, overall, was *further* from apes and people than those two groups were from each other.[36] They did *not* walk upright, but had a unique rolling locomotion. Most importantly, of course, he concluded that they were not ancestral to people at all.

In February 2011, a tiny foot-bone (4th metatarsal) was found at a site that had yielded a number of *afarensis* bony remains. From this, it was concluded that Lucy must have had a medial arch, like humans, hence walked upright like us. Despite the media hype, however, other evolutionist sources pointed out that this was an unsafe conclusion from a single bone, especially given that other studies had already concluded that Lucy's kind were

36.   Oxnard, C.E., The place of the australopithecines in human evolution: grounds for doubt? *Nature* **258**:389–395, 1975.

flatfooted—the very opposite.[37]

For years, now, there has been one variety of australopith after another trumpeted as the latest spectacular find allegedly supporting human evolution. One recent announcement involved a fairly incomplete specimen dubbed 'Big Man'. It was touted as Lucy's 'big brother'. But a closer look at the fossils suggests that (shades of Laetoli) the 'dating' is the only reason that it's assigned to that category. The fossil evidence instead fits much more naturally into the *erectus* category above.[38]

The upshot of it all is that any number of future finds of new varieties of australopiths is not likely to change this big picture. The reason is straightforward; the notion that humans evolved from ape-like creatures, besides stoking the fires of racism, is simply wrong.

Not the Flintstones—the Denisovans

Since the first draft of this section on human evolution was written, some new results on a recent finding have appeared. They turn out to be a useful illustration of how such new finds come to fit into the existing 'big picture'.

In 2008, a single finger bone, allegedly '30,000 years old' (see the section 'Racism and Time' on p. 223 for a brief comment on dating methods) and from a young girl, was found in Denisova Cave, an archeological site in southern Siberia. It looked like that of a modern human. Later, a solitary tooth was found that was said to look a bit different from both modern and Neandertal teeth, and more like *Homo erectus*.[39,40] DNA in both

---

37. For a referenced summary, see Wieland, C., "Lucy walked upright!" (Or did she?), 17 February 2011, creation.com/lucy-arch.
38. Line, P., He ain't my brother: no apparent family ties between Big Man and Lucy, creation.com/bigman, 23 September 2010.
39. Fossil finger bone yields genome of a previously unknown human relative, sciencedaily.com, 22 December 2010, accessed following day. See also Reich, D. *et al.*, Genetic history of an archaic hominin group from Denisova Cave in Siberia, *Nature* 468:1053–1060, 2010, doi:10.1038/nature09710.
40. *Homo habilis* was mentioned in this context, too, but see the earlier discussion on this 'phantom taxon'; this does not contribute meaningfully to the description. Surprisingly, however, the diagram of the tooth in the Reich *et al.* paper looks more australopithecine than anything else.

specimens (the preservation was "almost miraculous" according to one researcher) has yielded a draft genome, which shows the following:

- The two specimens were in fact from the same population, though from different individuals.
- The genome was neither typically modern nor typically Neandertal. It is regarded as a distinct population, a 'sister group' to Neandertals, dubbed the 'Denisovans'.
- Denisovans have, like Neandertals, also clearly had genetic intermingling with modern populations; in particular, the Melanesians found today in places such as Papua New Guinea.

As with Neandertals, such evidence from hybridization scotches any notion that these were other than post-Babel descendants of Adam.

Small groups coming into sporadic contact with each other before migrating to more distant regions is the most likely cause of the fact that in certain Melanesian populations, some 5% of the genome shows 'Denisovan' ancestry.

One of the leading researchers on this project was Richard Green, from the University of California at Santa Cruz (UCSC). He said:

> "Instead of the clean story we used to have of modern humans migrating out of Africa and replacing Neanderthals, we now see these very intertwined story lines with more players and more interactions than we knew of before."[41]

It is likely that there may be yet more such distinct (but distinctly human) populations turning up. Such genetic isolates likely resulted from further breakup of the already fragmented human gene pool post-Babel, especially during the harsh centuries of the post-Flood Ice Age in the temperate to polar latitudes. Neandertals are extremely closely related to each other. One interesting possibility is that the Neandertal/Denisovan group became

41.   Ref. 39.

somehow genetically isolated from the main Babel population *prior* to the dispersion recorded in Genesis. The biblical account seems not to totally preclude this possibility. This group would then have subsequently split into the Neandertal and Denisovan people, respectively—probably early on.

The main point is best summed up by Professor Clive Finlayson, Director of the Gibraltar Museum, who says: "The irony is that the scientific community is going to have to come round to the acceptance that the Denisovans and the Neandertals also belonged to the species which we call *Homo sapiens*."[42] In other words, all part of this *one human family*.

∞

42. Finlayson, C., All change: Theories of human ancestry get an overhaul, www.bbc.co.uk/news/science-environment-12093345, 31 December 2010.

8 DIFFERENT PEOPLE, DIFFERENT LANGUAGE

One of the many points of difference between the various groups of people within the human family is that they speak often vastly differing languages. No doubt this has been a factor in people seeing each other as more different than we really are. But here, too, there is much to learn from such differences about our overall unity.

We've already seen that a sudden division of people via imposed language differences has great explanatory power in understanding the genetic differences. Understanding the biblical history of humanity also helps us see how the language patterns in today's world are more consistent with the predictions based on this understanding than with those based on evolutionary ideas.

Born to communicate

All members of the human family have an incredible drive and ability to communicate with one another. Clever animals like chimps may have special sounds to warn about the approach of a hungry leopard, for example. But we communicate using language, in ways which set us apart from all other creatures. The Bible states we were made in God's image; other creatures were not (Genesis 1:27).

Dominated by the Creator-evading philosophy of our age, researchers have tried hard to narrow the huge 'communications gulf' between animals and humans, whom they regard as simply evolved animals. Some chimps have been trained by people to associate words with particular objects, and some have achieved a fairly basic form of sign language. But such limitations seem to serve largely to frustrate researchers, who are under considerable pressure to show the sorts of results that would match evolutionary expectations.

Dogs, too, have performed better than expected, given that they are not supposed to be closely related to us on the evolutionary tree. A border collie named Chaser "has been taught the names of 1022 items... [and] can also categorise them according to function and shape, something children learn to do around the age of 3." A researcher from Hungary's Eötvös Loránd University remarked that the study "shows that this dog has good skills for comprehension but the production side of communication is missing".[1]

'Bird-brains' outsmart chimps

iStockPhoto

Some birds, also not supposed to be our close evolutionary cousins, are even cleverer than either dogs *or* chimps. 'Alex', an African gray parrot like the one pictured, learned to be able to recognize and name some 100 different objects, as well as their color, texture and shape. He could also count up to six.[2] But Alex's remarkable trained talent pales into insignificance next to the built-in abilities his human teacher would have had, even as a very young child.

From an early age, we share information with each other—not just about the objects in the world around us, but about abstract things like thoughts, feelings and ideas. We can use language to

1. Griggs, J., Border collie is fluent in toyspeak, *New Scientist* **208**(2792/2793):8, 2010/2011.
2. See creation.com/bird-brain-matches-chimps.

project into the past and future, too.

Who are we?

Our communication also reflects that we have true self-awareness, an idea of ourselves and our place in the world as unique individuals. For some time, evolutionists became optimistic that they could show that chimps and orangs also possessed this; when the apes saw an unexpected marking or object on themselves in the mirror, they would inspect that part of their actual body. Elephants, apes and dolphins also pass this 'mirror test'. Orangs go even further—they interact with the reflection, even preening with the object they see.[3]

However, more than one researcher is realizing that this does not mean true self-awareness. Evolutionist Daniel Povinelli, from the University of Southwestern Louisiana, said in 1996 already that he was becoming "much more open to the possibility that chimps may not develop a mental understanding of themselves and others, at least not to the extent that preschool children do".[4]

Humans are indeed capable of much more than this mirror test. Even very young children have been shown capable of having a 'theory of mind'; they can speculate about what another person might be thinking. Povinelli said: "By 3 to 5 years of age, children conclude that their peers behave according to unseen beliefs, intentions, and other mental states"—while "chimps may not try to decipher others' minds in this way."[3] A chimp mother may be seen to grieve on losing an infant, but other chimps, unable to consider what she is feeling, will not comfort her.

Povinelli's negative results on chimps were reported with cautious wording—almost grudging at times. Nevertheless, he concedes that the results of his studies indicate that "humans operate in a mental realm that may stay off-limits to apes and other animals ... ."[3]

One of the leading researchers claiming to show human-like features in the behavior and abilities of animals is Harvard

3.　Kluger, J., Inside the minds of animals, *Time*, 16 August 2010, pp. 26–33.
4.　*Science News* **149**(3): 42–43, 1996.

professor Marc Hauser. At the time of writing, there is a huge cloud over all of his published work, a lot of which involves such claims. He has just been investigated for major irregularities in his data.[5] Despite the probe's results being kept secret so far, Hauser has gone on a year's leave of absence. The investigation has apparently turned up "eight instances of misconduct", and one of his papers, alleging that certain monkeys "can learn to distinguish between different patterns of vowels and consonants, just as human infants do", has already been withdrawn.[6] The *Nature* report on this describes how researchers are under pressure to "produce something new and exciting that can be summed up in three pages".[6]

Humaniqueness

However, even Professor Hauser, as keen as he seems to be to see results that support a lessening of the gap, has conceded that when it comes to comparing humans and other creatures, there is a huge gap in cognition that "shows we truly are something special". People have "a suite of cognitive skills" he calls "humaniqueness", which includes "the ability to recombine information to gain new understanding, a talent animals don't have." He says, "Animals have a myopic intelligence but they never experience the 'aha' moment that a 2-year-old child gets."[7]

And when it comes to language, there is still more. No ape, nor any other animal, exhibits 'recursion'—i.e. expressing one concept inside another one. Young children regularly use recursive concepts, e.g.: 'Samantha thinks Susan doesn't want to play with her.' (Susan's unwillingness to play is the concept within the concept of Samantha having thoughts.)

The gift of language

The spoken word is our primary means of communication, but

5.   Harvard star in misconduct probe over monkey minds, *New Scientist*, 21 August 2010, p. 14.
6.   Ledford, H., Harvard probe kept under wraps, *Nature* **466**:908–909 (2010), published online 17 August 2010 in the Nature News section of www.nature.com.
7.   Ref. 3, p. 33.

language can exist independent of speech or hearing, as the sign languages used by deaf people demonstrate. Language involves using a *code*, a sequence of symbols placed in a *particular sequence*, to represent the ideas we want to convey. When we speak, the code symbols are particular sounds. Writing and reading is another way of expressing our gift of language using *visual symbols*—the letters of a particular alphabet replace the sound symbols they represent. A message can, however, be transmitted using different symbol types. For example, there are the dots and dashes of Morse Code, the smoke patterns in Amerindian smoke signals, or the 1's and 0's of digital coding, stored as magnetic patterns on a hard drive. In sign languages, hand shapes and gestures form the symbols.

Symbols are arranged into groups—words—each with a particular meaning. In spoken and sign languages, the words are then strung together using certain sets of rules called grammar, in specific patterns or sequences known as syntax.[8]

When we understand a message, it means we have deciphered the code—we can do so because we have learned the *convention* behind it. Neither symbols nor words mean anything in themselves. For example, if you, blindfolded, drew four Scrabble® letters in the order G-I-F-T, to someone who has learned the 'key' to unlocking the code of English, that sequence means a 'present'. But if you had been brought up to speak German, which has a different convention for assigning meaning to letter sequences, it would mean 'poison'! Each convention is arbitrary, in the sense that the convention need have no connection to the symbols utilized or the items being represented.

When young children learn a language from their parents, they don't need complicated lessons in vocabulary, comprehension and grammar—all those rules are just picked up naturally as they grow. Once past our early childhood years, that ability mostly disappears, and we have to learn new languages the hard way.

---

8.   In English, 'The cat has bitten the dog' is the proper syntax or word order, whereas in German, it is 'The cat has the dog bitten' (*Die Katze hat den Hund gebissen*).

FEATURE

No 'Primitive' Languages

Contrary to the racially tinged expectations of evolutionary thinking, so-called 'primitive' (i.e. low-tech) cultures do not have 'primitive' or less complex languages. When Darwin first encountered the people native to Tierra del Fuego at the tip of South America, he wrote:

> "The language of these people, according to our notions, scarcely deserves to be called articulate. Captain Cook has compared it to a man clearing his throat, but certainly no European ever cleared his throat with so many hoarse, guttural and clicking sounds."

And in a letter of 23 July 1834, he said:

> "There is in their countenances an expression which I believe, to those who have not seen it, must be inconceivably wild. Standing on a rock he [a Fuegian] uttered tones and made gesticulations than which, the cries of domestic animals are far more intelligible."

He concluded that about a hundred words would cover their entire vocabulary. Yet we know now that their language was "infinitely richer and more expressive than English or Spanish". A first attempt at a dictionary listed "no fewer than 32,000 words and inflections". They had different words for five types of snow. For family relationships, they had as many as fifty different words, "each descriptive of a particular, and often involved, relationship."*

Many languages that are utilized by cultures or peoples that were traditionally regarded as 'less evolved' turn out to be far more complex than our own, sometimes astoundingly so.

*For details and references, see Grigg, R., Darwin and the Fuegians, creation.com/fuegians.

Jemmy Button 1833   Jemmy Button 1834

A native Fuegian who traveled back to England with Darwin and later 'reverted'.

I was fortunate enough to have grown up bilingual.[9] It is not uncommon for children to learn three, four or even more languages before the age of seven or so. They are automatically able to keep them separate and mostly unconfused, despite sometimes greatly differing rules of grammar among the languages. They just absorb them with effortless ease from the people in their surroundings.

Incidentally, trying to explain how our astonishing language ability could have evolved from 'primitive grunts' has proven very difficult; there are *no* proposals even partway convincing to most evolutionists themselves.

For some time, it was thought that language was just something 'learned', but it seems likely now that the capacity for developing language and grammar is something 'hardwired' into us from birth.

Observed—the birth of a language

One of the most fascinating evidences for this innate capacity for language involves some 500 children in Nicaragua, deaf from birth. Until 1980, when schools for the deaf were set up there, they had been living all over the country. They gestured to communicate with hearing relatives, but had no established form of sign language. When they came together in the schools, though, they quickly developed their own unique sign language among themselves. This had its own vocabulary, rules of grammar, and syntax—a fully-fledged language that had no precedent.[10] The 'hardware and software' that must already be in our amazingly designed bodies to enable such a thing to develop 'naturally' is inconceivably complex—imagine some futuristic computer program, itself able to design totally new programs.

Recent ingenious studies[11] have increasingly shown that languages are not just some passive acquisition, either. The particular language you speak actually does influence the way

9.   German and English.
10.   May, K., Born to communicate, *Creation* 31(2):40–42, March 2009, creation.com/born-to-communicate.
11.   Boroditsky, L., How language shapes thought, *Scientific American* 304(2):43–45, 2011. This is the primary source of this paragraph, including quoted text.

you think. This was long suspected by many linguists before it was fully demonstrated. Such findings also indicate that the development of a culture will be influenced by a language just as surely as the influence flows the other way. The structure of our language can also "make it easier or harder for us to learn new things". For example, children that grow up speaking languages (e.g. Mandarin) where there is no troublesome interruption to the 'base-10' pattern of numbers (as in the English 'eleven' for instance) grasp the concept of that pattern significantly earlier. Interestingly, language's effects on thought are also apparent in experiments involving bilingual people. Their results from various tests vary depending on which of their two languages the questions are being asked in.

Researchers have also noticed that Indo-European languages, contrary to most others, will tend to describe things in reference to oneself (e.g. someone will be standing on the 'right of the tree') as opposed to some outside reference, like compass points. This is in turn reflected in cognition and behavior. Researchers taught a group of German children, and another of Namibian children from a hunter-gatherer society, each the same dance routine. It involved hand movements relative to the body with a *right, left, right, right* sequence. When the children were asked to repeat the routine after being turned around 180 degrees, most of the German children reproduced the same pattern. But the Namibian children mostly switched to *left, right, left, left*. This indicates that while the former were using a frame of reference that was related to themselves, the latter were utilizing one that was 'outside' of themselves.[12]

Behavioral scientists are beginning to realize that many 'firmly established' results and conclusions of their discipline will have to be revisited. This is because they have been based on subjects from the same sorts of societies as themselves. However, these societies are characterized by patterns of language and culture which have quite a deal in common with each other, but different from those patterns in the societies in which most of the world's

12. Spinney, L., Who's the oddball? *New Scientist* **208**(2786):40–43, 2010.

people live. And it is now clear that such things can affect not just the way we think, but likely some of the 'hard wiring' as our brain develops from infancy.

This has huge implications for issues of 'race'. For one thing, it helps explain why people groups can be so closely related genetically, yet appear to act and think in such very different ways. It is also directly relevant to the issue of IQ testing—see Chapter 11—where many of the questions involve pattern recognition, whether visual, verbal or numerical. If one came from a culture with an absolute reference frame, like the dance situation just mentioned, what if an IQ test question were framed on one's ability to reproduce or recognize the same pattern after rotation? The Namibian child dancers would have been marked 'wrong' by a person who was themselves using a 'self-centered' frame of reference. Yet their use of an absolute frame of reference appears to be, if anything, more intellectually impressive.

The real origin of language

The Bible indicates that the first couple were not created from animal ancestors, but were direct creations of God. Like ours, their bodies contained incredibly complex micro-machinery, programmed to be able to pass on those programs to their descendants. Even though many speak of the 'miracle' of birth, we were not miraculously created in the way our first parents were.[13] Rather, the incredible mechanisms for reproduction, which show us massive amounts of programmed information being transmitted down a chain,[14] speak of the immense creative power and intelligence of God, the master Programmer and Designer.

Consider this, too: Adam and Eve, created as adults, had to have full language ability from the first, so as to understand

---

13. That does not mean that God is not involved when things occur 'naturally'; He is, but it is a part of His everyday upholding activity, and does not involve the extraordinary operation of God as in miracles like raising the dead, and creation itself. See also creation.com/miracles.

14. Reproduction is not just about things making copies of themselves. It involves passing on the programs that enable the functioning of all biomachinery—including that for passing on the programs to the generation after that again.

God and each other in that perfect world before sin. None of us pops into the world with that ability; even though we have

Artist's reconstruction of the Tower of Babel. The ancient historian Herodotus, who saw it on his way through Babylon, describes it as having eight levels, and standing a colossal 60 m (about 20 modern stories) high. This view, modelled upon ancient ziggurats, is probably very similar to how it actually appeared.

Composite graphic by Brendon O'Loughlin and Steve Cardno

the mechanisms to learn, even create, language with astonishing ease, we have to absorb word meanings and the rules of grammar from the world around us as we grow up.[15] We do this via our designed auditory and vocal equipment and brain machinery. But the first couple required more—they needed to have a 'built-in' knowledge of the language rules (grammar) and word meanings (vocabulary).[16] Unless they *already knew* the meaning of each word God spoke to them soon after their creation, they could not

15.   The rare and tragic cases of truly 'feral' children, only ever having had interaction with wild animals rather than humans, show the need for human contact to properly acquire language—even to develop the necessary brain 'wiring', it seems. If reclaimed by society beyond a certain age, it appears they are *never* able to speak.
16.   Some have speculated that the original language was Hebrew, but we can't know for certain what it was, or whether it even survived the Babel event. Even if it did, languages may become extinct, as many have done in modern times.

have understood Him.[17] For a Creator capable of programming all the information in the genes of the first population of each kind of creature, such language programming presents no difficulty.

Languages—always changing

Equally, the events described at Babel (Genesis 10 & 11), so instrumental in forming what we see today as 'races', had to have involved a direct programming of new language into people —in fact quite a few languages.

Papua New Guinea's many tribal groups offer an astonishing and colorful array of cultural variety as well as an unrivaled linguistic diversity.
Dave Christie

There are *thousands* of languages in the world today. The most 'language-dense' country in the world, Papua New Guinea (PNG), has well over 600 separate languages.[18] Does that mean that *each one* of those thousands of languages arose at Babel? Definitely not. As we have seen earlier, the breakup seems to have been along extended family lines, and being so soon after the Genesis Flood, this was not a huge population. So it is likely that there were at most several dozen languages created instantly.

All the other languages in the world today arose afterwards from these 'stem' or 'root' languages. This was by means of a straightforward process of language change, of a sort that can

---

17.   This provides an obvious answer to the Genesis-compromiser's claim that there must have been death before Adam's sin, otherwise he could not have understood God's warning of death. By that reasoning, Adam could not have understood "Do not eat…" since he had not yet experienced a 'not' (negation). It's also relevant to Adam being able to rapidly and efficiently name some (not all) of the kinds (not species) of land creatures as God brought them to him.

18.   This more conservative figure has been chosen over the commonly cited 800 or so, to avoid any hairsplitting over those that should really be classed as separate dialects, rather than fully fledged languages.

FEATURE

The Constantly Changing English Language

Chaucer's *Canterbury Tales* were written in the English of 600 years ago (officially called 'Middle English'):

Chaucer	Modern English
The tendre croppes, and the yonge sonne	Upon the tender shoots, and the young sun
Hath in the Ram his half cours y-ronne	His half-course in the Ram [Aries] has run,
And smale foweles maken melodye,	And small birds are making melody
That slepen al the nyght with open yë	That sleep away the night with open eye

Even though today's King James Bible (the 1769 revision) is not modern-day English, it too is very different from its original 1611 edition (officially 'Early Modern English'). Tens of thousands of changes were deemed necessary to make it comprehensible to a populace whose own English had changed and continues to do so. The spread of writing slowed down the pace of language change, which can be dramatic in cultures with no writing.

be shown to have occurred in English, for instance, in relatively recent history. Imagine a group of people, all speaking the same language, which breaks into two smaller groups, and that these then live apart without further interaction or communication between them. Language changes so rapidly (see feature above) that after only a few hundred years, they might very well no longer be able to understand each other.

A likely factor contributing to PNG's plethora of languages

is its many rugged mountain ranges—groups living only a few miles apart 'as the crow flies' may have had no interaction for centuries. However, geography is not the only factor isolating people groups so as to enable such language splitting. Social and religious factors, taboos, and fiercely defended tribal land boundaries, etc. can also operate. In Papua New Guinea, some languages seem to have developed where there are no mountain ranges—e.g. Roro, Nara, Gabadi, Mekeo, and Kuni. All of these language groups exist in the small, flat Kairuku sub-district of PNG's Central Province.[19]

Modern Dutch, German and English (and the Scandinavian languages) are very obviously related (see Table 1 below). This shows they came from a common source; so the more we go backward in time, the less they will have deviated from one another, i.e. the closer they will be to each other.[20] That's why, visiting a centuries-old Dutch cemetery in Melaka, Malaysia, my German-English background enabled me to understand almost everything written on the tombstones, whereas I can decipher only a *much smaller* percentage of *modern* Dutch text. The changes from old to modern Dutch were obviously rapid and substantial.

English	Dutch	German
water	water	Wasser
dog (hound)	hond	Hund
clock	klok	Uhr (related to Latin *hora* → English 'hour')

Table 1: Just a few examples of the obvious relatedness between German, Dutch and English.

19.   David Christie, Ph.D., personal communication, 4 February 2011. Dr. Christie, a former management consultant, spent years in PNG as a patrol officer.
20.   Globalization and television operate to oppose this by bringing languages closer together again, but in a different way—borrowing. E.g., since World War II, hundreds of English words have found their way into German.

French, Spanish, Portuguese, Italian and Romanian (called 'Romance' languages) are also obviously related to each other, and thus have also diverged from a 'common ancestor' language— all part of the same language family. But are these languages completely separate from the Germanic group discussed earlier? No. The evidence in Table 2 below shows that the ancestral language for this group is in turn related to that of the Germanic group. In short, many such groups can in turn be 'joined together' going backward, forming one large related 'language family'. This particular family is called 'Indo-European', and all the languages within it would have started off as one language.

English	German	Danish	Latin	Spanish	Italian	French	Greek)	Russian	Hungarian
One	Eins	En	Unus	Uno	Uno	Un	Ena	Odyin	Eggy
Two	Zwei	To	Duo	Dos	Due	Deux	Dhyo	Dva	Kettö
Three	Drei	Tre	Tres	Tres	Tre	Trois	Tria	Tri	Három
Four	Vier	Fire	Quattuor	Cuatro	Quattro	Quatre	Tessera	Chyetirye	Négy
Five	Fünf	Fem	Quinque	Cinco	Cinque	Cinq	Pente	Pyat'	Öt
Mother	Mutter	Mor	Mater	Madre	Madre	Mère	Metera	Mat'	Anya
Father	Vater	Far	Pater	Padre	Padre	Père	Pateras	Otyetz	Apa
I	Ich	Jeg	Ego	Yo	Io	Je	Ego	Ya	Én
You	Du	Du	Tu	Tu	Tu	Tu	Esy	Ti	Ón
House	Haus	Hus	Domus	Casa	Casa	Maison	Spiti	Dom	Ház
Dog	Hund	Hund	Canis	Perro	Cane	Chien	Skylos	Sobaka	Kutya
Cat	Katze	Kat	Feles⁻	Gato	Gatto	Chat	Gata	Koshka	Macska
Lion	Löwe	Løve	Leo	León	Leone	Lion	Leontari	Lyev	Oroszlán
Monkey	Affe	Abe	Simius	Mono	Scimmia	Singe	Maimouda	Obiez'yana	Majom
Bear	Bär	Bjørn	Ursus	Oso	Orso	Ours	Arkoudha	Myedvyed'	Medve
Snake	Schlange	Slange	Serpens	Serpiente	Serpente	Serpent	Fidhi	Zmyeya	Kigyó
Horse	Pferd	Hest	Equus	Caballo	Cavallo	Cheval	Alogo	Loshad'	Ló
Cow	Kuh	Ko	Vacca	Vaca	Vacca	Vache	Vodi	Korova	Tehén

Table 2: Comparisons of nine Indo-European languages plus Hungarian (red font). Hungarian is in a different language family, despite being in Europe, and shows no pattern of relatedness to the others in this table, as they obviously do to each other. The ancient Sanskrit of India is also in the Indo-European family.

Naturally, it would suit evolutionary ideas, and contradict the Genesis Babel account, if all or most languages could be traced back to one stem. But the evidence supports Genesis, not an evolutionary origin of language. For example, Table 2 shows that

Hungarian (in red) is very different. It is part of another language family which includes Finnish and Estonian.[21] The total number of language families in existence is controversial, but it is of the order of dozens rather than hundreds. In spite of some valiant attempts to join the dots, at least the well-known major families show no evidence of being related to any other such family. In short, there is no 'tree of language' with one stem, but rather a mini-orchard of language families. The stem of each tree likely represents one of the original totally separate languages created at Babel. That's why the tips of the branches in each 'family tree' (today's languages within any one family) show no connection at all to those of any of the other trees—except by borrowing, totally unlike any evolutionary model. Once again, we see that relying on Genesis history makes sense of the evidence in the real world.[22]

∞

21.   Generally called 'Finno-Ugric', but there is some controversy over the nomenclature and other issues. This group has been much less studied than Indo-European.
22.   To salvage their core belief system, evolutionists need to postulate that human language arose more than once, independently, and/or that the groupings we see today have deeper roots, but the connections have been lost in the mists of time.

9 ECHOES OF GENESIS

As we saw earlier, all groups of people diverged from that Babel event, some two centuries or so after the devastating worldwide Flood. One would therefore expect to still find a faint echo of these two catastrophes (especially the more devastating, larger one) in the cultural memories of at least some of these groups. That is, in their stories and traditions. Many of the details would be distorted in the telling and retelling over the millennia, especially in those groups which did not rapidly develop a form of writing for their new language. Perhaps 're-establish' writing is a better way of putting it, because writing quite likely preceded the Flood. Internal evidence suggests that Genesis was compiled by Moses from pre-existing written documents. These may have been copied from earlier ones by that time of course. And this does not *necessarily* mean that the original language was like ancient Hebrew—for one thing, pictographic writing could be decipherable by people not speaking the language of the original writer. This is similar to the way in which a person who knows Cantonese, and not Mandarin, can nevertheless understand a piece of text (if written in the traditional script, not Mao's simplified one) produced by someone who speaks only Mandarin.

FLOOD STORIES

What is surprising, really, is just how strong these traditions are when it comes to the Flood.[1] There are Flood stories in literally hundreds of cultures across the world. In a very few instances, it might be possible to see these as merely distorted memories of some local flood. But what is especially striking is to see how many of the rest have substantial details in common with the Genesis account. Usually a fair proportion, though seldom all, of the following impressive list are found in any one account:

- A warning by the deity (or deities) of the flood to come
- The flood is in response to transgressions of some sort
- A vessel of safety (e.g. giant canoe, boat, or raft)
- All people and animals are wiped out except for those in the vessel
- The only people on board are the family of the key figure who received the warning
- Bird scouts (sometimes rodent scouts) are sent out to see if the waters have abated
- The world is repopulated from the occupants of the vessel
- Following the flood, there is a sacrifice to the deity/ies, who often express(es) satisfaction/approval
- A rainbow marks the end of the flood

Note that the stories closest to the original in Genesis are often closer to it geographically, a key example being the flood account in the Babylonian Epic of Gilgamesh. This is what has led to the biblioskeptical claims that Genesis borrowed from the surrounding cultures.[2] This shows how one's presuppositions make all the difference to one's conclusion. The presupposition that Genesis gives us the original account, with the others being derivatives inevitably distorted by time and retelling, fits all the facts. In addition, the alternative (Genesis is an imitation of,

---

1. See, for instance, Connolly, R., and Grigg, R., Flood!, *Creation* **23**(1):26–30, 2000. Also, *Funk and Wagnall's Standard Dictionary of Folklore, Mythology and Legend*, New York, 1950.
2. See Safarti, J., Noah's Flood and the Gilgamesh Epic, *Creation* **28**(4):12–17, 2006, creation.com/gilgamesh.

e.g., a Babylonian legend) has great difficulty in coping with the widespread similarities found scattered across the globe. That only makes sense if there really was such an event.

For a committed evolutionist, such a testimony to the reality of Genesis can be uncomfortable. It is common to claim that these sorts of things must be the result of contamination of local stories via missionary contact. But these indigenous stories are almost without exception telling of biblical events that *preceded* the time in biblical history when people groups lost contact with each other. The stories are either about creation, sometimes mentioning things like the temptation and Fall, or about the dispersion of languages, or (mostly) about the great Flood. For instance, though they might exist somewhere in the world, we have never come across indigenous stories featuring a parallel to Moses parting the waters, or Jonah and the massive fish. But if the stories of pre-Babel biblical matters came from missionaries, one would expect at least as many stories of later events and characters.[3]

For those unwilling to accept humanity's real history, the 'missionary influence' idea can become not just a self-serving opt-out, but a self-maintaining one. To elaborate—decades back, I was shown a large, hardcover book that was a very impressive collection of Aboriginal legends. In it were several that were clearly reminiscent of incidents recorded in the Bible from before people dispersed at Babel. The book subsequently went astray without my recording them. So, many years later, when I came across an updated, much later edition of the same book, I was keen to document these biblical-sounding stories—but couldn't find one remaining in the book.[4] I don't think it was some sort of conscious conspiracy to deny the Bible. What likely happened was that scholars, seeing things through the lens of their worldview, just assumed that these particular ones must have been the result of missionary influence.

3. For the rare instance in which a detailed post-Babel parallel arises, it might well be the result of missionary contact, but it is also not impossible for an isolated group to have migrated from the Middle East subsequent to, e.g., the time of Abraham.
4. Without a record of the book's name, and given the vagaries of memory, this anecdote can only be 'for what it's worth'.

FEATURE

Genesis and the Ancient Chinese

The culture of the original inhabitants of China shows many signs of having originated from the immediate descendants of Babel. Chinese-language researcher Ethel Nelson and others have shown the remarkable parallels to Genesis in the early pictographic writing (see illustration). She writes that ShangDi, the creator-god of the ancient Chinese, "surely appears to be one and the same as the Creator-God of the Hebrews."*

*Nelson, E., The original 'unknown' god of China, 1998, creation.com/china.

boat

vessel   eight   people

The Discovery of Genesis, C.H. Kang and Ethel Nelson, p. 55

Characters reveal GENESIS account

Oracle bone (ancient) characters | Modern characters

woman + trees = desire, covet
Genesis 3:6 A woman, facing one tree, coveting the fruit, with her back to the other tree conveys the idea of coveting or desiring.

serpent + trees = negative, no, not
Genesis 3:1–5 The serpent (Satan) lied about the trees and the negative consequences.
used in classical writing

mouth (eating) + tree = restrain
Genesis 2:16–17 God's command was 'Don't eat; restrain yourself'!

tree + enclosure (garden) = difficulty, trouble
Genesis 3:16–24 Eating of the tree in the garden brought trouble, difficulty

hand + lance me + sheep = righteousness
Genesis 3:21 The sheep, like a garment, covers me. But 'me' is composed of a hand and a lance, a weapon, which suggests that I am ultimately responsible for the death of the Lamb.
Traditional
Simplified script

noble person + Lamb, sheep = beautiful
When the Lamb covered their sins they were beautiful in God's sight. This was fulfilled in Jesus. John 1:29; 1 Peter 1:17–21, cf. Romans 4:1–8

Thanks to Annie Yum for assistance with this diagram.

The character for 'boat' is comprised of the elements 'vessel', 'eight' and 'people'. Eight people were saved on Noah's Ark. Added to the many other possible echoes of Genesis in pictographic script, the combined weight of evidence seems considerable.

In fact, missionaries who have lived among tribal Australian people, learning their language and showing love and concern for their welfare, are far more likely to get the 'real stories' of the tribe than are academic researchers breezing in and out. I recall many years ago visiting what was then still a Lutheran Aboriginal mission at Hermannsburg, not far from Alice Springs in Central Australia, in the southern part of the vast Northern Territory. The head of the mission at the time was Garry Stoll, the cousin of my brother-in-law Walter Stoll. Garry (pictured overleaf) had spent many years with these Central Australian tribal people, and had a high and passionate regard for them.

Watching his speech and mannerisms while squatting on his haunches in the dusty Centralian outback, it was hard to believe that he was not at least a part-Aboriginal, rather than the 100% ethnic German he is. He had learned to speak the Western Arranta tribal language fluently, and his services were regularly called upon by government sources as a translator. He had even been invited to attend initiation and other ceremonies by the elders—a very rare honor, that meant becoming very familiar with their songs and stories.

Interestingly, these people saw aboriginality in a somewhat 'color-blind' way. Knowledge of *culture*, especially of 'men's law', was for them the key. Because he had witnessed and learned much of this 'law', Garry was treated as one of them. By contrast, there were several young Aboriginal men who were of age, but who had declined to be initiated. These were not seen by the elders as men, but were treated more like children, despite their age—since important knowledge cannot be passed on to an uninitiated person in that society. In one sense, Garry was more of an Aboriginal 'insider' than they were, regardless of their age, ethnic identity or skin color.

On more than one occasion over the years, Garry told me, Ph.D. candidates in anthropology from universities in the 'big smoke' cities would visit this outpost in Australia's remote heart. They would ask various of the old men of the tribe to tell them their stories and legends. This was for recording within their theses as 'straight from the horse's mouth', so to speak.

Like most Aboriginals prior to the real exacerbation of social decay described later herein, their cultural norm was to be gentle and polite, unwilling to refuse. So they would duly be seen talking to these anthropologists-in-waiting at length. One day, Garry related, he happened to be in earshot of one such elder, who spoke reasonable conversational English, sharing a story with such a Ph.D. candidate. Garry listened for a while in rapt fascination to a detailed story he had never heard before, involving strange and spectacular tales of the desert animals, dreamtime ancestors, whatever.

Garry Stoll (2nd from left) at Hermannsburg during the era described (see text).
Garry Stoll

It took a while for it to dawn on Garry what was happening. He spoke to the elder afterwards in his tribal language, saying something like, "Hey, that's not a story from our tribe—were you making that up?" To which the elder, surprised that this was even an issue, replied something like, "Of course. What did you think, that we would let some non-initiates have access to our stories?" Ever since, I've wondered just what proportion of all recorded legends from earlier tribespeople, who still took such things as their sacred stories seriously, are genuine; and also, how many of the genuine ones have been lost.

I know that there are other missionaries who have similarly drawn close to tribespeople and their languages. Some of them, realizing that these were links to biblical history, have shared some of these stories with our ministry. One of them was missionary Harold Coates, who passed on the following story from the Wunambal Aboriginal tribe, of Western Australia. The text is unedited; the bracketed explanations are not CMI's. The story-teller was an old man of the tribe named Mickie Bungunie, who asserted that this was a story handed down from earliest times. Mickie's way of putting it was, "This is an old time story told by the earliest, profoundly knowledgeable elders". (A very similar story to this, by the way, had originally been recorded by anthropologists in the 1920s, from a group of newly 'discovered' western desert people who had not yet had contact with any missionaries.)

In those ancient days Gajara was still a human creature, living along with his wife and with his sons who themselves were also married.

It came about that the earliest-time children living in those far-off days mocked, tormented and ill-treated the Winking Owl, Dumbi. They plucked out his feathers; they spat on him; they pierced him many times with grass spears, even thrusting a hole through his nasal septum.

Up into the air they tossed him, jeering at him, "Now fly!" But he fell down on to the ground with a thud. This they did again; and again Dumbi thudded to the ground. A third time those children threw him up into the air, but this time Dumbi continued to go up and up through the clouds out of sight and right on up to Ngadja, the Supreme One.

"What has happened to you?" asked Ngadja, the Supreme Being. "What have they done to you?"

The owl then presented his complaint to him, saying, "The children mocked me; they held me in ridicule and persecuted me."

Ngadja, the Supreme One, was inwardly grieved and felt deep sorrow for him, so he gathered his followers together and held a council with them. Among the many followers of Ngadja gathered to this council meeting were Maguriguri [the sidewinder lizard], Windirindjal [another kind of lizard], the eel, the freshwater turtle, and the black goanna.

"Go," said Ngadja, "see where these people are; peer over the range and see if they are still camping in that same area, then come and tell me." This he said to his followers for he was truly sorry that these children had mocked Dumbi.

The first one to be sent was Maguriguri. He, the quick-legged one, ran to the place called Dumbey which is the range that lies across the country in that place. On returning he reported that they were all still there. Ngadja sent him again, saying, "Go again to the same place; see if they are still there." Maguriguri went to spy once more and returned again with the same report to Ngadja.

Ngadja, the Supreme Being, then instructed Gajara [who at that time was still a man], saying, "If you want to live, take your wife, your sons and your sons' wives and get a double raft. Because of the Dumbi affair, I intend to drown every one. I am about to send rain and a sea flood.

"Put on the raft long-lasting foods that may be stored," he told him. "Foods such as gumi, banimba, and ngalindja, all these ground foods." So Gajara stored all these foods. He also gathered birds of the air such as the cuckoo, the mistletoe-eater, the rainbow bird, the helmeted friar bird and finches—those he took on the raft, and also a female kangaroo.

Ngadja then said, "All is ready now." He thereupon sent Maguriguri to peep at the people for the last time. "Ah!" the lizard said, gesturing in their direction. "They all remain in one place!"

Gajara gathered his sons as the crew, and his own wife and his sons' wives together. Ngadja the Supreme One gave Gajara some of his own foods. Then Ngadja sent the rainclouds down, shutting the clouds in upon them. The sea-flood came in from the north-northeast and the people were closed in by the saltwater flood and the tidal waters of the sea. The flood began to sweep all the living creatures together and was pushing them all along to one place, Dumbey. Here the waters were spinning in a whirlpool and the people were screaming as they looked for a way of escape. Ngadja whirled the flood waters and the earth opened, drowning and flattening them all. He finished them at Dumbey.

Meanwhile, the flood carried all those who were on the raft with Gajara along on the current far away to Dulugun where the world ends and the waters flow over. That is where the flood had been taking him all the time, the place of the dead, where there is no land. The waters were rolling him this way and that way and spinning him around for a long, long time.

At last, however, the flood-waters brought Gajara back in this direction. He sent some birds out from the raft, first the cuckoo. The cuckoo found the land and did not return to him. Gradually the waters were going down. The first land that Gajara sighted was the hilltop at Ngumbindji [Doubtful Bay]. "Oh!" he said, "I have found a hill!" and he was glad within himself. Then, as the waters continued to go down, he sighted Numbuzare [Mt Waterloo].

Later on, the other birds returned to Gajara and he sent them out again the following day. They arrived on the land and met Dumbi, the owl who said, "Oh, you have returned already!" and invited them to stay. The land was already drying the waters up and the living creatures found a home and food. Soon in many places the owls were breeding.

As the flood subsided Gajara noticed that it was leaving a water-mark like a painting along the hills. This is the flood spirit line, left there where the flood made it. The waters were taking him past Munduli [Montilivet] when he bumped into a rock. [Munduli is "the tomahawk place" where they used to get stone for tomahawks.] Gajara was bumped off the raft with a splash and sank to the bottom. On the bottom of the sea he walked to the shore of the mainland.

His sons and his wife paddled the raft towards the shore where they met him. His sons wailed for him, crying. "Father has come out to us with a lot of heavy seaweed and oysters all over him," they said among themselves. They removed some of the oysters, prising them off, and threw the seaweed into a heap. The heap turned into a lump of rock, where it remains a monument to this day.

The Wandjina's spirit went out into the cave where he is painted. "I want to turn off here," he said; so he turned off, and for this reason the place is called "The Turn-off Place". He went into the cave and lay down. The hornets are numerous down in that cave; we do not touch it; it is taboo. That is, the Gajara cave is taboo.

With regard to the kangaroo which they had taken with them on the raft and which was still with them when Gajara went down, and forced his way through the sea, and came out on the shore, they killed it after landing; and Gajara's wife Galgalbiri put it in the earth oven and cooked it with other foods.

The smoke rose slowly until it reached through into the sky. Ngadja, the Supreme Being, said, "Oh, what is that smell? Ah, they are cooking a good kangaroo! The marrow smells; I can smell the odour." He could smell the steam and smoke rising from the female kangaroo as it was cooking and he was pleased.

Ngadja, the Supreme Being, put the rainbow in the sky to keep the rain-clouds back.

The rainbow lies bent across the sky; he ties up the clouds behind it and the rain does not come. The rainbow keeps the clouds back and protects us so that the rainfall does not rise too high. Our people understand the significance of it. When we see the rainbow we say, "There will not be any abnormally heavy rain."

Our ministry has been told of other such Aboriginal Flood stories, including one said to be from the people living near the site of Ubirr, or Obiri Rock. This is in the north-east of the Northern Territory's Kakadu National Park, famous for its rock paintings and more. The story is about a great Flood, and also refers to three brothers being the origin of people after the Flood.

Of course, such evidence is, by its very nature, anecdotal— but then so is every story ever collected by an anthropologist. Normally scholars would be very careful about dismissing things when there are such large-scale patterns, as in this matter of Flood stories.

Other Genesis memories

Pastor George Rosendale 2000.

Indigenous people also have stories about the Tower of Babel, though they are not as common as flood stories. When I lived for a few years in Far North Queensland, I had the privilege of meeting George Rosendale (pictured), a third-generation Lutheran pastor of the Gwguyimithirr people. During an interview with him for *Creation* magazine, he said that the first time he had heard the Tower of Babel story in Sunday School, he raised his hand in indignation, saying, "You white-fellas have it wrong, the origin of languages didn't happen in the Middle East, that happened up here, near Cooktown.[5] My grandmother told me

5.   Black Mountain, to be exact. As stories are told and retold, it's not surprising that they will become identified with local landmarks.

our story, it's just like that one." His grandmother had heard it when she was a young girl, well before these Aboriginal people had had contact with missionaries.

Many of the people of the Pacific, from Hawaii to New Zealand, share an ancient belief in Io, a great Creator God who is good, and whose stated attributes fit the God of the Bible to a remarkable degree.[6] This fits with an interesting phenomenon often observed by missionaries once they become very close to a tribal group which, on the surface, seems to only worship such things as spirits and idols. That is, the missionaries become aware that buried deep within the group's shared belief system is some sort of overarching background knowledge of a 'Sky God' or 'Creator God'.

The group may often not be worshipping this God at all; it is more a recollection of the time their ancestors did so. It is as if they are echoing Paul's comments in Romans 1 about people having abandoned the knowledge of the true Creator in favor of multiple gods.

Missionary Don Richardson, known for his book *Peace Child* and the film of the same name, recorded several such situations in various tribes worldwide in his subsequent book *Eternity in their Hearts*. In this book, there is no mention of the history in Genesis, and the reader seems to be meant to conclude that God supernaturally placed this in their hearts. That is not impossible, of course. But it makes more direct sense of the evidence to explain this as evidence of the straightforward connection, through Babel, that all cultures once had back to the time when all knew of the one true Creator God.

STAR CONSTELLATIONS IN VARIOUS CULTURES

I first heard about the names that were given to various constellations, like the Hunter, the Bear, the Seven Sisters and

---

6. See Bates, A., A witness at the 'ends of the earth' (an interview with *Graham* and *Tui Cruickshank* about the knowledge of the one true God—preserved for millennia in Polynesian culture), *Creation* **32**(1):16–18, 2009, creation.com/maori-creator-io.

so on, as a young lad. I wondered how such names could have arisen. I mean, it's not as if they look anything like the objects they are named after. What I learned on growing up was even more intriguing. On some occasions, more than one ancient society, even though widely separated by geography, time and culture, had come up with the same name for some of the constellations.

Nowadays, of course, that makes much more sense to me, knowing that these cultures all descended from the dispersion at Babel (ancient Babylon, where astrology and star-worship was strong). The instances that can be well documented are modest in number, but are both fascinating and hard to put down to coincidence.

The Pleiades' seven ladies

One of the best examples is that of the Pleiades. These are sometimes called the Seven Stars, or the Seven Sisters— even though there are more than seven in the cluster. (Six are reasonably easy to see with the naked eye, but it's often hard to see a seventh one unaided.) The stories of not a few cultures, including Australian Aboriginal ones, associate the Pleiades with rain or flooding, or a great Flood.

That may not be such a big deal, but what is intriguing is that several ancient cultures called them the Seven Sisters—here, too, this includes some Australian Aboriginal ones. Since nothing about their appearance suggests sisters—or even women, for that matter—it would be a strange coincidence if the same association had occurred by chance once, let alone several times.

Recently, a CMI supporter who is on very good terms with famed Aboriginal artist Donny Woolagoodja commissioned him to paint a picture of his tribe's creation story for us (see feature 'Genesis and Aboriginal Art' p. 204).[7] Mr. Woolagoodja lives in the remote Kimberley area in Western Australia's north. A lot of his paintings illustrate the traditional stories of his people, the

---

7.   He kindly did this so we could sell it to help the ministry, having had Donny do it for him at a very reasonable price, and we did. Donny's paintings are highly sought after and valuable.

FEATURE

Genesis and Aboriginal Art

Picture: Paintings of the Worrora Aboriginal stories about the creation (below) and the Pleiades (at right), by renowned artist Donny Woolagoodja. The latter constellation is associated with stories of Seven Sisters in disparate cultures that are not supposed to have had any cultural links for tens of thousands of years.

Photo: Graham Corney

Photo: Graham Corney

Worrora tribe. When we received this one, it was accompanied by his handwritten telling of the story from the elders. It is reproduced below unedited. You will notice that it contains hints of the earlier story we listed about the Flood, which came from over a thousand miles (1,500 km) further south—e.g. the teasing of the owl as the flood's cause. But notice that in this Worrora story, the Pleiades feature, and are called the Seven Sisters.

In the dreamtime as the stories were told to us about the wandjina, Namarali created the land and sea. As they came down from the sky the gjorn gjorns (Bradshaw figures) were there with the seven sisters in the milky way which the old people call Wallagunda.

And the ungud snakes represent fertility.

The crocodile is called Koi Koi, is the wandjina animal which has a skeleton inside its body that looks like a wandjina.

Widgignardi is the dreamtime quoll[8] that was married to the black-headed python. When he died the black-headed python shaved her head and painted it black with charcoal. That's why today in our custom when a man dies the women cut their hair and paint charcoal all over her face.

The owl went up to the wandjinas when it was hurt by the 2 boys who were mocking it, they said if you are a wandjina bird go and fly to the wandjinas which it did.

That's when the wandjinas sent the flood down to drown the 2 boys and their people. Only 2 people swam towards a kangaroo and jumped on to its tail to safety. The brolgas[9] were dancing to make the ground quicksand.

Djandad the wandjina is a lightning man, so when it rains he shows you all the different smaller lightnings.

The ta-ta lizard called Mugguddigoodi was waving to the wandjinas to tell them where the 2 boys and the people were.

The same supporter then commissioned Mr. Woolagoodja to paint a picture of the Pleiades, also asking him to incorporate the Aboriginal story. Sure enough, there were the figures of seven sisters (see feature at left). The picture was accompanied by the following story from the artist (also unedited):

In the dreamtime there was eight sisters living on earth.

They roamed the country, they were wondering what's it's like to live in the sky.

They kept on dreaming about life in the sky, then the sky heard their voices and lifted them up to the sky only one sister remained here on earth.

The one left behind cried and cried for her sisters but they never returned again.

That's why the seven sisters are shining up in the sky today.

That's what our dreamtime story is all about.

---

8.   A quoll is a small, carnivorous marsupial, often with a spotted coat. It is sometimes called the Native Cat.
9.   Brolgas are birds in the crane family native to Australia. They are known for their intricate mating dance.

Various cultures around the world see the Pleiades as all sorts of things, sometimes even as dogs, or doves. But there is a core of stories that see them as seven women, most often sisters. In Ukrainian folklore, as well as in the Amerindian Kiowa tribe, the Pleiades are seven maidens. To the Seri Indian tribe of Mexico, they are seven women giving birth. In early Guatemalan cultures, they were the Seven Sisters. In the Greek legend about the Pleiades, there are actually nine stars in the cluster named after mythical figures; two are Atlas and Pleione, and the other seven are their daughters, who were known in Greek mythology as—yes, the Seven Sisters: Sterope, Merope, Electra, Maia, Taygete, Celaeno, and Alcyone.

It seems significant, if not striking, that this association of the Pleiades with seven women, generally sisters, should feature in such disparate cultures as the Aboriginal inhabitants of Australia's Kimberley Ranges and the ancient Greeks, for instance. Secular sources, too, have puzzled over such associations. There is definitely not supposed to have been any cultural exchange in ancient times between Greece and Australia. To believe that the Pleiades being Seven Sisters had a common origin seems at least a little more reasonable than that it is all coincidence. In which case, this would be one more faint, residual echo of the Babel dispersion.

Zodiacal connections?

The constellations that make up the Zodiac (Hebrew *Mazzaroth*, see Job 38:32) are those through which the sun traces its annual circuit. Like most other constellations, their names require considerable imagination to see the resemblance. In representations of the Zodiac around the world, some of the same symbols and names appear in diverse cultures (including our own). For example, the constellation we know as Virgo (from the Latin name for 'virgin') bears that same name in several disparate ethnic groups—including the language of the remote Hindu kingdom of Nepal, for instance.[10]

10. Personal communication from Ken and Gwyn Brookes, former missionaries to the Nepali people and fluent in their language, 6 March 2011.

I want to avoid too much focus on this more ephemeral sort of evidence, but it does at least suggest the possibility of a primeval link. In the traditional (evolutionary) view, nothing of the sort is supposed to be there. For those wanting more, Dr. Jonathan Henry, a creationist chemical engineer who has authored the popular *The Astronomy Book*,[11] has written a very interesting paper on this whole subject of constellations and Babel in CMI's *Journal of Creation*.[12] It includes an attempt to weigh up the matter of the 'Gospel in the Stars'. This idea of a primeval revelation in star names is complicated by sloppy documentation and overenthusiastic claims. God may well have intended any such matter (if indeed it was there) to fade away as His written Word became available.

Dr. Henry's article documents some intriguing 'Babel' links regarding constellations, and is appropriately sober and cautious. I would re-emphasize those last three words, because there are a few claims floating around about various cultural links to ancient Babel/Babylon that do not merit that description. These 'strong' claims about cultural connections include, but are not restricted to, constellation names, and the details go way beyond the biblical account.

One example of this genre appears to have been the inspiration and/or source of some of the others. It is the book *The Two Babylons*, written in the 1850s by Alexander Hislop. His claims sound fascinating, and are presented authoritatively. Some of the connections might even be valid. But for most of the claims, trying to check the sources is like chasing will-o'-the-wisps fading into the mist—the same thing one experiences when trying to track down things that have turned out to be 'Christian urban legends' in modern times.[13] That is a pity, especially when there is so much solid evidence around. Christians, of all people, need to

---

11.   Part of the "Wonders of Creation" series available from creation.com/store.
12.   Henry, J., Constellations: legacy of the dispersion from Babel, *Journal of Creation* 22(3):93–100, 2008.
13.   E.g. 'The NASA computer that found Joshua's long day' (see creation.com/nasa-computer) or 'The Russians drilling into hell'.

avoid the temptation to 'gild the lily' in our passion for defending the faith.[14]

THE WORLD'S MOST SPECTACULAR ART GALLERY

In one of the Worrora stories, you will notice mention of the 'Bradshaw figures'. This is the name given to a very distinctive style of rock art and/or the figures that characterize it. Sometimes just called 'the Bradshaws' or 'the Bradshaw paintings', they are named after pastoralist Joseph Bradshaw, who came across them in 1891. They are found in a fascinating 'gallery' of rock art in Australia's remote north-west Kimberley Ranges region. It consists of over 100,000 sites spread over 50,000 km² (20,000 sq. miles)! The number of such paintings is simply staggering.

The Bradshaws, which make up the bulk of this outdoor art gallery, have been described as mysterious and very sophisticated. The latter refers to both their style of execution and the level of complexity of the culture they portray. They include things that do not feature in any other Australian Aboriginal art, nor in any other known Aboriginal culture. Instead of showing animals, the Bradshaw paintings generally feature highly decorated humans with relatively sophisticated cultural accompaniments. They show people with tassels and hair adornments, and possibly sometimes depict clothing. There are several paintings showing boats. One has 29 people on board; another has four people, and also features a rudder. There are also what may be pictographic symbols.

Not surprisingly, these artworks have inspired a number of theories, some much more on the 'flaky' end of the spectrum than others. Many of these incorporate subtle racist assumptions about the intrinsic biological inferiority of the area's local Aboriginal people, who are never given the credit for having been able to produce this level of society in times past. These attempted explanations often have the 'crude and primitive Aboriginal aggressors' wiping out this superior alien culture. A

---

14. See also creation.com/arguments-we-think-creationists-should-not-use.

Top: The ruggedly beautiful Kimberley rock 'gallery' region, home to two different rock art styles. Below: Several of the controversial Bradshaw (*gjorn gjorn* or *gwion gwion*) figures showing characteristic features such as tassels and headgear.

Photos Top: © Kerry Lorimer, Lonely Planet Images
Bottom L: © Jeff Gresham R: © Grant Dixon, Lonely Planet Images

far simpler and more straightforward explanation is of course that the Aboriginal people who settled Australia came from a background that, in terms of culture and know-how, was the equal of anything in the ancient world.

The amateur archaeologist Grahame Walsh (1944–2007) developed such a passion for the area, he accumulated over one million photographic images of this art, and became undoubtedly the world's leading authority on the Bradshaws. The art is very different from the 'Wandjina' style of the local Aboriginals, such as Danny Woolagoodja's. This style is also found on rocks in the same area. The latter lack the same fine detail in construction, for one thing.

Significant controversy has taken place surrounding Walsh in relation to these Bradshaw paintings. He was one of those who believed they were created by a pre-existing civilization that has since vanished, possibly wiped out by the present-day tribesmen. This was perceived by many as having both racist and political ramifications against the interests of local Aboriginals, who were involved in various land rights claims. It was thought that it might affect their claim to having had continuous connection with the land. So Walsh's funding from mainstream sources dried up.

Even though I personally do not think Walsh's theory very likely, it is always a pity when considerations of political correctness interfere with rational assessment of evidence. In any case, the local Aboriginal style of art is there side-by-side with the Bradshaws, supporting their claim to a long association with the land. Also, their local stories, like the one published above, show that the Bradshaw figures (known as *gjorn gjorns*, with various alternative spellings, most commonly *gwion gwions*) are very much a part of the local folklore, whether incorporated later or not.

While proof is hard to achieve with all such historical questions, a straightforward explanation of all this evidence is that the Bradshaws were painted by people arriving post-Babel, and local tribes are likely their descendants. As we will see shortly, the *loss* of some aspects of a culture is neither surprising nor unprecedented. Nor need it be seen as denigrating the people involved—especially given the harshness of the region.

A Bradshaws–Bible link

What drew my attention to these figures was an article in a Brisbane, Australia, newspaper in 1992, while Grahame Walsh was still alive. It cited Walsh as claiming that there were aspects of the art 'closely linked with Christianity'.[15] Because of this, he was proposing that, about a thousand years ago, some Christian seafarers must have reached the group that drew them.

It seemed more likely to me that, rather than postulating a mysterious and speculative missionary journey ten centuries ago, these were simply cultural memories of Babel and before. That would not be the case, of course, if the drawings were showing the Crucifixion, or even Moses parting the Red Sea, for example. So I wrote to Walsh for more details. He held his cards close to his chest, saying that he was working on a publication on the matter. But his reply seemed to confirm my assumptions, because what he did say about the alleged missionary influence revealed in the artwork was that it concerned "the Great Flood and the rebirth of the people from one family". It is therefore much easier to explain as just one more example of an Aboriginal people's cultural memory of the Genesis Flood, rather than evidence of the region having been visited by ancient missionaries.

∞

---

15.   *The Courier-Mail*, 10 February 1992.

10 HIGH-TECH *VS* LOW-TECH HUMANS

Languages, cultural memories, and genetics are not the only issues relevant to the dispersion of people after Babel. It's also a fair question to ask about the differing levels of cultural and technological sophistication and know-how evidenced by finds at various excavations around the world. There are many sites where one finds a stone-tool technology only, lending support to belief in a so-called 'Stone Age'. For example, sites associated with the Neandertal people, or even with modern-type skeletons such as the Cro-Magnon folk.

It seems natural at first thought that if people dispersed from one population which had city-building technologies, they would *all* have this same level of know-how. In fact, many sophisticated civilizations are acknowledged as having arisen quite rapidly in, or radiating from, the Mesopotamian area in which the Babel/ Babylon dispersion took place. One can, therefore, reasonably assume that the level of technology represented by the ancient cities of Babylon and those in Egypt and Sumer, for example, was directly 'transplanted' from that prevailing at Babel. This was, in turn, likely a reflection of that prevailing immediately pre-Flood (see feature 'No Laptops on the Ark' p. 218). But what about when a stone-tool-using culture is excavated? Since people assume that technologies inevitably progress from simple to complex, they naturally think that stone tools are always a sign that the associated culture simply had not progressed any further yet. Linked with this is the assumption that the people themselves, and their brains, had not yet evolved far enough to devise anything beyond stone technology.

Such 'understandable misunderstandings' require clarification. It would actually be very *improbable* for all these groups to have been able to take with them, including inside their heads, all the technology and know-how prevailing in their Babel culture of origin. This would have been necessary, though, in order to be able to transplant or recreate it. Remember that the effect of the sudden language confusion would have been socially quite catastrophic, to a degree unprecedented in human history, before or since. Think only of the likely estrangement, suspicion, and probably even hostility that would arise between groups which all at once could no longer understand each other. The resultant rapid breakup involved many groups moving off into unsettled areas around the world, without the luxury of planning the excursion for months or years ahead of time.

I have tried to consider what would happen if my own extended family had to leave our current civilization quickly and move off into totally uninhabited areas. We would be *aware* of all the technology of our culture, but we would not actually be carrying the requisite know-how in our heads to be able to reproduce more than a fraction of it. For example, in my own extended family, there are teachers and doctors and architects and so on, but nobody I know of with the know-how to identify ore bodies. Or, for that matter, to be able to smelt ore, once discovered, into metal. For us, stone tools would be a necessity, despite having come from a society with cell phones and nuclear power. Living in a cave would be a great option for shelter. Even then, we would find it difficult to immediately be able to manufacture the sorts of stone tools that one finds in the archeological record. In time, and with practice, we would get better and better at it.

There are of course families which would have people with the right know-how to do these things. So in the case of Babel, one would expect that some groups would have taken more of the relevant know-how of their world with them than others. Some would have had to 'start over', as it were, and use stone tools. And stone tools, once designed and utilized optimally, can actually be far more efficient and sophisticated than most people realize—see feature 'Sophistication in Stone' p. 216. There may on occasion be little incentive for the group using them to strive to rediscover metal use. And, particularly in harsh conditions, the details of their previous world, apart from 'big picture' things such as the Flood etc., could be rapidly lost in a generation or two—especially without redevelopment of a written language.

TECHNOLOGY LOSS

The notion of people groups 'losing' pre-existing technology following the Babel event would be harder to sustain if all around us one only ever saw examples of cultures going 'uphill'. However, in recent decades it has been shown that cultures can indeed go 'downhill' in the sense of losing significant levels of pre-existing know-how. The original Aboriginal inhabitants of Tasmania are a classic example. When first encountered by Europeans, they were regarded as being the most primitive people known to that point.

The way anthropologists commonly told the story, the Tasmanians appeared to know nothing about simple devices which just about all other tribes had—such as friction tools to light fires, bone needles to sew clothes, and the like. Despite the cold climate of this sizeable island, they would mostly go around naked apart from being smeared with animal fat. Having no way of starting a fire, they had to carry burning firebrands with them (from previous campfires or lightning strikes). Their shelters were mostly crude windbreaks of bark and branches, and their stone axes (unlike those of mainland Aboriginals) had no handles. Nor did they seem to have any of the spear-throwers, boomerangs, or

FEATURE

Sophistication in Stone

Evolutionists have named different types of stone technology or 'culture' in association with the different types of humans with which they were found, depending on how primitive or advanced they believed the fossil types and technology to be. For instance, the tools of the so-called Acheulean culture had been found with *Homo erectus* (see p. 168 for a discussion of this fossil human) so often that wherever such tools were found without fossils, it was always assumed that *erectus* must have made them. Until, that is, such tools were found with undoubted *Homo sapiens* as well.

A very common Acheulean artefact was the stone hand axe. Far from being a primitive tool, Elaine O'Brien from the University of Georgia found that it was a highly sophisticated device.* Creationist fossil human researcher Marvin Lubenow writes:

"Her experiments led her to conclude that the hand axe was actually a flying projectile weapon, thrown discus style and used in the hunting of large game. To test this idea, she had a fibreglass replica made … When thrown, the hand axe spun horizontally as it rose, like a discus. However, when it reached its maximum altitude it flipped on to its edge and descended that way. It landed on its knife-sharp edge 93 per cent of the time, and 70 per cent of the time it landed point first. The average throw was over 30 meters (100 feet), and it was usually accurate to within two yards right or left of the line of trajectory. … O'Brien believes that ancient humans could have attacked large animals perhaps 200 feet [60 meters] away with great accuracy."[†]

An Acheulean hand ax c. 27 cms (11") in length, in various views. Fashioned out of chert, the device was found at a site in France alleged to be 300,000–500,000 years old.
Public domain

*O'Brien, E., What Was the Acheulean Hand Ax?, *Natural History*, July 1984, pp. 20–23.

†Lubenow, M., Axing evolutionary ideas—stone dead! *Creation* **16**(3):28–30, 1994, creation.com/axing.

fish-catching technology common on the mainland. Even though many lived on the coast, the idea of eating fish seems to have been regarded by them as odd.

Not surprisingly, then, observers thought that they had simply never had this technology in their culture. These tales were to some extent exaggerated by bias and selectivity in the stories told of early contact. For instance, more careful and less prejudiced observers noted that they did indeed know how to light fires, and had some rudimentary clothing.[1] Nevertheless, they certainly did have a much lower level of technology than their mainland counterparts. But the idea that this was because they had simply never advanced that far was overturned by the discoveries of the late Welsh-Australian archaeologist Rhys Jones, from the Australian National University. It is now regarded as indisputable that in earlier times, the Tasmanians *did* have things like fish traps, and bone needles to make more sophisticated clothing. So it has to be accepted that cultures can indeed lose technology.

Evolutionists and creationists alike believe that the Tasmanians migrated across from the mainland by foot during the Ice Age (we only disagree about the dates involved). At that time, with so much water locked up as huge ice sheets in the high latitudes, sea levels were much lower than at present, and the two land masses were not separated by Bass Strait, as now. It is now thought that during the process of migration they lost some of the technology that they had had while on the mainland. In fact, it is now generally believed that small, rapidly migrating groups are particularly prone to technology loss. This is of obvious interest in the context of Babel.

But even once on the Tasmanian land mass, further technology loss occurred, because the evidence of past fish traps and needles comes from sites *in Tasmania* itself. Secular researchers have proposed that this may have developed as a result of religious taboos. Given the ways in which religion can affect culture either for better or worse (see Chapter 16), this would not surprise.

1.   See Wieland, C., Culture clash, *Creation* **17**(3):42–44, 1995, creation.com/culture-clash.

FEATURE

No Laptops on the Ark

The Bible records that such things as farming, metalworking and musical instruments arose quite early in Adam and Eve's descendants. Some have therefore wondered about the level of technology in Noah's day. Sometimes the imaginings have been so unbounded as to involve power tools, and even lasers, before the Flood. But some commonsense considerations should serve to limit such speculation.

Remember that Noah had many years of warning that he and others would have to begin again in a new world—ample time to ensure that he took the know-how of his world with him. The civilizations that sprang up quickly in the Middle East following the Babel incident, such as Egypt and others (and Babylon itself) therefore almost certainly represent the heights of technological prowess reached just pre-Flood. While they showed great levels of ingenuity (i.e. ancient man was just as highly intelligent as today, if not more so), their technology was obviously not at modern levels.

Some look at the rapid development of technology in the last few hundred years, and wonder why pre-Flood people would not have reached a more high-tech level during the 1,600 years preceding this catastrophe. What is often forgotten is that this 'tech surge' in recent centuries really only fired into life after more than 3,000 years in the post-Flood world. Also, that it was hugely dependent on ways of thinking about the world resulting from the Bible, in particular after its post-Reformation rediscovery. See 'Science and technology—the biblical links', p. 324; the benefits of our modern Western way of life are not from some inherent racial advantage, but because the West was transformed by the Bible and the widespread preaching of the gospel. Righteousness exalts a nation (Proverbs 13:4). By contrast, the very reason for the Flood was that the world prior to it was not exactly renowned for righteousness (Genesis 6:11–12).

See also Sarfati, J., Computers on the Ark? *Creation* **33**(2):40–41, 2011, creation.com/ark-tech, 2010.

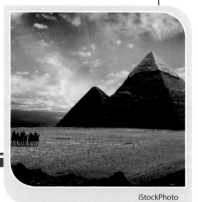

iStockPhoto

Modern examples

There are other instances of proven technology loss within social groups. Evolutionists have had to reconsider the history of some tribes which use 'Stone Age' technology and live by 'primitive' hunting and gathering. These tribes had been considered relics of the 'Stone Age' that had never evolved culturally any further.

Such groups include the Bororo, Pume and Awá (Guajá) people of South America's Amazon Basin. They were considered by evolutionists as some of the 'most primitive' hunter-gatherers on earth.[2] But archaeological evidence now shows that they descended from sophisticated cultures which made fine pottery and had advanced settlements with agriculture. The effects of the Spanish conquest (including new diseases) and the subsequent dispersion of these people into small groups meant their previous technology and lifestyle was abandoned.

Anthropologist Anna Roosevelt, of the University of Illinois, says that to take the lifestyle of one of these "most primitive groups on earth" and project it onto the past "is not really a legitimate scientific enterprise". One such group of 'primitive hunter-gatherers' turned out, on closer study, to be surviving by 'hunting' cattle off ranches and 'gathering' produce off farms.

Another tribe in which men, not women, did the gathering was the subject of much socio-evolutionary speculation until it was discovered that this was only because the women had been molested by ranchers during gathering forays.

Notice the parallel between the two forced, socially catastrophic dispersions: that of the South American conquest and that at Babel. Both resulted in some groups of people quickly *becoming* 'Stone Age' by the usual criteria.

It is clear from such real-life examples that it does *not* follow that just because a society has a very basic technology and a non-farming lifestyle, therefore its ancestors did not build cities and grow crops. This is true for 'fossil' cultures (e.g. those deduced

---

2.   For references, see Wieland, C., Modern 'Stone Age' reconsidered, *Creation* **15**(4):51, 1993, creation.com/tech-loss.

FEATURE

The People That Forgot Time

In jungle exile, the Mlabri soon forgot their ancestors' farming knowledge.
Bunyuen Suksaneh

The Mlabri tribe of Southeast Asia was first 'discovered' by Europeans in 1936. Without agriculture, they were forest nomads who hunted and foraged. Thais called them 'the people of the yellow leaves', because their temporary bamboo-framed dwellings thatched with banana leaves would be abandoned after a week or so when the leaves turned yellow. Anthropologists regarded them as having descended through the ages unchanged, as relics of the Stone Age—people that 'time forgot'.

However, the Tin Prai, a hill tribe of farmers in that region, have long had a story handed down about the origin of their hunter-gatherer neighbors. They say that several hundred years ago, a boy and a girl were banished from the Tin Prai's midst and sent downriver on a raft. They escaped and survived by hunting and gathering. They grew up, had offspring and thus became the founders of the Mlabri.

This story did not fit the prevailing ideology that technologies always go uphill, so it was long relegated to tribal myth. But genetic investigation has shown all of the Mlabri to be near-identical genetically—and so close to the Tin Prai, that the researchers concluded that exactly this sort of a 'founder' event must have happened!*

*To read a fascinating and fully referenced account, see Catchpoole, D., The people that forgot time (and much else, too) *Creation* **30**(3):34–37, 2008, creation.com/forgot.

Linguists confirm that the Mlabri language recently diverged from Tin Prai.
Bunyuen Suksaneh

by finding relics left by extinct groups of alleged 'Stone Age' humans) as well as current ones.

In any case, the process by which technology advances within a culture is often misunderstood. It does not come from groups evolving to 'get smarter'. The average person from a tribe in, say, Irian Jaya using stone technology is not less intelligent than the average person from a group which uses nuclear and computing-age technology. Take a baby from our culture, and bring him up in the 'Stone Age' group, and he will grow up using stone technology. (And he would probably amaze us; when crafted and wielded with the proficiency and skill of those in such cultures, trees the size of a telegraph pole can be chopped down with a stone axe in less than ten minutes.) Conversely, a baby from that culture could be brought up and raised in the US, for instance. She might end up the CEO of a large corporation, or flying a jet plane. The issue is culture, upbringing and education, not racial superiority or inferiority.

If we apply this understanding when considering the artefacts of societies past and present, things more readily fall into place. Societies advance technologically as individuals make discoveries or conceive of innovations, and these are then added to the level of existing know-how. Note that this is rarely a smooth step-by-step progression. Also, individual discoveries are not necessarily always adopted by the group, and thus many are stillborn. Discoveries are often serendipitous, too. So, one might have two widely separated groups, whose know-how (and average intelligence) is equivalent—yet many generations later, their level of technological sophistication may be quite different.

The environment makes a huge difference, too. For example, in Australia's harsh outback, Aboriginal technology/know-how is highly appropriate for survival. If I were caught out waterless in one of Australia's many vast, arid deserts, and staying alive depended on locating water, I would rather be in the company of a group of local tribesmen than a convention of nuclear physicists.

In the early days of European colonization of Tasmania, the

settlers would often force the Tasmanian Aboriginals to wear clothing, thinking they were doing them a favor. In fact, the natives who wore clothes were mostly worse off than those who followed their traditional practice of rubbing their bodies with fat to insulate and repel water. This is because, with Tasmania's frequent and sudden squalls, those wearing clothes were much more likely to die from pneumonia through wearing soggy clothing.

The environment may also have been a reason why the Tasmanians abandoned the hunting boomerang and spear-thrower after arriving from the mainland. They were of little use in wetter Tasmania's much denser forests, as opposed to open grasslands.

'Stone Age' flour and textile manufacture

Very recently, the website of the prestigious journal *Nature* announced a discovery that is highly relevant to the whole picture of post-Babel groups and their level of civilization. Re-analysis of stone tools from a range of so-called 'Paleolithic' sites across Europe has found evidence that the users were not 'stone age carnivores' as widely believed. Patterns of wear on the tools, as well as several kinds of microscopic starch grains from plant material, indicate that the people concerned were grinding and milling plant foods. In short, as the report puts it, "early humans ate ground flour".[3] This flour is believed to have come from the root of a cattail species and the grains of the grass *Brachypodium*. The possibility of agriculture is not yet admitted.

The report, and an associated *New Scientist* item,[4] makes it clear that this is the first time anyone has even *looked* for such plant residues. Evolutionary assumptions about the 'primitive' nature of the makers of the stone tools meant it was simply not expected. But it makes great sense in a post-Babel context. These were fully intelligent humans, with city-building technology in their past. They would have readily wanted a diet that included carbohydrates similar to the cultivated starch sources they were

3. Callaway, E., Stone Age flour found across Europe, *Nature News*, www.nature.com, 18 October 2010.
4. Van Gilder Cooke, S., Stone Age humans liked their burgers in a bun, *New Scientist* **208**(2783):18, 23 October 2010.

used to. It is no surprise that they would use their stone technology to extract such items from locally available plants.

This adds to other recent evidence of unexpected sophistication associated with stone tools. For instance, a textile factory of sorts. In the Republic of Georgia, scientists recently discovered evidence that

> "the early cave dwellers processed textiles in the cave. While searching for ancient pollen grains, they found tiny flax fibers in the dirt. Some of these fibers were woven, some were cut, and some were dyed black, gray, turquoise, or pink. They also discovered evidence that these people were processing fur (for clothing) and animal hides."[5]

In summary, following the Babel dispersion, the world soon became a mix of societies with greatly differing levels of technology and know-how, all living on the earth at the one time. The same is still the case today, even though, for many years now, there has been far more opportunity for cross-cultural fertilization than back then. In addition, modern-day people using stone tools, and modern hunter-gatherers (some of whom can be shown to have descended recently from sophisticated agricultural societies) are not some part-evolved brutes but sophisticated, intelligent members of our *one human family*. Apart from evolutionary prejudice (paleo-racism, if you like) there is no reason to think otherwise about people associated with excavated stone technology.

RACISM AND TIME

In the context of technology and progress, there has for decades been a constant emphasis on how Australia's Aboriginal people have supposedly been on the continent for '40,000 years'— sometimes even 50,000 or more. Few stop to consider how demeaning to them this actually is in practice.

In 1993 former Australian Prime Minister Sir John Gorton

---

5.   Carter, R., An ancient textile factory? New discoveries continue to push human technologies back to the earliest times, 1 October 2009, creation.com/textile.

FEATURE

'Primitive' Tribesmen Exact High-Tech Retribution

Retribution (or 'payback' in local parlance) is said to play a prominent role in the culture of many tribes in Papua New Guinea. Popular science writer and committed evolutionist Jared Diamond wrote an article recently for *New Yorker* magazine, based on recorded conversations with tribespeople in that country. In it, he tried to explain this aspect of their culture in evolutionary terms, "to draw an overall lesson about the human need for vengeance." Apparently, his subjects were not impressed; some of them, far from being 'primitive', have high-paying jobs and are internet-savvy. As a result, reports *Science* magazine, Diamond has been served with a distinctly modern $10 million lawsuit.*

Modern-day Papua New Guineans in differing dress, each associated with either a high-tech or low-tech culture. Individuals from any culture have the same potential for high-tech achievement, given the same opportunity and education.

Dave Christie

*Balter, M., "'Vengeance' bites back at Jared Diamond", *Science* **324** (5929):872–874, 15 May 2009.

expressed what are unfortunately the sentiments of many Australians when he said, "You can't reconcile with Aborigines" because "they're not as good as the white people are". Attempting to justify his remarks, Sir John asked, "Why did they never understand after 40,000 years to build a house?"[6] The more that people keep assuming, and the media keeps stressing, that Aboriginal groups have been here for such massive time-spans, the more they will continue to be seen as 'primitive' for this alleged cultural stagnation.

Of course, they haven't been here that long at all. Some think that they must have been, due to the 'assured results' of radiometric dating. Major creationist websites, such as creation. com (and icr.org, the site of the Institute for Creation Research), have much information about the problems and fallacies of radiometric dating. A good place to start is creation.com/dating which has an extensive list of linked articles on the subject. One of these, by my colleague and CMI geologist Dr. Tas Walker, highlights dating problems with respect to Aboriginal sites. It refers to, among other things, the way in which the archaeological fraternity in Australia is "still embarrassed by the Jinmium rock shelter fiasco, where a claimed [radiometric] age of 116,000 years was later reduced to 5,000 years".[7]

Some years back, I visited the renowned Kakadu National Park in Australia's Northern Territory, real 'Crocodile Dundee country'. (Well, the huge crocs are certainly real.) This is where the well-known 'X-ray' style of Aboriginal rock paintings, among others, can be found. Like all visitors, I was told that the paintings were as much as tens of thousands of years old.

A letter to the editor of an Australian newspaper around that period made a telling (and humorous) point. I recollect it went something like this:

"I've just bought a can of the best house paint around, and I'm told if I'm lucky, it'll last 15 years. Yet I'm

6.   *Sunday Telegraph* (Sydney), 31 October, 1993, p. 7.
7.   Walker, T., The Dating Game, *Creation* **26**(1):36–39, 2003, creation.com/the-dating-game.

shown where some Aboriginal has blown some soggy ochre onto a rock and I'm told it's lasted 40,000 years. Where can I get a can of that stuff?"

Some of the 'ancient' paintings I saw at Kakadu had had a silicone strip or dripshield applied around their rim to deflect water run-off. I couldn't resist asking the park ranger why this strip was there. He explained what it was, adding, "We had to do that to stop the water from running over the paintings. You'd be amazed how quickly they fade when it rains." I didn't find that amazing at all. What I *did* find amazing was that no-one had thought about why the paintings were still there at all, if they had been sitting there exposed to every passing shower for thousands of years before there were park rangers with silicone-loaded caulking guns.

Some might argue that they were kept from fading away by being touched up from time to time. But to have to assume careful and ongoing maintenance/restoration (rather than just drawing new ones) happening consistently over such a huge time period further begs the question of whether the great ages assigned can have any credibility at all.

In one section of the park, I could see how the red, white, yellow, orange and brown of the mineral colors in some of the paintings were beautifully supplemented by lines of a striking electric blue, enhancing the 'X-ray' effect. I could not think what mineral readily accessible in the region would give such a blue color—certainly not ochre. So I asked the guide, who actually seemed a little reluctant to let me know. Becoming almost furtive, he eventually revealed that this had been done by "old Billy", a local Aboriginal, using Bluo (then a common Australian brand of laundry bluing powder).

In another part of the same park one finds paintings of Europeans smoking pipes, and of sailing ships—also in the same 'X-ray' style. The bottom photo at right shows a Kakadu painting featuring a rifle. Naturally, everyone is going to accept *these* as 'recent'. The incongruity, that these paintings in the same style are next to others claimed to be tens of thousands of years old, is

Left: X-ray paintings at Nourlangie Rock, Kakadu. Above: Nourlangie Rock from a distance.
Carolyn McPherson

This Aboriginal rock painting of a rifle in Kakadu National Park was clearly painted in modern times.
Peter and Cathy Sparrow

glibly passed over with the aid of phrases like, 'the world's oldest unbroken record of culture'. The biblical creationist is aware that

Aboriginals themselves only arrived after the Flood, perhaps even several centuries after it. So he has no difficulty accepting the evidence at face value, namely that the paintings are probably all just a few centuries old at most. We sometimes forget what a very, very long time period that is.

Reasoning in circles

Evolutionists have argued that at least some of the Kakadu paintings must be tens of thousands of years old, because they show animals which became extinct tens of thousands of years ago. It seems obvious, however, that one evolutionary/long-age assumption is being used to prop up another. It is perfectly feasible that the animals in question only became extinct a few centuries ago.

Unfortunately there is a strong *emotional* component to this issue of the allegedly long Aboriginal sojourn in Australia. The perception is that 40,000 years makes their historical dispossession from many areas of the country somehow *more* immoral than if they had been here for only 2,000 or 3,000 years. But this hardly follows, even if the 40,000 year story were real. In Australia, the 'ancient' theme has also become closely linked with not just land rights but 'black pride' in general. Not to mention the added mystique (and therefore commercial appeal) when marketing such things as Aboriginal art and souvenirs. Even Aboriginal rock music has been given the '40,000 years' hype treatment to help it sell.

Under such fashionable social strictures, it is no wonder that there is pressure for 'dating' results to be as high as possible. That's why there was so much excitement when the Jinmium rock shelter date of over 100,000 years was publicized, before being shrunk by a factor of 20. In reality, the weight of evidence is consistent with the fact that the Aboriginal people, as descendants of Noah's family and thus part of the *one human family* on this planet, have been in Australia only a few thousand years—certainly less than the date of the Flood, about 4,300 years ago.

Population growth figures show that people in general could

not have been here much longer than that in any case. Starting with eight people at the time of the Flood, one comfortably arrives at today's world population in 4,300 years.[8] And this is using conservative assumptions for growth rates, ones that are considerably *lower* than the actual rates observed today, to try to account for natural disasters, wars, etc.

∞

8.   Batten, D., Where are all the people? *Creation* **23**(3):52–55, 2001, creation.com/people.

11 NATURAL SELECTION, RACE AND INTELLIGENCE

Earlier we saw how natural selection can help explain some of the patterns of distribution of skin color. Also, how it can influence the frequency of genes for disease within a population, using the example of sickle cell anemia. But natural selection is also likely to be relevant to the distribution of other genetic traits within groups.

Selection and athletic ability

It has been suggested, quite plausibly, that the reason why there are so many huge, strong individuals available to rugby teams in Pacific island nations like Fiji and Tonga has to do with selection. The islands were colonized by crossing immense stretches of open water in canoes, and many would have perished from the hardships of such a journey. Paddling through high seas in an open canoe for months on end involves prolonged physical exertion. Endurance may not always correlate with physical strength, but all else being equal, it seems likely that larger, stronger individuals would generally have been at an advantage. If so, then such individuals are more likely to have survived and passed on their genes. They may also have been more likely to have elected (or been elected) to undertake the journey in the first place, because of the perceived advantages of their physical stature and prowess.

A similar thing likely applies for slaves brought from Africa to the Americas. The adversity of the journey, often including a tortuous first stretch over land, would have been a considerable selection pressure in favor of the strongest and hardiest. Plus there is the likely selection bias among kidnappers, traders and plantation owners in favor of the bigger, stronger and more muscular individuals capable of doing more work. As horrible as it sounds, it's a logical scenario that could explain the superior average athletic ability in African Americans, compared to other groups in the US.

The matter of whether intelligence can also be related to varying genetic distributions is a 'hot potato' area. But if varying patterns of genetic distribution can affect such things as muscularity, for instance, I see no reason in principle why traits related to the brain (an organ which is also constructed under the influence of genes) should be immune from such effects. If, for instance, someone were to show that genetics helps explain why Asian-Australian students generally do better academically than European-Australians like myself,[1] I'd like to think I would not feel particularly threatened. Today, many decry any discussion of, or research into, the whole issue of race, genetics and intelligence as racist. Of course, some in the field might have such motives, just as the Darwin-inspired anthropologists of an earlier time eagerly sought ways to prove that the brains of non-whites were inferior. But we should all embrace established facts, regardless of our preferences.

Blacks and IQ in America

African Americans, especially in years past, have scored significantly lower on IQ tests than the American population as a whole. Today, their IQ scores average some 15 points lower than among whites. For many, this has reinforced these

---

1.   I.e. on average. There will be many European-Australians that outperform many Asian-Australians academically, but on average it's the other way around.

Darwinian racial/genetic inferiority theories. The reality, however, is that the weight of evidence shows *no* consistent link between intelligence (which is notoriously difficult to measure, anyway) and racial 'genetics'. IQ scores can change in given people groups dramatically over time, for various reasons that have nothing to do with race or biology. Former Harvard economics professor Dr.

Thomas Sowell (pictured left) points out that many particular ethnic groups within the *white* American population were once behind the average of the whole population by a similar margin to this 15-point difference. They later showed rises that substantially narrowed, and often closed, the gap.

Dr. Thomas Sowell
The Hoover Institution Stanford University

Take Jews in America as an example. Given their enormous rates of professional success, and the disproportionately high number of Nobel Prize winners who were Jewish,[2] few would be likely to suggest that they were a less intelligent group. Yet during World War I, Jews as a group recorded *dismal* scores on US Army intelligence tests. As a result, they were widely assumed to be second-rate people. Yet their IQ scores have risen to now rank near the top.

The same has happened with East Asians in the US, who also originally scored very poorly. Black IQ scores are now going through a similar process, despite the fact that their progress in such tests is inadvertently concealed by the practice of 'norming'. This refers to redefining baselines over time, such that what was considered normal in 1960 would be subaverage today. If one recalculates from original baselines, not only blacks but whole nations show substantial IQ rises over time.

All of this is without even looking into such things as possible

2.   Some 20% of Nobel Prizes have been awarded to this group which makes up far less than 0.1% of the world's population.

cultural bias in the questions posed in IQ tests, or the additional 'types' of IQ claimed to exist. As we saw in our discussion related to the dancing children from either Germany or Namibia (p. 184), to suggest that the way tests are framed is very much culture-dependent is far from a politically correct cop-out. Even the way our brains develop increasingly seems to be culture/language dependent. Most of the world's ethno-linguistic groups tend to think 'holistically' rather than the 'analytical' way we see as 'correct'.

> "There are questions in the standard IQ test, for example, for which a possible analytical answer is considered correct, and a possible holistic one incorrect. The majority of humanity would respond 'wrongly' to those questions."[3]

In fact, the way in which certain groups within, for example, US culture rise in their IQ scores over time could in part reflect the increasing way in which the children within those groups come to assimilate the ways of thinking of the rest of their society.

There is, on the other hand, a solid link between academic achievement and the culturally determined *attitudes* that are often transmitted consistently within people groups. For example, the better academic performances on average of Asian-Americans (or Asian-Australians) may well reflect the fact that their families place an immensely high value on education and achievement. Examples of such cultural incentives—and pressures—to achieve are not hard to find, sometimes even in the personal experience of people with Asian acquaintances.

One of my colleagues in CMI, New Testament specialist Lita Cosner, noted an interesting phenomenon during her post-graduate education. At the American divinity school she attended, Asians (mostly from overseas) would routinely, though not always, far surpass most of their fellow students. This was in a program where the selection process ensured that all in the class would be in the top percentiles academically.

---

3.   Spinney, L., Who's the oddball? *New Scientist* **208**(2786):43, 2010.

Her European-American classmates would sometimes express a racially tinged frustration at this. Their presumption was not that the 'other group' were intrinsically inferior, but the *opposite*. They assumed that their Asian classmates were naturally endowed with superior intellects. Thus, it required less effort for them to achieve high marks than it would others, so it was 'unfair'.

My colleague said that she soon saw indications that the real issue was culture, not biology. The Asian students had mostly come from backgrounds where studying for long hours was the norm. Lita said, "I personally learned from their dedication. I wanted to be in their study groups because they were harder on themselves and each other than most of my American friends, so I had to do better just to keep up." Though it might not seem a 'racist' thing to assume that another group is intrinsically superior, it can have the effect of downplaying the other group's accomplishments.

Pressure to perform

This culture-derived 'being hard on yourself' can have its downsides, of course. I encountered an extreme case many years ago while practicing as a family physician. A young ethnic-Chinese man from a Southeast Asian country presented with severe anxiety and depression. He had been sent to Australia by his family to study medicine and make a career for himself. He had succeeded in becoming a GP or family doctor, the same as I was. He practiced in a country area of South Australia, where his income was higher than most urban family doctors. It was certainly several *times* the average wage in Australia, a wealthy and fairly egalitarian Western country. Nevertheless, as unbelievable as it might sound, his major problem was that he felt an absolute failure in the eyes of his family 'back home'. Why? His income was too low. Doctors in the society he came from were expected to make far, far more. Why hadn't he at least become a specialist?

His shame was as surprising to me as it was real to him. It took an extended series of sessions to walk him through the effects of his cultural expectations and toward eventual wellness. The idea was to get him to adopt a realistic view of his rather fortunate circumstances, relative to most of the world. This led to a substantial amelioration of his problems.

In short, the differences between the averages of various people groups in such things as measured IQ, behavior, attitudes, and achievement, are largely, if not exclusively, the results of the culture transmitted to each generation, as the next chapter will expound further.

∞

12 RACIAL DIFFERENCES IN ATTITUDES AND OUTCOMES

BIOLOGY OR CULTURE?

By 'culture' here I mean much more than a particular group's shared heritage of such things as literature, art or folk dancing. It refers to the entire web of influences that an individual absorbs from the family and society of which they are an embedded part. These are profound and powerful, though often so subtle as to be subliminal. They help mould just about everything about the way we think and act—our attitudes, mannerisms, behavior, ways of speaking, and tastes—and our ways of looking at the world and other people. The group helps shape the individual, and the group in turn gains its characteristics from the combined expression of those cultural characteristics in the individuals of which it is comprised.

It involves even such trivial-seeming things as the food to which we are accustomed. I grew up in an immigrant family in the Australia of the 1950s. The vast majority in that society were also descended from immigrants (often convicts). But that was long enough ago that they thought of themselves as 'real Australians'. At that time, most such Australians were relatively intolerant of the other cultures immigrants brought with them, and largely unappreciative of their richness. I venture the same would have been true of all other 'Anglo' nations.

Their approach to foreign food gives an indication. When our family arrived in South Australia from Germany in that '50s era, the standard Australian dinner (apart from a roast on Sundays) varied little from a hunk of meat, accompanied by boiled or mashed potatoes, and vegetables—mostly peas, sometimes carrots, too—boiled to death. For a long time, the shops in the country town in which we lived during my school years carried only one variety of bread, one type of cheese, and only two or three types of sausage, one of which seemed mostly composed of fat and blood.[1]

This was somewhat of a challenge for my parents to handle, given their German culinary heritage, plus my father's added background of Middle Eastern foods. Just to obtain the ingredients for the sorts of dishes they had grown up with meant driving 80 km (50 miles) to the 'big smoke' of the state's capital city, Adelaide. Even then, the pickings were slim. For the first few years, for instance, there was only one outlet in the whole of that city that sold either garlic or olive oil! It provided a great incentive to grow, process and preserve as much as we could ourselves.

By the standards of the day, the school lunches prepared by my mother were nothing short of exotic; rye bread sandwiches with various types of continental sausages or cheeses, olives, capsicum, dill gherkins and the like. Even such still-unusual things as preserved capers and pickled kohlrabi featured. But rather than these making my fellow students jealous, they were an object of derision. 'Wog food' was a common slur. My childhood foolishness coupled with this sort of peer pressure caused me to regret, rather than appreciate, my lunches. I fervently wished that I could have what filled the other lunchboxes; sandwiches with drab fillings which most Australians would nowadays see

---

1.   For the curious (or nostalgic): Bread: white sandwich loaf; cheese: foil-wrapped blocks of processed cheddar; sausage: 'fritz' (aka devon in other states of Australia, similar to bologna/baloney in the US), plus black or white 'pudding' (both seemed to be mostly fatty offal; the black had blood as well).

as less than appetizing.

Those days are, fortunately, long gone. Thanks to a strong migrant influx commencing in the postwar era, Australians have long had ready access to a cornucopia of delights, with food from a huge range of cultures and nations freely available. Immigrants have greatly enhanced the life of the nation, and in far more ways than food, too.

Multiculturalism and the evolution link

However, the reaction to the narrowness of the past may have caused the pendulum to have swung too far the other way nowadays. The word 'multiculturalism' today generally means much more than just being keen to maintain knowledge of the language and customs of immigrant cultures. It has been mostly used to promote such postmodern notions as that all aspects of all cultures should be embraced as 'equal'. This is closely related to the notion that 'all religions are equal'.

In a strange way, the prevalence of evolutionism has contributed to all this. Evolution is increasingly being taken to its logical conclusion—if the world made itself, then there is no Creator who made us and who cares about what we do or say. There is then also no-one who has the right to 'set the rules' for all mankind. If we are just reorganized pond scum—if our number just happened to come up in the great casino of the universe—then there is no basis for any absolute right or wrong. Values and morality are a matter of mere opinion. And so, what may be wrong for person A may be right for person B. We can all write our own rules.

Even the idea of truth has fallen under the wheels of this bandwagon. We hear of things being 'true for you and not for me', even though the world is not like that. The law of gravity will apply to you and me with equal validity whether or not we disbelieve it, or try to ignore it.

The very idea is even self-refuting, as Plato demonstrated in his 4th–century-BC dialogue *Protagoras* (paraphrased):

Protagoras: Truth is relative. It is only a matter of opinion.

Socrates: You mean that truth is mere subjective opinion?

Protagoras: Exactly. What is true for you is true for you, and what is true for me, is true for me. Truth is subjective.

Socrates: Do you really mean that? That my opinion is true by virtue of its being my opinion?

Protagoras: Indeed I do.

Socrates: My opinion is: Truth is absolute, not opinion, and that you, Mr. Protagoras, are absolutely in error. Since this is my opinion, then you must grant that it is true according to your philosophy.

Protagoras: You are quite correct, Socrates.

Once the idea of absolute standards of values and morality is abandoned, the philosophical vacuum is quickly filled by all sorts of other rules and decrees. Now that all values are widely believed to be relative, not absolute, it's not surprising that the ultimate transgression in fashionable Western circles is anything which smacks of forcing your values down someone else's throat. Along with this comes the notion, relevant to our discussion, that there must be no hint that any culture—or even any of its aspects—is regarded as superior to any other.

I purposely started this discussion off with my reminiscing about the cultural chauvinism of an earlier Australia, so that the reader could be reassured that I'm not advocating heading back to that sort of thing. My chief concern with the postmodern overshoot into the multiculturalism of today is that it can actually inflame racism. For example, it has frequently meant that the assimilation of immigrants into the culture and language of the host country is seen as not just of low priority but almost something to be discouraged. It's as if encouraging such rapid language assimilation, for instance, would be to imply that the local language was somehow superior, rather than it being essentially a practical matter to ensure that immigrants' lives are much easier.

Mastery of the local language will of course aid functioning in the host society. In addition, it will decrease the chances of being perceived as an outsider unwilling to adopt the norms and values of that society, and so reduce the chances of intergroup tensions. And in the situation where that host society's language is English, it will also help the immigrant in any international travel situation as well as in the online world. This is not because English is a 'better' language, but because by historical happenstance English is the generally accepted *lingua franca*[2] for travel and the internet.

Finally, of course, there is the matter of simple courtesy. If I were to choose to move permanently to 'Callathumpia', then it would be discourteous of me to continue to insist on mixing only with English-speakers, and refusing to learn or use Callathumpian. It would be equally inappropriate to expect the government of Callathumpia to make special provisions to help me avoid assimilating, or to flaunt aspects of Australian culture which were offensive or provocative to the average Callathumpian. If I and fellow Australian expatriates regularly did these sorts of things, then, especially if our appearance distinguished us from the average Callathumpian, we should not be surprised to find a 'racist' backlash in that culture. Yet these are the sorts of things which today's postmodern and politically correct (PC) multiculturalism has cultivated in most Western countries.

As a result of the de-emphasis on language assimilation, some immigrant groups have felt little incentive to rapidly obtain proficiency in the language of their chosen new home, or to embrace its values. Within any culture, this tends to promote a ghetto mentality. When 'locals' observe this happening, it will serve to heavily reinforce negative perceptions and stereotypes, often with racial overtones that tap into the evolution-based notions that have been simmering in the background. This in turn makes the immigrant group feel isolated and threatened, enhancing this ghetto mentality further.

---

2.   I.e. a language that is regularly used to communicate between two parties who do not necessarily share a mother tongue. This is actually Italian for the 'language of the Franks' as most Europeans were once called by non-Europeans, especially their Muslim antagonists of the Crusades era and before. At that time it was mostly Italian, with words borrowed from Turkish, French, Spanish, Greek and Arabic.

German's Chancellor Angela Merkel:
"Multikulti ist absolut gescheitert."
(Multiculturalism has absolutely failed)
Public domain

The backlash in Europe against such overdone PC notions is already apparent, with anti-immigrant parties at the time of writing (early 2011) strengthening their vote right across the continent.

Unfortunately, because many immigrant groups share identifiable biological characteristics, the backlash too often involves overtly racist sentiments. At the same time, people with no racist agenda, but with genuine and appropriate concerns about the lack of assimilation, particularly in the area of language, have been fearful to voice these lest they be seen as racist.

Because of its recent past, German society is particularly sensitive to any suggestion of racism. Even there, however, Chancellor Angela Merkel has recently stated that multiculturalism (called 'Multikulti' by Germans) had "failed".[3] This was followed a few months later by a similar statement from British Prime Minister David Cameron. He called for "better integration of young Muslims to combat home-grown extremism", saying that "the 'hands-off tolerance' of those who reject Western values has failed."[4] Indeed so—and "Western values" were, as Chapter 16 shows, derived from a Christian worldview based on the Bible. One hopes these are signs of a long-term rise of common sense, and not just politicians trying to ride the wave of a populist backlash.

---

3.   Multiculturalism in Germany has failed, says Chancellor, *Sydney Morning Herald*, 18 October 2010. The backlash in many areas means that there are now many moves to re-emphasize assimilation.
4.   Multiculturalism policies in Britain a failure, says PM David Cameron, www.heraldsun.com.au, 5 February 2011.

Our Genesis-derived worldview assumption of *one human family* should help us here, too. To view people in such a biblically color-blind way, free from any background notions of biological or group inferiority, would for one thing be more likely to focus attention on culture and behavior, which are not seen as immutable in the way biological differences have been. Once the existence of a Creator is assumed, it means there are such things as objective standards from which one can try to assess everything—including aspects of culture. So one would be freed from the fetters of our PC, postmodern society when it says that one can't make rational assessments of culture or behavior that are in any way critical.

True tolerance *vs* PC 'tolerance'

At the same time, the primacy of the gospel built upon that Genesis foundation should inform us of matters of *true* tolerance, in the sense of putting up with something even if not particularly liked (very different from the PC notion that 'everything goes, 'cos there ain't no rules'). I refer to the biblical imperative toward humility, neighbor-love, and the primacy of criticism of self over others. As Jesus Himself stated:

> "How can you say to your brother, 'Brother, let me take out the speck that is in your eye,' when you yourself do not see the log that is in your own eye? You hypocrite, first take the log out of your own eye … (Luke 6:42)."

CULTURE AND GROUP DIFFERENCES

The notion that culture is totally 'neutral' fails to meet the test of reality, even of simple commonsense. For one thing, cultures give rise to significantly different practical and tangible outcomes, as will be discussed shortly in this chapter. These can not infrequently have large impacts on the wellbeing of those within the group.

Of course, it's important for everyone in a given society to try to understand the influences and traditions that have helped mold someone from a quite different background. That's just part of the respect owed to everyone—their right to be treated and regarded with dignity, on the basis that they are not only part of

FEATURE

Racial Slurs and Political Correctness From the Days of Empire

It's proved nigh-impossible to verify this story or the reverse, but it's worth relating.

In the days of the British rule of India, the colonial government was becoming disturbed at the tendency of Brits working there to refer to indigenous Indian government employees by disparaging names like 'coon' or 'nigger'.

So a directive went out that henceforth, such names were forbidden. All official references to the native Indians were to either use the term 'Worthy Oriental Gentlemen' or 'Worthy Oriental Persons'.

Instead of this early form of political correctness changing things, what happened was that a new set of derogatory words arose from the acronyms—the terms 'wogs' and 'wops'.

Whether apocryphal or not, the anecdote highlights that merely sanitizing our language is not likely to really change things in regard to racism. Words are important, but what's needed is a change of heart, a different way of looking at the world.

The Star of India Red Ensign from when Britain ruled India.
Public Domain

our *one human family*, but made in the image of God. We need to be aware, too, that a lot of the time our own culture may look 'better' just because it's more familiar to us.

It does not follow from that, though, that all cultural traditions are equally worthy of respect and deference. Obvious examples would be if one were faced with a culture steeped in cannibalism or child sacrifice—or Nazi culture. But—more of that later in Chapter 16, which discusses the effect of religion on culture. What I want to get into here is something which has become virtually taboo to mention or discuss, because of the PC overreactions highlighted. Namely, the simple fact that among the many distinguishable groups in our *one human family*, there are substantial and consistent differences between groups in terms of such things as behavior, achievement, attitudes and social outcomes.

Since the groups in question are very often defined on the basis of ethnicity and race, such differences will often be seen as genetically determined. Where one group is underperforming consistently, it is not difficult to see this as reinforcing ideas of the racial or biological inferiority of one group compared to another.

Australian Aboriginals, for example, are statistically much more likely than the average of the Australian population to be major abusers of alcohol. They are also overwhelmingly more likely to be unemployed, and often semi-literate. More often than not, they are 'written off' by the average Australian, who assumes that this is 'just the way they are', with all that this implies about alleged biological inferiority.

That potential racist connotation is probably the main reason it's become politically incorrect even to acknowledge that there are these differences. Regardless of the good intentions that might underlie this taboo, simply changing the way we speak, or what we choose to speak about, is not going to change any of the facts of the real world. What it mostly does is to add a layer of artificiality and hypocrisy to social discourse. In this brave new PC world, people often feel intimidated into talking to each other in a way that politicians call 'dog whistling';[5] they mention things without mentioning them, hoping the other person will pick up the subtle cues.

In any case, the evidence indicates that such differences are not genetic, but rather cultural. It's easy to underestimate the powerful

---

5.   A dog whistle is ultrasonic, so humans don't hear it, only the dogs for which it's intended. For example, a politician could appeal to racial prejudice within her constituency by referring to certain 'hot button' issues known to be associated with racial matters. Without ever mentioning anyone's race, she has alerted those 'with ears to hear' to what she really means. But often demagogues seize upon racial connotations where none are intended, e.g. innocent advocacy of personal responsibility can be seen as 'code language' for racist views on minorities.

effects of culture, the more so because we are generally unaware of the extent to which we ourselves have been shaped by them. The individuals from whom we most readily absorb our culture are firstly those within our own home, and then those of our 'peer group', while growing up. These are going to be the people to whom we are most closely related, i.e. our own ethnic group or race. This is why it's so hard to disentangle culture from 'race'. It's also why it's just not possible to meaningfully discuss race or racism without considering the effects of culture.

Believing that people are intrinsically of equal worth is *not* the same as believing that all people are equal or behave equally. We are obviously not all equal—not all are tall enough or strong enough to be useful army commandos, or good enough at mathematics to be university professors in the subject, for instance. And we don't all behave the same. That's self-evidently true of individuals. But what is not often discussed is that it's also true of entire categories of people. This includes groups defined ethnically or racially, which often exhibit consistent differences in behavior and outcomes.

I have previously mentioned economist Dr. Thomas Sowell, and his reputation for dispassionate analysis. As a Hoover Institution Fellow, he has done a monumental series of studies into several different groups of people around the world. For something as complex as human society, no analyst is going to be 'spot on' all the time. But, though he is not a Christian, I and several others I know among my colleagues regard Sowell as perhaps the most insightful student of humanity alive today. He is one of the few well-known public minds who has a reputation for dispassionately following the evidence, regardless of whether that makes him popular with the academic 'herd' or not.

Institutional funding allowed him to travel the world for many years to research his subject matter as perhaps no-one else ever has. The trilogy of books he is most renowned for is: *Race and Culture*, *Migrations and Culture*, and *Conquests and Cultures*. I think Sowell should be compulsory reading for everyone trying to understand the forces that have helped shape our modern world.

It might mean, though, that they will have to unlearn a lot of what they think they know.

US ghetto culture—neither authentic nor African

For example, in the US, large numbers of African Americans share particular mannerisms, ways of speaking, behaviors and attitudes that have been summarized as 'black ghetto culture'. Many have sought to use this as a source of racial pride and cohesion, even going so far as to call it 'authentic black culture'. However, Sowell argues persuasively that it is neither authentic nor black in its historical origins. Instead, it was absorbed and inherited from a particular white redneck culture in the antebellum South.

He convincingly identifies this culture's origin, in turn, as an import of the so-called 'cracker culture' of the Anglo-Scottish border areas. The clans in this rather lawless region, who would historically shift allegiances at will between Scotland and England, developed a particularly dysfunctional society. Their approach to life was characterized by work aversion, a propensity to violence, sexual promiscuity, drunkenness and lack of entrepreneurship. The value of education was particularly despised. Even the preachers used dramatic oratory, repetition, yelling and exaggerated cadences. Significant numbers from the region emigrated to pockets of the southern US, where clusters of many of these attributes became endemic in segments of white society. Here they were picked up early by many black communities, too. Sowell's point is straightforward; continuing to embrace a culture in which many of those elements feature prominently is not helpful for African Americans, but rather the opposite.[6]

There are significant groups of black Americans whose culture has, for historical reasons, never been influenced by this 'authentic' cracker-derived one. He convincingly shows how such groups

---

6.   Sowell, T, *Black Rednecks and White Liberals* (a collection of six essays), Encounter Books, 2005. One reviewer wrote (and I agree): "This is an articulate, searching text that goes well beyond the traditional Liberal/Conservative ping-pong."

have dramatically outperformed their 'authentic' counterparts in the academic and professional arena. This applies also to such social parameters as the frequency of two-parent families, in which they outstrip whites—the reverse of the situation that generally prevails.

The lower educational and job outcomes of the bulk of American blacks, relative to the rest of the community, makes sense in the light of a peer group that undervalues such things. Yet it is that lesser performance which tends to reinforce the deep-seated beliefs of many whites about their 'racial' inferiority.

In one of his many books, Sowell pointed out that at times, American blacks from such a highly functional cultural background have become particularly peeved at the bad name the so-called 'authentic black culture' has given them. Such groups of African Americans have sometimes joined the white exodus from certain neighborhoods. The issue for them at least was not race, but culture/behavior. Yet for most of the whites, no doubt, the culture-derived behavior of the other African-American group would have mostly reinforced the evolution-fueled biological-racist stereotypes. The message is clear. It is culture that makes the difference, not race. And this is no surprise given the biological closeness of our *one human family*.

Sowell's research also reinforces this matter of culture, not genes, in another way. He shows that immigrant people groups who are of the same 'race' as their host country nevertheless show distinct differences in behavior and outcomes. These differences carry on through generations. This even extends to the types of occupations they gravitate to and excel in. For instance, Germans migrating to other parts of the world are disproportionately represented in beer brewing enterprises and the higher military ranks within their new homeland. Pershing, Eisenhower and Schwarzkopf, top US generals in World War I, World War II and the first Iraq war respectively, were ethnic Germans and obvious examples. Sir John Monash was often hailed as Australia's top soldier ever—and even "as the best general on the western front in Europe" according to Field Marshal Montgomery.[7] He was of Prussian Jewish ancestry.

Similarly consistent patterns are seen where race is different, too. Jewish people in Caucasian-dominated societies are statistically overrepresented in the 'rag trade', or clothing industry. Such patterns are not likely to reflect the influence of any genes, but rather the cultural heritage they have absorbed. The Jews in Europe had for generations been subject to pogroms[8] and frequent forced moves, often without much warning. It's not surprising that they would tend to gravitate to occupations in which everything that was needed to carry on their livelihood could be thrown into a wagon at short notice—or could even be replaced without excess hardship.

Work and enterprise

The important influences on us as young children, gleaned from our parents and other significant people close to us, come not so much from what they teach us in words. They are mostly from what is transferred and absorbed without even trying—by osmosis, if you like. It's not hard to understand how the group characteristics of various 'race-defined' communities differ widely in such things as the drive and motivation to work and achieve.

In Malaya (now Malaysia), in the heyday of rubber plantations and the last embers of the British Empire, there were widely noticed differences in work ethic and output between the Chinese immigrants and the local Malays. Over time this translated into a widening economic gap between the two groups, with the Malay community lagging considerably behind.

---

7.   Monash's revolutionary strategy of co-ordinated use of infantry, artillery, tanks and aircraft won the Battle of Hamel in 1918 in only 90 minutes with low casualties; taking such objectives had previously taken months and cost hundreds of thousands of casualties. This was also the first engagement of American troops in WWI. Monash's strategy was applied on a much larger scale in the Battle of Amiens, the turning point of the war.

8.   A violent riot against an ethnic minority either instigated or approved by authorities. The term (Russian погром) mostly arose in reference to anti-Jewish actions in the former Russian Empire.

The differences make sense from the facts of history acting on their respective cultures. The Chinese came from a background in which they had regularly experienced great famine and hardship. Their culture accordingly valued hard work and thrift, and encouraged making the most of every opportunity for economic advantage and advance. The Malays, by contrast, came from a much more idyllic background. A combination of fertile soils, plenty of rainfall and continual warmth meant that a much lesser amount of work was needed to acquire and maintain the basics of food and shelter.

It was common knowledge that European plantation owners would pay their Chinese coolie laborers about twice as much as they paid Malays for the same type of manual work. This is because the employer would generally get about three times the amount of work done by the Chinese as by Malay laborers. In time, the Chinese came to dominate in business and ownership of resources, leading to great tensions between the two populations. The obvious differences in group behavior could be attributed by either side to innate racial/biological characteristics—they could be conveniently written off by each other with epithets such as 'lazy' on one hand and 'greedy' or 'sneaky' on the other.

Not surprisingly, even in the absence of any racist assumptions about Malays, the Chinese would generally prefer doing business with those sharing their cultural outlook and ways of operating. In this way, they got the reputation of being 'clannish', so the tensions (and the racial stereotypes) would be further reinforced. And these were enhanced by the fact that each group was recognizable on the basis of biological/racial characteristics. One can readily see how perceptions arose of the Chinese as a 'favored immigrant elite'[9] whose actions were intended to exclude Malays, the 'true inhabitants', from economic benefit. The wealthier the Chinese became, the easier it became for individual Malays to blame their own economic standing on someone else's 'greed'—in this case an entire group of people.

---

9. The fact that the forefathers of some Chinese had been in Malaya for centuries did not exempt their descendants from this perception.

A similar situation developed in the South Pacific nation of Fiji between the indigenous Fijians and the Indian immigrants (who today make up some half of the population). The native Fijians had, like the Malaysians, also been blessed in their natural environment—and without the really sweltering equatorial heat, either. In these islands, surrounded by easily available seafood from the fringing reefs and lagoons, there was no shortage of readily accessible protein. Coconuts were plentiful, as was other natural bounty.

The Indians had mostly been brought to the islands as indentured laborers. They had effectively been forced into slavery to pay off debts. Obviously, their background reflected greater material hardship and insecurity than that of the locals. In their culture, it was much more the norm to be continually working to ensure bare security for oneself and family. Making the most of whatever opportunity presented itself—including sometimes where that was to another's disadvantage—was also going to be more prevalent among the Indians than the native Fijians, whose more easygoing village culture encouraged ready sharing. Here, too, Indians came to own virtually all the businesses in Fiji. Many Indians see Fijians as lazy, and many Fijians see Indians as greedy, and feel threatened by their economic dominance. Thus, in Fiji, also, huge tensions have arisen between these two populations, and have helped to ensure chronic political instability in recent times.

To deny (or avoid discussing due to PC considerations) such group differences is not only avoiding reality, it is unhelpful in seeking to reduce inter-group tensions. The people involved in the situation will trust their own experiences over any sort of PC-based denials. And these experiences will often tend to reinforce the 'racial' aspects in their minds. How much more likely to benefit the situation if those differences were both faced realistically, and continually understood for what they are—generated by culture, and not the biology of race. Culture gives a basis for greater understanding of the background to the behavioral differences. And behavior seen as learned is less likely to be regarded as 'incorrigible' in anything like the same way as if it is thought of as biologically or 'racially' derived—for example, from being 'less evolved'.

It might be argued that it is over-idealistic to expect a Genesis-based worldview to gain wholesale acceptance in an evolution-soaked world. But considering the fact that the history of Christianity encourages one not to 'think small', even modest advances in this direction are worthwhile. They can even be vital. Ethnic tensions generated by such group differences have more than once led to open conflict and bloodshed. It is of real practical importance for all of us, in our own circles of influence, to promote and maintain a high level of awareness of this truth— our close relatedness, as part of this *one human family*.

∞

13 DISCRIMINATION AND RACE— ANOTHER LOOK

RACIAL OR RATIONAL DISCRIMINATION?

In the instance described in the previous chapter, where the employers were paying Chinese more than Malays, this was 'racial discrimination', certainly. But it was not from any inherent bias against any people group so much as it was a rational reflection of the plantation owners' legitimate commercial self-interest. Remember, when referring to group differences, we're talking about 'on average'. There would have been some Malays who worked much more diligently than some Chinese; the point is whether this group discrimination matched the probability of the likely outcome for the employer. Obviously, it did so often enough for employers to keep backing that proposition with their own money.

Much of what passes for 'discrimination' today, and is definitely politically incorrect, is not what one could call 'real racism' or 'true racial discrimination' at all, but is similar rational behavior. By real racism I mean attitudes or actions which unfairly and consistently target people as inferior, to be despised or rejected, treated unjustly, or even harmed—simply by virtue of being a member of a particular people group. Overdoing the PC antiracism bandwagon can, by targeting things as racist that are not racist at all, be counterproductive, as we saw in regard to the backlash occurring in Europe.

Profiling and probabilities

So-called racial profiling during airport screening procedures is another situation in which discrimination can make sense as a form of sensible probability-matching. Unless there are unlimited resources available for the screening, it might be more rational to pay extra attention (while not overlooking any) to gentlemen of Middle Eastern appearance and dress compared to a group of Belgian nuns. Israel faces perhaps the most danger from aviation terrorism, but has some of the safest airlines in the world, and its security forces are not afraid to use profiling—especially behavioral.

Countering real racism and true racial discrimination is ultimately an issue of the heart and of morality. As in other matters, to try to impose morality 'from the top' is seldom effective unless there are simultaneous efforts to change the heart. In this case, that also means changing the way people view other races.

While legislation is sometimes necessary where flagrant injustices are happening, in most cases imposing morality only achieves a legalistic morass. The social rules, PC sanctions and even legislation in the area of 'discrimination' of all sorts can border on the absurd.

It used to be regarded as rational and highly appropriate behavior to discriminate, hence terms such as 'discriminating gentleman'. Today, employers in some parts of the West are scarcely able to discriminate (openly at least) in favor of employees that work harder. Consider, too, a person being interviewed for a job requiring a lot of very heavy lifting and bending. They may be obviously unsuitable—perhaps grossly obese, or perhaps, if say a slightly-built female, clearly too weak. Employers in many countries simply don't tell people what the *real* reason is when informing them that they are 'unsuitable'. The risk of being the target of an antidiscrimination suit is too high. This encourages a lack of openness and honesty, and more than a little cynicism.

RACISM TO FIGHT RACISM?

Applying biblical principles consistently not only addresses racism, it makes it impossible to support measures to address racial inequities, perceived or real, by applying 'racism in reverse'. In Malaysia, such 'affirmative action' transparently favoring indigenous Malays over citizens of other ethnic groups has taken place for years. It seemed to reach new heights under the regime headed by former Prime Minister Mahathir bin Mohamad.

While I was still a GP (in Adelaide, South Australia), a Malaysian Chinese doctor responded to my advertisement for a Christian partner for the family practice I had commenced (such an advert might result in lawsuits in many PC-dominated countries today because of 'religious discrimination'). I was puzzled; he seemed far too qualified for a humble family practice. He was a fully trained and registered specialist in not just general surgery, but also the even more specialized area of urological surgery. I later found out that he had been in line to become the Professor of Urological Surgery at the University of Kuala Lumpur. (In Malaysia as in most British-derived systems, that meant being head of the Department.) But it was not to be; the Malaysian government had apparently decreed that only people of Malay descent—called 'Bumiputra', i.e. 'sons of the soil' (short plural form 'Bumis')—could be the actual Professors of any Department.

Former Malaysian Prime Minister Mahathir bin Mohamad.
Public domain

Note that this particular instance of society-wide racial discrimination never fell foul of world opinion as did South Africa's (see Chapter 15). This may again reflect a racist view— of not expecting Asians to have, or be able to live up to, the same ethical standards as Europeans. Clearly disillusioned and quite likely disgusted at this sort of blatant racial discrimination, my colleague-to-be had decided to emigrate to Australia. With him came his equally brilliant wife, a clinical microbiologist.[1] Australia's gain was definitely Malaysia's loss.

Who knows how many other times this sort of 'brain drain' has taken place in response to these policies—to the detriment of Malaysia's economy and the health of its people, no doubt. So, regardless of how it was supposed to benefit the majority Malay population, in reality it would have done the reverse overall. Indeed, in neighboring Singapore, a majority-Chinese nation where Malays have no special privileges, the *Malays* are better off on average than in Malaysia.

Sometimes such situations are made much worse when politicians and rulers cynically exploit racial stereotypes. This happened in 1972 when Idi Amin, then the dictator of Uganda, expelled all the country's Asians (mostly Indians). This was ostensibly for the benefit of the indigenous Ugandan population. The ones expelled, however, were responsible for most of the activity of business and commerce in that nation, for similar sorts of cultural reasons as in previous examples. Predictably, the Ugandan economy crashed.

There have been other significant-scale social experiments in modern times involving such 'reverse racism'. It may sound great in theory, especially to the previously disadvantaged group. However, outcomes almost never match expectations, no matter how noble the intentions may be. The main beneficiaries in the preferred groups are those who are already best off, and the most harmed are the poorest in the 'privileged' groups discriminated

---

1. She is the 'Irene' in the 'knee healing' anecdote in my book *Beyond the Shadows: making sense of personal tragedy*. The book is centered around a major motor collision in which I was involved in 1986.

against.

Like affirmative action, Marxism, too, can sound great in theory, and can also appeal to one's sense of justice and fair play. But that does not prevent it from being a deeply flawed system that has never failed to hurt the bulk of the people it is meant to be helping. This is mainly because it ignores the biblical teaching that man is fallen. Desire for gain is a human universal. A system that confiscates wealth from the productive to give to the unproductive removes the incentive—from both groups—to produce in the first place.

Humans are also not omniscient; no group of central planners can possibly have the knowledge to decree how much of each of millions of different types of goods should be produced. Ironically, many blame Marxist failures on butchers like Mao, Stalin, and Pol Pot. But for a government and its bureaucracy to be able to redistribute wealth and plan a whole economy, it must be huge, powerful and controlling—just the sort to attract and enable these types in the first place. Marxism is not just a useful analogy to reverse racism, either—when the two are applied together, it generally compounds the difficulties inherent in each.

Head and heart—both needed

Having said that, however, things in this complex world are not always black and white (perhaps, given our subject, I should have used 'blue and green'). Christians need to consider whether their support of any particular ideological position traditionally associated with free enterprise really does reflect mere rationality and biblically derived principles. There is sometimes a fine line between rational economics and an economic rationalism that owes more to the Darwinian laws of the economic jungle than to rationality. Sometimes hardness of heart can be an issue. Are we really supporting something because we think it's more likely to be for the greater good of our fellows, or because we will be the chief beneficiaries (perhaps even at the expense of others)?

Zechariah 7:9–12 applies to both the individual, and to groups of individuals:

"'Thus says the LORD of hosts, Render true judgments, show kindness and mercy to one another, do not oppress the widow, the fatherless, the sojourner, or the poor, and let none of you devise evil against another in your heart.' But they refused to pay attention and turned a stubborn shoulder and stopped their ears that they might not hear. They made their hearts diamond-hard lest they should hear the law and the words that the LORD of hosts had sent by his Spirit through the former prophets. Therefore great anger came from the LORD of hosts."

We need to also understand something about how a group historically disadvantaged on the basis of race in recent history may feel about the pain of their previous situation. It may be so acute that, for them, the sense of satisfaction/justice/relief gained from the role reversal itself is primary. So much so that they may be willing to put up with substantial—even astonishing—deprivations resulting from the socio-economic failure of any such approach.

On a milder scale, affirmative action in favor of minorities has been in vogue among the intelligentsia, especially in the USA, for quite some time. As an unmistakably African American, Thomas Sowell (pictured p. 233) certainly has experienced the full brunt of real racism and racial discrimination in his lifetime (b. 1930), including the infamous Jim Crow laws of the American South.[2] But what counts with him is whether the *evidence* supports a particular idea or a proposed solution. On this basis, Sowell has consistently made a principled, and often rather lonely, public stand against affirmative action.[3]

Affirmative action and bad loans

For one thing, some of what has been blamed on discrimination in

---

2.   A series of state and local laws passed between 1876 and 1965 that mandated racial segregation in public places. The name comes from a standard character in minstrel shows of the mid-1800s. This became a stereotypical image of black inferiority in popular culture and ultimately a racial slur. A 'Jim Crow' law was thus one which was based on such notions about blacks.
3.   See his book *Affirmative Action Around the World: An Empirical Study*, Yale University Press, New Haven CT, 2004.

the US has not been from that cause at all. Take, for example, the widespread allegation that African Americans applying for loans have been routinely discriminated against by financial institutions on racist grounds. This is so widely stated, even used as the basis for laws mandating loan quotas for minorities, that for many people it requires no further justification. Sowell shows, however, that the facts and statistics simply do not bear this out. Rather, they show that financial institutions, until forced to do otherwise by affirmative action, were simply making rational decisions based on normal lending criteria, such as loan history, ability to repay, and so on. If they were discriminating on racial grounds, he asks, why is it that Asian-Americans have a consistently higher success rate in obtaining finance than whites? Are the majority whites who control the lending institutions racially discriminating *in favor* of non-whites in this instance?

Obviously, financial institutions are in business to make money—ideology, even racism, is seldom going to get in the way of that. Even at the height of apartheid, bankers in South Africa would often find ways to circumvent various government policies and practices so as to make loans available to blacks. Their only proviso: applying the usual lending criteria needed to indicate that they would likely make money on the loans. There is no evidence that this indicated some sort of social conscience on the bankers' behalf; it was simply in their obvious (and understandable) self-interest. For similar reasons, private owners of buses and railroads in the Jim Crow South fought against segregated seating requirements of their governments, which Rosa Parks famously challenged.[4]

Affirmative action policies in the US encouraged—even forced—lenders to ignore the rational norms of lending practice. This is particularly relevant in light of the US subprime mortgage collapse of 2008, which led to a financial crisis of global proportions. Previous to this, the catchcry was of racist lenders denying loans to hapless minorities. After the collapse,

4.   Sowell, T., Rosa Parks and history, www.jewishworldreview.com/cols/sowell102705.asp, 2005.

260 ~ ONE HUMAN FAMILY

the trend has been to condemn the 'predatory' lending practices of institutions, who are now seen as having targeted minorities to force loans on them that they could not afford.

Reverse racism—reducing respect

Sowell points out that in addition to affirmative action policies being market-distorting and based on false assumptions, such racism in reverse is patronizing and demeaning. This is especially so for those many members of US minorities who have, like himself, achieved academic and professional stature on their own merits. Where such achievements take place in an environment of widespread affirmative action, onlookers are likely to assume that they are the result of some quota system. This devalues the qualification or position, as well as the one holding it.

Artificially imposed reverse racism does nothing to enhance respect by groups for each other, but rather the opposite. In Malaysia, the affirmative action policies already mentioned have included laws requiring that native Malays need to have a substantial share of ownership in new businesses. This has led to the widespread creation of countless ventures known to locals as 'Ali Baba' enterprises. On the surface, 'Ali' (a common Malay name) owns the business. Behind the scenes, though, 'Baba' ('grandpa' in one Chinese dialect) is the Chinese person who pulls the strings and makes all the decisions. He is the business owner in reality, the one with the experience and skills to operate it, and the money to set it up in the first place. Ali gets paid as a front-man, simply for the use of his 'race'.

Such a situation involves an unproductive diversion of capital, and is one in which reward is not based on outcome or merit. It is an inevitable drag on a nation's economy, in addition to any 'brain drain' effect via migration. It also does nothing to lessen any racist or other negative attitudes by Babas toward Alis—if anything, the inevitable resentment toward 'Ali' and his 'cash for nothing' ensures the reverse. Such overt hypocrisy and phoniness also encourages public cynicism towards the institutions of law and government.[5]

Ethnic favor is to an extent built into the Malaysian Constitution. Nevertheless, there are currently definite signs that the government of Malaysia wants to make substantial moves away from this notion. This may be an implicit acknowledgment of the failure of such race-based policies.

The belief that one can redress group imbalances and injustices by artificially imposing further ones in the opposite direction seems to superficially 'make sense'. It appeals to our notion of justice, too, when wrongs appear to be righted. A little thought on the matter, though, will indicate how unlikely it is that imposing further injustice is the appropriate remedy. For one thing, the perpetrators of offenses in the distant past are not at all affected by making others of their ethnic group suffer in return. It may be understandable that group X, which sees itself as the victim of racism by group Y, may want to effect some sort of redress. It might also seem to be 'fair', or to expiate perceived guilt in the collective conscience of the historical oppressor group. Yet the people benefiting are mostly not those who suffered. It is overall a strategy doomed to long-term failure, and fails to deal with the root causes and attitudes.

∞

5.   Interestingly, a friend who is a research professor at a major Western university lived in East Malaysia (Sarawak and Sabah) for some years. He told me that the 'Bumi' policies there worked against Malays (unlike people groups such as the Kadazan, Dayak, Iban, etc. Malays are not indigenous there. So in similar arrangements, 'Baba' was sometimes actually a Malay).

14.
INDIGENOUS ISSUES

This chapter will focus on the Aboriginal people of Australia, since this is the indigenous issue with which I am most familiar. However, there will be some similarities to indigenous communities in other countries colonized by Europeans where the original inhabitants have long been a minority group. To the extent that this is so, readers from such countries may be able to identify some useful general principles and applicable insights.

Looking at the disastrous living conditions in many Aboriginal communities, it's easy to see how these would reinforce any racist assumptions, subliminal or otherwise, that non-indigenous Australians might have. The facts seem too obvious to deny; whenever significant numbers of Australians who share that ethnicity, with its particular external features, including skin color, live together, the same sorts of problems arise. Yes, the average non-indigenous Aussie thinks, I know it's not nice to be racist, but … . Deep down, there is often at least an uneasy feeling that the biological inferiority theory may well be right.

The problems in these communities are huge and undeniable. One of my two daughters is a medical doctor. Lara (see feature 'One Human Family' p. 266) has devoted much of her life to working with, and standing up for, the poor and disadvantaged in her Australian homeland, specifically Aboriginal communities.[1] This has mostly involved the so-called Cape communities (on remote Cape York Peninsula in the far northeast, around the Gulf of Carpentaria), one in particular.

Alcohol, violence, sexual abuse, and suicide

The statistics in such townships are discouraging, to put it mildly. The health problems and life expectancy of the people in them are mostly worse than in many very poor developing nations, despite Australia's thoroughly first-world economy. And if trends continue, the average teenager in such communities entering high school can expect that before she reaches 20, a substantial percentage of her current classmates will already have committed suicide, mostly by hanging themselves. Of the remainder, more than half will be well down the road to established alcoholism, with the bulk of these highly likely to become alcoholics, too, in subsequent years. Nearly all the girls will be single mothers already, and most of the boys will have criminal records, or will even have spent time in jail. Only the tiniest percentage, if any, is likely to have achieved gainful employment.

What is particularly distressing is the level of alcohol-related physical and sexual abuse, particularly of young children. It's not unusual for doctors in the Cape communities to see cases of sexually transmitted disease (STD) in prepubescent children, both male and female.

When people find out about the very poor educational outcomes for children in these communities, the 'racial' conclusion comes very quickly to mind. But outsiders have no idea of either the lack of incentives or role models, or the horrendous conditions under which a child would have to do homework. For most of us it's hard to imagine the difficulty of even getting a regular night's sleep, with a background of noise, violence and threats of violence. Many grandmothers spend much of the night trying to

---

1. Newspaper hails creationist 'Angel of the Cape': What a difference it makes when you believe in the Bible's real history, 6 January 2003, creation.com/angel-of-the-cape.

shield their grandchildren with their own bodies, to protect them against drunken sexual abuse when there is alcohol in town. This is fortunately not as regular as it used to be, since the alcohol restrictions in Queensland lobbied for by Aboriginal activist Noel Pearson (feature p. 272) and others.

Until very recently, and even now to an extent, it was taboo to highlight such things, for fear of being called racist. The denial, including by the same sectors of society who are most vocal about Aboriginal rights, has been appalling. But in 2007, the problems among Aboriginal communities in Australia's quasi-state known as the Northern Territory became too great to ignore. Perhaps more significantly, they became too *public* to ignore—the Territory government had published a bombshell report on the level of child abuse, titled *Little Children are Sacred*. The Federal Government formally decreed the situation to be a National Emergency, and sent hundreds of soldiers and police into the Territory's Aboriginal communities in a response that became known as 'The Intervention'.[2]

It seemed well-intentioned, if heavy-handed and partly politically motivated, and it received cautious support from several Aboriginal leaders, including Pearson. Nevertheless, many of the self-styled champions of 'indigenous rights' seemed to have less concern for the suffering of the children than for ideology, widely condemning the move as 'racist'. Currently, however, several years and a change of government after the *Little Children* report triggered the Intervention, the great majority of its recommendations remain unimplemented.

There is a somewhat encouraging sign emerging from a small coterie of individual journalists and editors in some sectors of the Australian media. Over the last few years, these have started to work in a semi-coordinated fashion to heighten awareness of these deep-seated problems. They have helped to push for commonsense reforms, including the obvious one of empowering these communities to impose draconian restrictions on the sale

2.   See Walker, T., *National Emergency in Australia*, creation.com/aboriginalemergency, 29 June 2007.

FEATURE

One Human Family

Dr. Lara Wieland* and her husband, Ron, shown here with two of the boys referred to in the main text who have come to live in their home during school term. They live about 600 km (c. 400 miles) south of the Cape community in which Lara works, mostly on a regular roster basis, flown in and out for a week at a time by the Royal Flying Doctor Service.

She and Ron also drive up during school holidays to operate vacation activities and gospel outreach. They founded a non-profit charity (see www.outtherekowanyama.com.au) supported by Christians and unbelievers alike. When they first surveyed the community's youngsters about what they most wanted to do in their vacation period, they uniformly indicated that their key desire was for 'a youth center run by someone who is strict with us'. This can be a shock to those of us who live in a culture where most of its children would think it was great not to be hovered over or restricted in what they do. It's hard to imagine living as a child in a situation where you yearn

for someone to love you enough to care where you go or what you do.

*Female doctors in Australia tend to retain their maiden name professionally if they graduated in that name.

and consumption of liquor. But the 'sweep it under the carpet' mentality in such matters has been deeply ingrained for a long time. It meant that Lara was at one point overtly opposed by health officials when she tried to notify authorities about active STD in a child of seven years. Believe it or not, she was 'encouraged' to conclude that the infection, which is only spread by sexual contact, had likely been caught from a toilet seat, or was simply a false result!

It probably didn't help that acknowledging the obvious abuse would have meant spending money on such things as flying pedophilia investigative teams up to the Cape. If this laboratory result in a seven-year-old had occurred in one of the residents of the leafy suburbs of Brisbane or Sydney, how different the response would have been! It's not hard to see how the underlying community assumptions and beliefs about 'race' are significant in understanding why there is such markedly differential treatment for the two sets of Australian citizens.

Education and literacy

The educational outcomes in places like these Cape communities, already alluded to, are similarly depressing. Many children in the communities leave school functionally illiterate. It's far too easy for people to just assume that this is simply part of being Aboriginal—that 'biological inferiority' thing again. People are generally unaware of the many factors involved that put these children behind the eight-ball (in pool parlance) from the outset. For one thing, many of their mothers were drinking heavily during pregnancy. So-called fetal alcohol syndrome is rife in the communities, and can severely stunt a child's intellectual potential from before he or she is born.

Add to that the malnutrition from neglect, and in some instances the horror of even young children 'petrol-sniffing' (inhaling the fumes from gasoline) and one can get some idea of the insults to which their developing brain cells are subjected. A large number have severe deafness from chronic middle ear infections, a further educational handicap.

Starting with the right assumptions, i.e. the biblical facts about the true history of mankind and our close relatedness, Lara and her husband, Ron, knew that 'race' was not the factor that was holding so many of these kids back from any sort of future. The issue was their environment, the dysfunctional aspects of the social culture surrounding them. So they decided to help at least the few they could. They offered their home during school term as a haven for maybe two or three youngsters at a time. These were those whose parents (or carers—often these are grandmothers where the parents have abdicated responsibility in a haze of alcohol) wanted them to have a chance. The first child they took in after this fashion was a boy who, after six years in primary school, was still almost illiterate. This is so common in the communities, it's just seen as 'normal'.

In 'white Australia', by contrast, the public education system would not permit such children to progress to higher and higher grades without having learnt to read and write. The alarm bells would have been triggered at an early stage, with willing expenditure on remedial measures. If our nation truly believed in the close relatedness of our *one human family*, would we have tolerated this sort of thing, year in and out, just passing kids on to ever higher classes, even though they can't read? I doubt it.

With their starting assumptions that it was not a racial issue, Ron and Lara were pleased, but not surprised, when they saw that the young lad quickly gained full literacy and started to achieve at normal levels, even excelling beyond his peers in some academic areas. Proper nutrition, and a peaceful and caring Christian environment (including both affection *and* loving controls on behavior) had made a huge difference. And similar positive results are apparent in the other youngsters so far.

Sure, children are not laboratory rats, such that switching environments on and off is all it takes. Their emotional ties to family and community are maintained as much as possible, and will remain strong. And there may well be scars from their childhood experiences yet to surface, not to mention the nutritional handicaps during fetal development and early childhood on the developing brain. And of course there are bound to be the occasional factors that affect learning in any ethnic group—of which dyslexia, attention deficit problems and various parts of the spectrum of autism are just a few. But the turnaround in health, achievement and happiness is already astounding. It shows how much of a positive difference can still be made by having the right starting beliefs about our *one human family*.

Merely giving lip service to antiracism may be trendy, but is clearly not the answer. Real non-racism, and real caring for Aboriginal people as people, as our full relatives, does not go along with putting one's head in the sand about the problems in their communities. Nor does it help to blame the racism of past generations of 'white Australians'—as real, and sometimes horrific, as this book has shown that to have been. In fact, that sort of notion can be counterproductive, by feeding into a victim mentality and distracting from the social urgency of the huge current problems.

And they *are* huge. Even with the sorts of descriptions I've given here, it's really hard for those of us in comfortable suburbia to understand the sort of living hell these kids come from. When Ron and Lara took in their first two young boys from the Cape, the youngsters began to literally shake with fear as they entered the kitchen. Why? They had spotted a sharp knife out in the open on the kitchen bench. Where they came from, leaving anything like that lying around in easy reach would mean it could far too easily be snatched up and used with deadly effect in an alcohol-fueled rage.

I find it almost hard to write about the way in which, more than once, Lara has shared with me and other family members her heartbreak at finding one of her young patients hanging lifeless from the end of a self-constructed noose. Adding to the sadness, these were sometimes youngsters she thought had real potential to break free some day from the grinding constraints of their social environment. Imagine how much more heartbreak there must be in such cases for direct relatives and friends, even though already numbed by the rolling trauma of daily life in that setting.

Soaked in an environment like that day and night, it's not difficult to imagine even young teenagers already wanting to drown out the pain with whatever is handy—whether that's petrol fumes, or, more readily available, the alcohol that fostered most of the distress in the first place. Or even a joint or bong—there is currently a worrying graduation to marijuana as the emotional painkiller of choice. And so the cycle goes on.

Modern history shows that the intelligentsia (remember, not the same thing as 'all intelligent people') are notoriously resistant to the influence of facts on their cherished beliefs concerning what is best for the rest of us.[3] This has unfortunately been true of their approach to indigenous issues, too. Though their antiracism is often sincere, the solutions proposed for indigenous problems have, in Australia at least, been both paternalistic and largely counterproductive. They have, for instance, actively discouraged the idea of Aboriginal people progressively becoming fully integrated into mainstream Australian culture, with eventually the same restraints and incentives as the rest of us. In this they have often been aided and encouraged by some sectors within Aboriginal leadership, possibly concerned about losing out on various privileges not available to other Australians.

Money, work and welfare

The general principle which most Australians uphold and live under is that those capable of gainful employment should have to engage in it in order to be meaningfully sustained, while having a welfare safety net in case of temporary or unavoidable hardship. The idea that this principle, also iterated in I Thessalonians 3:10, should apply to Aboriginal people, too, does not seem to suit the vision of the intelligentsia. They often react, too, against the perceived 'racism' of having strict community-policed alcohol controls. Yet for some reason, the racist implications of treating Aboriginals differently from non-Aboriginals when it comes to work and money are lost on them. The end result has been a soul-destroying welfare dependency that feeds into, and in turn is reinforced by, the rampant community problems already

---

3.   Here, also, Thomas Sowell has laid the evidence out brilliantly, in two of his books: *Vision of the Anointed* (1996) and *Intellectuals and Society* (2010).

described.

The idea that market constraints should apply to housing in Aboriginal communities too, or that they should be encouraged to own their own dwellings, has also been anathema in such circles. Instead, 'community-owned' (really bureaucracy-administered) land and houses became the norm in Aboriginal communities, with peppercorn (nominal) rentals and no incentive to repair or look after buildings.

Billions of dollars have been spent on 'solutions' to Aboriginal problems, but many of them seem to mostly serve the idealistic visions of the intelligentsia (that small media contingent I mentioned excepted). The money mostly seems to dissipate within layers of self-serving bureaucracies, rather than reach where it is needed. The Cape townships, like most remote indigenous communities, have for decades had only a fraction of the medical services that most Australians take for granted. In proportion to the numbers of people and the actual health needs, the spending is very much below that in non-Aboriginal parts of Australia.

Nonetheless, mainstream Australia knows that large sums of money are being spent, but can't see the corresponding benefits. Not knowing the realities on the ground, the mainstream largely resents the expenditure of its taxpayer dollars, and the blame is put on the Aboriginal people for not showing any improvement despite 'all that money'. That's why reading articles about the ongoing third world conditions in the Aboriginal communities will often *increase* that resentment. And it also serves to reinforce racist thinking about Aboriginal people, even if social fashion decrees that it should remain suppressed beneath the surface.

These past few decades, one trendy fad was a push for Aboriginal people to not only return to their homelands, but return to their tribal culture. There are aspects of that culture which are certainly beneficial. For example, large numbers of Aboriginal people suffer from type 2 diabetes, a lot of it brought on by the chronically high carbohydrate overload from beer, white flour and so on. When the people spend time out 'in the

FEATURE

Cape Crusader

Aboriginal community leader, lawyer, and activist Noel Pearson. Pearson was raised on a mission at Hope Vale in the rainforest region of Far North Queensland. Though he experienced the sometimes patronizing aspects of Christian attitudes of the day, he is very aware of the positives, and has indicated that in many ways they were the 'good old days' for his people, compared to the present. He is an activist for more government support for Cape communities in areas that are currently underfunded compared to the rest of Australia, but opposes welfare dependency and has worked hard to see tighter alcohol controls in communities.

Noel Pearson
Public domain

At varying times both disowned and embraced by the right *and* left of politics, he has not gone along with the 'trend' of assuming that a return to tribal culture will benefit his people. While wanting his people to still retain their language and knowledge of other aspects of their culture, he is keen for Aboriginals to join the modern world and be able to achieve economic independence by their own efforts, breaking free of the cycle of welfare dependency and alcoholism.

Pearson has very much experienced the "daggers of impediment, [racial] prejudice, difficulty and strife"* that dog his people within Australian society, conditioned by decades of racist assumptions. But his approach does not dwell on fostering an ongoing victim mentality. He founded and directs the non-profit *Cape York Institute of Policy and Leadership* (www.cyi.org.au). Acutely aware of the importance of education, and of the difficulty of achieving this within the present conditions in Aboriginal communities, Pearson has (without public fanfare) also personally funded a string of scholarships. These permit a number of youngsters from such remote communities to attend quality boarding colleges in the big cities.

*This is from a landmark speech which he gave as the Ben Chifley 'Light on the Hill' Memorial Lecture for 2000 (Chifley was a famous former Prime Minister of Australia).

bush', hunting and living off the land, eating 'bush tucker' as it is called (including wild roots, berries, etc.), their diabetes tends to dramatically improve.[4]

Yet many aspects of that culture are counterproductive. This is not surprising, really. For one thing, we all live in a modern world that has reaped the benefits of the gospel in science and technology, as shown. The situation of Aboriginals has not been improved by this move back, but rather the reverse. Of the various Cape Aboriginal communities, the ones where this 'back to the culture' has been most thoroughly applied have consistently been the worst off in regard to the violence and chaos.

For years, enlightened Aboriginal leaders, like lawyer Noel Pearson (feature at left) have been urging their people and governments to recognize, and deal radically with, both alcohol and welfare dependency. In the last few years, the media coterie mentioned earlier has come alongside Pearson in his calls for such things, including permitting Aboriginal people to buy and sell the houses they live in, as one step toward proper, non-racist assimilation into modern Australia. Though some progress is being made, even now, such sane voices have a hard time being heard. They are often in danger of being drowned out by not just the intelligentsia, but those, including Aboriginals, who are beneficiaries of much of the government spending on what has been called the 'Aboriginal industry'.

What a difference it would make to this whole situation if large numbers of people, black and white, were to operate on the biblically derived assumptions that:

- We are all closely related, each having intrinsic dignity and worth, therefore:
- Culture makes all the difference, *not* race, where 'culture'

---

4.   Much of this seems related to glycemic index (GI); the higher the GI for a carbohydrate, the faster it is converted to blood sugar (glucose). White sugar has a GI of less than 65, yet white bread, and even the potatoes bred for today's consumers, reach into the 80s and 90s (pure glucose is 100). These are the 'cheap staples' in societies where income is low, and more so where expenditure is prioritized towards alcohol, tobacco and gambling.

includes the consistent behavior patterns in any group.

• We are all moral creatures. No matter what people group we identify with, the fact is that how we act, and the choices we make, affect us, our families and our communities, for good or evil. Issues of right and wrong are highly relevant when dealing with behavior. And behavior, as we have seen, is both influenced by a culture and at the same time forms part of it. The biblical term for the negative aspects of the behavior of both individuals and groups is *sin*.

The threat of being thought 'racist' should not intimidate us into ignoring, whitewashing or sweeping under the carpet the dysfunctional, and yes, evil aspects of any culture—including our own. Rather, we all, Christians in particular, should do our best to love in a practical sense any relatives of ours we come across who are bound and held back in such ways—regardless from what people group.

At the same time, we should do what we can to bring into their world the most hopeful factor of all for real change. That is the power of the risen Christ in the lives of individuals, which has repeatedly demonstrated its culture-transforming capacity in the history of our *one human family*. A recent *Creation* magazine article featuring an interview with Lara about her involvement with Aboriginal work received a flood of comments when it was posted on the web.[5] One of the respondents was a Mrs. Beverley Ferguson, who with her husband George commenced an Aboriginal church ten years ago in the remote outback mining community of Mt. Isa. She said they started the church in a dry riverbed, to be able to reach the many homeless and often alcoholic Aboriginal people there. She endorsed the article's comments, and added:

"We can testify of the power of God to dramatically set people free, in every aspect of life. For those who have accepted God's free gift of forgiveness and have a vibrant relationship with the living God, we have found

---

5.   Bates, G., Doctor to the disadvantaged: Gary Bates chats with Dr. Lara Wieland, *Creation* **31**(3):44–47, 2009, creation.com/LaraW.

that, without specific teaching or coaching in these areas, health improves, surroundings improve, school truancy drops off, children are well fed, clean, happy and loved. The difference comes from within, and no government program can achieve what Almighty God can when He is given a chance. Yes, there are still problems to work through, but there is a huge difference, and there is Hope, and 'tools' to work through problems and break out of the binding, destructive cycle."

∞

15 APARTHEID—COLOR AND CONUNDRUM

Any book on this topic would be incomplete without comment on *apartheid* ('separateness'). This term refers to the widely known system of racial segregation and 'separate development', formally implemented in South Africa by legislation in 1948, when the Afrikaner[1]-dominated National Party came to power.

What makes it significant here is that much of Afrikaner society was self-consciously Christian. And apartheid was supported by that country's largest church, the Dutch Reformed Church (DRC).[2] So it's not surprising that critics sometimes use that fact to try to play down or dismiss the connection between evolution and racism, despite the volumes of evidence.

Of course, as has already been demonstrated, this book's thesis is not that evolution is the solitary cause of racism—though it has been a factor *par excellence* in Western society for the last 150 years or so. It is, rather, that the real history of mankind in

---

1.　Used here in the modern sense to refer to whites (mainly of Dutch descent) whose mother tongue is Afrikaans. It encompasses those who identify with a Boer (Dutch for 'farmer') heritage, more associated with the Cape frontier and semi-nomadic pastoralists (Trekboere). It also includes the so-called Cape Dutch from the southwest, as well as those of German and French (Huguenot) background.

2.　Afrikaans: *Nederduits Gereformeerde Kerk* (NGK).

Genesis is, to the extent that its implications are squarely faced, a significant antidote to racism.

It is true that the DRC came to formally repudiate apartheid, and that some churches in South Africa opposed apartheid. But it is also true that in that country, if a church was theologically and biblically conservative, it was on the whole more likely to be associated with support of apartheid than the opposite. It's also true that there were attempts to justify apartheid biblically.

In short, if this book's thesis is to have value as an honest appraisal of the facts, apartheid (and racism in general in Christian settings) can't be sidestepped or lightly brushed aside.

This chapter goes into some background detail, but is not meant to be a definitive treatment of apartheid. It leads up to descriptions of the actual reactions of South African audiences to this message of *one human family*. They provide a practical demonstration of the positive value of presenting this biblical and scientific truth.

Searching for objectivity

It's never easy to obtain an objective view of an emotion-charged issue such as apartheid. The events are so recent, and many of the wounds are still so raw. Speaking to individuals who experienced the era, the differences in perception are often stark. So much depends on the lenses through which individuals view that history.

The sins of the apartheid era—and the suffering they caused to the black people in particular, including exploitation, oppression, injustice and humiliation (and worse)—are widely known. My own current pastor served in the South African Police for some years. Many of his closest friends were in the black community, and he has substantial recollections of blatant racism—exhibited by his work colleagues in particular. One of my relatives by marriage left South Africa well before apartheid's collapse, disgusted at the way that people groups other than whites were treated.

What is less well known internationally, yet useful to explore, is the way many Afrikaners perceive the protracted global condemnation of apartheid as having gone well beyond legitimate condemnation. To them it can even seem like a vilification of their cultural heritage, and more.

Many outside South Africa have come to see whites who even condoned, let alone participated in, such a policy as morally suspect at best, and frankly evil at worst. But characterizations like this are not helpful in understanding how such aberrations arise. I grew up in Australia at a time when the so-called 'White Australia Policy' was in force, blocking migration by individuals on racial grounds. It just seemed normal to most people.

Also, several of my relatives, as already indicated, were in Germany during the development of Nazism. We would find it horrendous today to consider how they were 'enculturated' to accept such things as the euthanasia of mentally defective people as normal. But then, most Western cultures now think it's OK to kill people for being unwanted, provided they are still in their mothers' wombs.

A search for understanding in the case of apartheid might be of help to future generations as well as our own. It might help avoid being led by the ideologies of one's time down paths that are out of step with the clear teachings and implications of God's Word.

Acceptance of apartheid by Afrikaners would have been made easier because much of the policy was presented in a somewhat idealized context, as something that would be for everyone's good—including the black people, whether or not they knew it yet. It would be helpful to know for sure how much of that was rhetoric for political expediency as opposed to idealism, no matter how naïve in hindsight. But in the context of understanding its impact on the average Afrikaner, that is a secondary question. The point here is that such rationalizations were in the 'ether' at the time. And as we shall see, they were tied up with non-racial issues of legitimate concern to Afrikaners as a group. Then there were also the seemingly biblical justifications, to be touched upon shortly.

Verwoerd and race

A key figure in all this was Hendrik F. Verwoerd (1901–1966), widely known as the 'architect of apartheid'. Verwoerd was elected to parliament shortly after the National Party won power in 1948. He became Minister of Native Affairs in 1950 and then Prime Minister from 1958 till his assassination eight years later. Reading many of his official speeches,[3] one is struck by the idealism expressed. This includes a seemingly vigorous determination that the black people should not be disadvantaged (a common catchword at the time was 'separate but equal'). Particularly, that they should not be exploited.

Looking back at the actual outcomes under apartheid, which included severe disadvantage and exploitation, as well as imprisonment and even death if one resisted, one has to ask whether those expressions were genuine or mostly for public consumption. I had the opportunity to speak briefly to his son, H.F. Verwoerd Jr.[4] My impression of him was of a sincere and

Left: Hendrik F. Verwoerd Jr., the son of apartheid's architect and a lifelong missionary to native people, c. 2010. Above: His parents in the 1960s.

H. F. Verwoerd Jr.

3.   Pelzer, A.N. (Ed.), *Verwoerd Speaks*, APB Publishers, Johannesburg, 1966. Pelzer was at the time Professor of History at Pretoria University.
4.   February 2011, by internet audio connection.

humble Christian. Surprisingly to many, the son has spent his whole life as a missionary to a black people group. And in fact, it was his father who encouraged him to learn that particular native language and to engage in missionary service to its people. So far as HFV Jr. is concerned, there is no doubt about the genuineness of his father's statements. He says he never heard him speak in other than positive terms of black people, and recalls him staunchly opposing those seeking to exploit native peoples.

The point here is not to make a judgment on something concerning one individual, in a situation where one can never have all the evidence (Proverbs 20:3 tells us that "the purpose in a man's heart is like deep water…"). It is rather to try to make some sense out of the fact that so many well-intentioned folk could have supported a policy which is so frankly repugnant. (Consider only the sort of signage of the apartheid era as shown overleaf, and the countless humiliations that represented.)

Surprising as it seems, frank biological racism (evolution-based or otherwise) was relatively uncommon in Afrikaner thought and discourse. Verwoerd Sr. taught at the renowned Stellenbosch University:

> "His lecture notes and memoranda at Stellenbosch stressed that there were no biological differences between the big racial groups, and concluded that 'this was not really a factor in the development of a higher social civilization by the Caucasians'."[5]

Afrikaner self-determination

For many if not most Afrikaners, the issues at the forefront of their minds in contemplating apartheid were their desire as a people for self-preservation and self-determination. In and of themselves, these are not wrong, of course. The fact that the policy came to fruition in this sort of context ensured the backing of many who would not have willingly supported anything immoral or unjust. Nevertheless, they ended up effectively doing just that.

---

5.   From a biography of Verwoerd at South African History Online, www.sahistory.org.za, accessed 6 March 2011.

In support of this, historian Herman Giliomee (1938–), in his renowned (post-apartheid) work on the history of the Afrikaner people,[6] shows how from an early stage of the policy's extended birth process, there were always those concerned with ensuring that the notion of 'white survival' was balanced with appropriate justice. He writes:

FOR USE BY WHITE PERSONS

THESE PUBLIC PREMISES AND THE AMENITIES THEREOF HAVE BEEN RESERVED FOR THE EXCLUSIVE USE OF WHITE PERSONS.

By Order Provincial Secretary

VIR GEBRUIK DEUR BLANKES

HIERDIE OPENBARE PERSEEL EN DIE GERIEWE DAARVAN IS ViR DIE UITSLUITLIKE GEBRUIK VAN BLANKES AANGEWYS.

Op Las Provinsiale Sekretaris

A typical sign of the apartheid era in South Africa.
Public domain

"In 1940 the Rev. William Nicol of Johannesburg delivered a much-discussed sermon in which he stated that while he labored for the separate survival of the Afrikaner people, he would rather see the Afrikaners swamped by other peoples if they tried to survive without God and His justice."[7]

For those like Nicol, in theory, the *afskeiding* (segregation) needed to incorporate full development and opportunity for each people group, and did not involve ideas of racial inferiority. But in practice, of course, in the hands of sinful humans (as we all are), things overall were very different. Exploitative motives, and racial superiority/inferiority notions drove much of apartheid's

---

6.   Giliomee, H., *The Afrikaners: Biography of a people (reconsiderations in Southern African history)*, C. Hurst & Co. (Publishers) Ltd, London, 2003. Giliomee was Professor of Political Studies at the University of Cape Town (1983–2002), President of the South African Institute of Race Relations (1995–1997) and is currently Extraordinary Professor of History at Stellenbosch University in South Africa.
7.   Ref. 6, p. 461.

later outworkings (and even the later framing of the policy and its unjust laws).

To further understand the complexity of how such a racist policy could develop in a culture in which there was a relative absence of overt racist *ideology*, a lengthy excerpt from Giliomee is helpful:

> "Many Afrikaner nationalist academics, including Verwoerd ... rejected the idea that blacks were biologically inferior to whites or that race had anything to do with intelligence or abilities. A leading Afrikaner educationist wrote: 'I maintain that nothing has been proven about the backwardness of the native mind.' [National Party] leaders increasingly purged racist expressions from their speeches.

> "... How does one square the absence of a racist ideology with a racist program? In some cases it was simply a case of packaging a racist product in inoffensive terms, hoping that this trick would make it less objectionable. But there was also another dimension. Afrikaner nationalists argued that that their survival as a volk[8] was inseparable from maintaining racial exclusivity and that apartheid was the only policy that systematically pursued that end. But apartheid with its racist outcomes was not a goal in itself; political survival was.

> "Afrikaner editors emphasized this theme. In his book *Het die Afrikaase volk 'n toekoms?* (Do the Afrikaner people have a future?), G.D. Scholtz, historian and editor of *Die Transvaler*, stressed the small numbers of Afrikaners as the dominant political factor in their demand for apartheid. The Afrikaners, Scholtz pointed out, had never experienced the luxury of 'safety in numbers.' He cited as a model the Lithuanians and Estonians whose freedom had been subverted by the Soviet Union.

> "Piet Cillie, together with Hendrik Verwoerd the most

---

8.   Afrikaans for people/folk (the 'v' is pronounced as 'f', as in German).

articulate apartheid apologist, wrote in 1952 that South Africa was 'remarkably free from racial mythologies'. For him the Afrikaners' desire to survive was a far stronger and more indestructible feeling than race prejudice. 'Like the Jews in Palestine and the Muslims in Pakistan, the Afrikaners had not fought themselves free from British domination only to be overwhelmed by a majority of a different kind. Eventually we shall give that majority its freedom, but never power over us ... They will not get more rights if that means rights over and in our lives.'"[9]

This desire for self-determination, for identity as a *volk* is crucial to understanding one of the common barriers to meaningful dialogue between Afrikaners and others over apartheid. Outsiders see it as racial segregation and oppression, period. Whereas Afrikaners will mostly want to distinguish between its initial aims and the worst of its outcomes.

Understanding *vs* approval

To understand is not to condone. Things such as perceived political, cultural and ethnic survival have been at the heart of all major racist movements in history. The facts about apartheid indicate that racism and white supremacism were obviously and painfully dominant factors. If it were merely a matter of cultural survival, why, for instance, were the so-called colored (mixed-race) people also excluded from white privilege, and unable to lawfully marry across the 'color bar'? Most of them overwhelmingly regarded themselves as Christian, spoke Afrikaans, and identified themselves with Afrikaans culture rather than black culture.

Also, despite many noble-sounding words about 'separate but equal' development, the incontrovertible facts are that the so-called independent homelands in which the 'other nations' were supposed to 'develop' were not exactly on prime land. They were small, fragmented and unsustainable. They were little more than labor reserves for South African industry. Men from these

---

9.   Ref. 6, pp. 469–470.

homelands working in South Africa were unable to bring their families with them. And in the 1970s, about ten times as much per capita was spent on educating the children of whites as on those of blacks.

Giliomee confirms (emphasis added) that

"… the sanitized vocabulary of apartheid made little difference to the reality that the policy resulted in the pervasive stigmatization of all people who were not white. It started from the premise that black and colored people were different, not because they were mostly abjectly poor *but because they were racially different.* The message that apartheid as a system conveyed offensively and obscenely, was that black and colored people were socially inferior, morally inadequate, intellectually underdeveloped and sexually unfit for intimate relationships."[9]

MORE BACKGROUND

Apartheid developed out of a complex history of more than 300 years of European colonization of southern Africa. This included the British colonial pass laws, instituted in the Cape Colony and Colony of Natal in the late 1800s. These were the forerunners of the pass laws under apartheid. Black people were not allowed onto the streets after dark. Also, they could not move into the British-ruled areas from tribal regions, or from one district to another, without a signed pass. They had to carry this on them at all times.

As Giliomee explains, the attitudes of South Africans of British background were shaped by different factors from those affecting Afrikaners:

"With the Western world experiencing an upsurge of racism in the 1880s, the Afrikaner and English-speaking whites tended to justify white supremacy in different ways. English South African politicians and journalists drew particularly on the concept of a biological hierarchy of races and on the (social) Darwinism theory of the survival of the fittest. By contrast, Afrikaans or Dutch publications seldom considered the biological concept of race. They focused on an idealized picture of paternalism, depicting the white master as caring for his faithful servants, and punishing them when they erred. The more modern among them sketched a world of competing organic nations, each with its own distinctive cultural heritage and needs, co-existing under the aegis of white supremacy."[10]

Social Darwinist and mining tycoon Cecil John Rhodes.
Public domain

The stance of well-known mining magnate and British South African Cecil John Rhodes (1853–1902) seems consistent with the assessment that racism in the English cultural stream was dominated by evolutionism. A member of the parliament of the British-ruled Cape Colony in the late 1800s, and later its Premier, Rhodes is well known to have been a strong advocate of Social Darwinism.

Black voters: once upon a time

At the time of Rhodes' election, black people in the Colony had the vote based on education and property ownership, the same as applied at that time to white Englishmen in England. Rhodes was instrumental in progressively removing this limited franchise from black people—and later from colored (mixed-race) people as well.

This process continued under the rule of Jan Smuts (1870–

10. Ref. 6, p. 286. NB see also the feature: 'Racism: New Sin or Old Sins?' on p. 58 for a comment on 'paternalistic racism'.

1950), one of the most well known of South Africa's prime ministers (1919–1924, 1939–1948). As leader of the United Party which lost to the National Party in 1948, Smuts is often held up as some kind of liberal who was supplanted by the 'evil' Nationalists. But Smuts was in fact also a convinced racist.

Zulu chieftain Albert Luthuli was awarded the 1960 Nobel Peace Prize. He was the leader of the (then banned) African National Congress, and rejected the use of force in opposing apartheid. Luthuli was also a strong Christian (as in fact were other early ANC leaders) and a lay preacher in the Methodist Church. Before his death in 1967, Luthuli wrote in a largely autobiographical book, which was for years banned and unavailable to South Africans, that Jan Smuts was "a world statesman beyond the Union's borders, a subtle and relentless white supremacist at home".[11]

Chief Albert Luthuli in 1960, the year he won the Nobel Peace Prize.

Smuts was one of not a few South Africans of the time who blended their Christian upbringing with evolution to end up with an amalgam which owed more to pantheism than to the Bible. His beliefs were overtly based on the assumption that evolution was 'scientific fact'.[12] Nevertheless, such a viewpoint was relatively rare among those of Afrikaner heritage, as he was. And it would be a mistake to assume that his (or Rhodes') views on evolution significantly influenced the bulk of Afrikaners. Many of them in fact viewed Smuts as somewhat of a cultural traitor for his identification with many things British. During World War II he even served as a Field Marshal in the *British* (not South African) Army.

So, while it would be deficient to altogether ignore evolution's effects in the development of racism and segregation in southern Africa, to blame apartheid on evolution would be to mislead. Giliomee's comments on the different influences on Afrikaner

11.   Luthuli, A., *Let my people go*, Tafelberg Publishers, Cape Town, with Mafube Publishers, Johannesburg, 2006, p. 92.
12.   Ambler, M., Be still and know … what God?, 11 October 2006, creation.com/smuts.

vs British South African cultures are pertinent at many points. There were relatively rare occasions when Afrikaners strayed into frank biological arguments for white supremacy. But these were more continuations of the pre-Darwinian influences discussed in Chapter 1 than having anything to do with Darwinism, as much as this clearly influenced *British* South Africans.

One possible exception to this emerges from a scholarly source on Werner Eiselen, the man who is regarded as almost a co-constructor of apartheid with Verwoerd. He was, for some time, head of the Department of Bantu Languages and Ethnology at Stellenbosch. Like Verwoerd, Eiselen himself seems to have avoided, even criticized, the idea of biological inferiority. But in his own department "there was a course on 'Race Hygiene', with its overtones of biological racism."[13]

Despite such exceptions, evolutionary influence on Afrikaner thinking seems to have been minor and very indirect.

Apartheid and the church

Given that theological conservatism is more likely to be associated with awareness of our common descent from Adam, why did it not correlate with opposition to apartheid, but more often the opposite? Part of the answer may be that these were also the churches most likely to be socially and politically conservative. One undoubted factor would have been what we have already seen about the idealized way in which apartheid was presented, as a program of national self-identity and survival for Afrikaners and their children. Reasonable biblical support for such legitimate desires is not hard to find. Unfortunately, there were also some seemingly convincing 'biblical' rationales for the segregationist aspects of the policy (see shortly) potentially available—both for idealists to assuage their consciences, as well as for use by those with more cynical motives. See chapter 4 on slavery for how many in the church rationalized this evil, along

---

13.   Kros, C., 'W.W.M. Eiselen: architect of apartheid education', in Kallaway, P. (Ed.), *The History of Education Under Apartheid 1948–1994: The Doors of Learning and Culture Shall be Opened*, Maskew Miller Longman, Cape T own, 2002, p. 60.

with black inferiority, in America.

We have seen that belief in the fundamental *biological* equality of all races, while by no means universal, was quite common in Afrikaner society (and thus the church).

However, the idea of *cultural* equality of whites *vis-à-vis* blacks was another matter altogether. We have already seen in earlier chapters the tremendous difference culture makes (with more to come in Chapter 16). And all but the most incorrigibly politically correct would agree that the Afrikaners had justification for believing that the culture they had brought to the African continent was in many ways very much superior to that of the locals. In addition to its greater industrial and military clout, there were also clear social and economic benefits.

Those in this Christian European culture would also have been very aware of some of the more unsavory pagan and animistic practices that were part of the tribesperson's heritage. For example, there is the practice, still occurring sporadically in southern Africa today, of using body parts, from people (including children) killed or mutilated to obtain them, as magical charms or *muti*. Such things would have made it harder for them to see the undoubted positives of many aspects of the black person's culture.

The reality is that someone's culture is a part of their heritage, their very being, interwoven with concepts of family, tribe, nation, and so on. Because of the inherent dignity to be ascribed to any individual made in God's image, their heritage is worthy of *a priori*[14] respect and sensitivity. At the same time, though, one should be willing to make considered value judgments about any aspect of a culture that is detrimental and immoral, such as the example cited.

Unfortunately, when a different culture to one's own is also associated with recognizable and consistent 'racial' differences, that simple, practical assessment of comparative cultures can easily morph into something more. It can in practice become a 'working substitute' for the untenable idea that there really are

14.   I.e. the starting baseline approach, before any information about the culture is in.

innate (biological) differences among races. So much so that it becomes a notion of *intrinsic* racial superiority after all, difficult to distinguish from a belief in biological superiority. For example, the other group's culture can be portrayed and viewed as so hopelessly degenerate that it has indelibly stamped its recipients, destined to forever be in that same mold.

The importance of heart motive

This illustrates the dilemma of trying to understand something in which 'heart motive', as it's called, is so all-important. In this matter of stark culture differences, one person in Christendom may humbly understand that they have, quite undeservedly, been blessed via the historical circumstances that go to make up their culture. (Hopefully, they would also acknowledge with equal humility the undoubted deficiencies in aspects of their own society.) For not a few godly Afrikaners, the motive to spread the gospel to native Africans included the conviction that its culture-transforming effects would in time elevate their society to a similar level as their own. As Chapter 16 demonstrates, this is far from a naïve or unrealistic view.

Whereas another professing Christian may, often without even thinking it through (and maybe even while giving lip service to the 'all people are equal' notion), take it as, 'Well, that's just the way it is'. This is similar to the way in which many of the 19th-century Darwinian racists saw that whatever biological benefit natural selection had chosen to bestow upon them, they had every right to enjoy its fruits. For those who were less endowed, well, it was just tough.

A similar analysis can apply to the idea that the race or nation which is in a superior situation at one point in time is so positioned because of God's favor. In the sense of it being by divine *appointment*, that proposition is actually correct by definition, given a sovereign, all-powerful God—even though such national (or ethnic) elevations mostly prove to be temporary. But notions of being part of a group with intrinsic divine *favor* have an unspoken corollary for many. That is, that the situation is 'obviously' because of that individual's group somehow 'deserving it' due to some inherently praiseworthy ('superior') qualities. Of course, this does not follow at all, and certainly has no biblical basis.

One of the ways in which the relative poverty and historical disadvantage of black people was explained in southern Africa was similar to the situation in the US—the biblically non-existent 'curse on Ham' (see p. 44). Such rationales do not have to represent some official theological position in order to have an effect within a given Christian culture. It is enough for them to be spread as quasi-folklore—perhaps with occasional reinforcement from a pulpit here and there, if only via a passing comment.

For some, belief in this 'curse' may have been a genuine attempt to explain the *status quo*. But it also provided a tailor-made escape clause from the implications of our common origin—we all started off equal, but then some were cursed along the way. Whether the effects of this supposed cursing were cultural, biological or some mix of the two was largely immaterial. If a group was of lower social status because of divine displeasure, that could in practice both justify and underpin notions of racial superiority.

Another factor which would serve to continually reinforce feelings of white superiority, even without any conscious assent to the notion, is 'social stratification'. This is the phenomenon where one racial group is repeatedly and overwhelmingly observed to be occupying the lowliest social strata (layers) in a given society. This observation then becomes a factor in perpetuating the situation.

Slavery and social stratification

Slavery was introduced into the Cape in 1658, and became widespread among farmers. We saw in Chapter 4 how and why slavery drives racism, more than the other way around. Originally, most of the slaves were not Africans, but imported from other continents. Many were Malays. Then slaves began to be imported from other parts of Africa, mostly captured first by other Africans as mentioned earlier. By the time the British captured the Cape Colony in the early 1800s, it was commonplace for Afrikaners to have African slaves. In addition, their manual labor was mostly done by cheap native laborers and also indentured servants, whose role is often hard to differentiate from that of slaves. That statement also applies to the conditions under which Africans worked on the mines owned by people like the aforementioned Cecil Rhodes, who founded the giant DeBeers diamond mining conglomerate in the 1880s.

This sort of thing was not unique to Afrikaners but was increasingly the norm for Europeans in general in the Cape Colony. It entailed a pattern of social stratification by 'race'. Such race-based layering, with blacks occupying the bottom rung wherever one looked, became part of the everyday background. For 'English' South Africans in particular, it would have fitted naturally with the notions of biological racism developing back home in Europe. For Afrikaners, it would have continually buttressed the idea that black people were naturally destined to occupy a lesser role. Whether this destiny was biologically or culturally determined would have been of no import, overall. Such a phenomenon is more psychologically determined than rationally thought through.

A personal anecdote will illustrate how seeing one group of people consistently associated with more menial forms of work 'enculturates' ordinary people to see such race-based stratification as normal. It concerns a very pleasant young couple from Namibia, whom I met because an in-law of mine was born there. Namibia is the former German colony of South-West Africa. This couple had bought a farm in South Australia.

I remember the husband, a nice fellow, telling me of the time he was doing extensive fencing work where his farm bordered a public road. He said that for the first few weeks of this task, he had to really fight against the impulse to dive into the bushes and hide whenever he heard a car coming. The reason was an intense feeling of shame at being seen doing manual labor, something that in his former homeland was done solely by black people. After a time of living in Australia, he had a different perspective, and was embarrassed at having ever felt that way.

A milder example is the common experience of African Americans staying at US hotels in past decades. They would often be asked by white guests, out of naiveté rather than malice, to perform menial tasks for them like bringing towels. They were simply conditioned, by the persistent association of one recognizable people group with lower-paying jobs, to seeing that situation as 'normal'.

We've already touched upon the fact that the laboring classes of India are more likely to be darker-skinned due to the legacy of the Hindu caste system (Chapter 3), environmentally enhanced by the greater sun exposure of outdoor work. That in turn would become self-reinforcing by this same stratification phenomenon.

Singapore provides a current example. Whenever visiting there, I am struck by one form of social stratification that is apparent just driving around. All the menial laboring work on roads is done by non-Singaporeans, the overwhelming majority from Bangladesh. Because of the low rents (by Singaporean standards) they are able to pay, they live in cramped conditions in the poorer suburbs. These foreign workers are permitted entry into the country for a limited time. They work for wages which are both more than they would get 'back home' and less than an average Singaporean would think was a livable stipend. In one sense it is a 'win-win', driven by economics, not racism.

After a while, one becomes totally accustomed to continually seeing these road gangs of dark-skinned Bangladeshis, either out laboring in the equatorial heat or seated on the backs of pickup trucks being carted to and from roadworks (see photo p. 295). It makes the association of dark skin with lower status seem 'normal'. The effect is mitigated to an extent by the fact that there are many dark-skinned Indian-extraction Singaporeans in high income brackets. One example is former cabinet minister and current leading businessman Suppiah Dhanabalan (1937–), of Tamil Indian background and a devout Christian.[15] But because

15. 'Race' considerations affected Dhanabalan; he was one of a handful of top ministers considered by Lee Kuan Yew as a possible successor, but Lee thought that the 76% Chinese electorate was not yet ready for an Indian Prime Minister.

FEATURE

Black, Yellow and Red Perils

A constant background concern for white South Africans over the centuries was being swamped by the native populations and cultures that surrounded them. To Afrikaners, it became known as the 'black peril' or *Swart Gevaar*, a concept prominent in the heyday of modern apartheid, too.

The term brings back memories of the 'yellow peril' from the days of the White Australia policy of my youth. This was the fear many in Australia had of marauding Asian hordes sweeping down from the north. It was likely driven more by cultural/racial fears than by rational strategic considerations. But the two 'perils' are not easily comparable. For Afrikaners, existing in a society (unlike Australia or the US) with a substantial black majority, *Swart Gevaar* could not be lightly dismissed as some abstract notion.

Related to both perils mentioned above was the so-called 'red peril' of expansionary communism. These days, the Berlin Wall, the Iron Curtain and the Cold War alike seem like distant memories. So it becomes all too easy for outsiders to dismiss the concerns of white South Africans with communism in the antiapartheid movement during that struggle.

Many would see it as a mere rationalization of white supremacy. It would certainly have served as a useful political foil for the NP government to help maintain support for apartheid in the face of mounting overseas condemnation.

But there is no doubt that the communist movement engaged in overt and ongoing efforts to cynically exploit racial tensions in the furtherance of its worldwide goals. This alliance of the antiapartheid movement with the radical left may well have worked against the interests of black South Africans overall. For one thing, it would have hardened the white establishment's resistance to change. Both it and the use of violence in the struggle would have provided politicians in South Africa with a way to keep  justifying their own increasing level of violent and cynical tactics. This included exploiting deadly tensions between the Zulu-dominated Inkatha Freedom Party and the African National Congress.

one ethnic group that has darker skin is so consistently and *visibly* identified with the least desirable jobs, it still causes a modicum of this 'stratification' to become part of the background. I've seen probably hundreds of these road-gang crews, and it was exceedingly rare to see a Chinese face seated among the Bangladeshis on those pickup trucks.[16] And I think that even in that overtly antiracist nation, it would cause surprise, at least, to most passersby were they to see a European face.

Returning to the Afrikaners of yesteryear; their resentment at various strictures of British rule was already acute, and was only heightened when in 1833 slavery was officially abolished throughout the British Empire. This abolition was thanks to the biblical passions of Wilberforce and others, as discussed in Chapter 4 (and more in Chapter 16 to come).

This discreetly captured 2011 image of a road gang of laborers being transported by open pickup is a typical sight on Singapore roads. Road laboring crews there have for years mostly been, like these men, from Bangladesh.

Benjamin Chong

It would have been perceived by Afrikaners as a humiliation, as well as causing further frustration at British interference with their affairs. Their sense of nationhood and identity was already under threat of being swallowed up by the culture of the British.

Many of them left the areas under British rule to establish their own nation in what became known as the Great Trek,[17] taking their slaves with them.

---

16.   It is becoming less rare as ethnic Chinese workers from other disadvantaged regional economies increase.

17.   Afrikaans: *Die Groot Trek*; called the *Voortrekkers* (fore-trekkers, i.e. those who trek ahead).

Intentions *vs* outcomes

The Boer/Afrikaner culture rests on a heritage of good intentions, with many genuinely seeking to honor God and His Word. While the abhorrent practice of slavery cannot in the slightest be justified, the fact is that the master–slave relationship of an earlier South Africa, while paternalistic, was also mostly not cruel. By 1835 most slaves in the Cape had been born there and were considered almost as part of the family—which in fact some were, having been born to black slave women of white masters.

White supremacist racism was also substantially tempered by a sense of Christian decency. This is likely why the effects of racism within Afrikaner society, baneful as they were, never approached the level of atrocities recorded earlier in regard to Aboriginal Australians. The outcomes were certainly far removed from the activities of the overtly Bible-rejecting hierarchy of Nazi Germany. And Afrikaner society never generated anything like the Darwin-inspired genocidal rampage carried out by German forces against the Herero and Nama peoples of neighboring South-West Africa.[18]

The Battle of Blood River

Many non-South Africans are unaware, too, of the impact of the 1838 Battle of Blood River, where less than 500 Boers faced more than 10,000 Zulu warriors. Before the outcome, it is said, the Boers had covenanted with God in return for their deliverance. Not surprisingly, the fact that they prevailed against such odds still resonates deep in the Afrikaner psyche. It helped cement their belief in their special destiny to be a Christian bastion in a sea of hostility and paganism—a nation chosen to bring Christianity and civilization.

The parallels with Old Testament Israel are obvious, and may well be legitimate if left in the realm of analogy or example. (The book by black antiapartheid activist Albert Luthuli, mentioned on p. 287, was titled *Let my People Go*, a clear reference to Exodus

---

18. Ambler, M., Herero genocide, *Creation* 27(3):52–55, 2002, creation.com/herero-genocide.

that similarly draws a parallel between his people and the biblical Israel.) But such an extrabiblical 'argument of circumstance', if it were to become quasi-doctrine, would automatically be out of synch with the great Reformation principle of *Sola Scriptura*. And even if it remained a mere analogy, applying it to Afrikaner society would have had to be cautiously done to avoid inconsistency.

Take for example the divinely ordained separatism of Israel, to keep itself from foreign gods and religious practices. It's easy to see how this could be used as a justification for apartheid's separatism. But this would be a misuse, because the divine command to keep the Israelite nation separate had to do with religion, not race. As we saw in Chapter 2, if someone converted to faith in Israel's one true God, their ethnic origins did not matter (e.g. Ruth, Rahab).

Further, if the parallels with Israel were to be strictly maintained, the Old Testament repeatedly *commands* something that, if applied, would have been the death knell of at least political and judicial apartheid. That is, it commands that a stranger sojourning with Israel was to be treated equally in every way—specifically, *the same law* was to apply equally to the stranger as well as the Israelite (e.g. Numbers 15:16, Exodus 12:49). This was not so under apartheid.

One can see how, in a fallen world, not just the 'chosen nation' sentiment but other biblically derived notions could become tools in the hands of political and economic interest groups. Many of the key players over the decades were, like Cecil Rhodes the social Darwinist, interested in the Christianity of the average devout Afrikaner only insofar as it furthered their own agendas.

But things were never simple. Missionary activity to native Africans was a sincere passion among many segments of the Afrikaner church. And so in time, there arose the matter of 'heathen' blacks who had become baptized believers.

The Afrikaner Church—originally multiracial

Unknown to many, shortly after gaining its full independence from the mother church in Holland in 1824, the DRC was in fact an interracial church. Blacks and whites worshiped together. Then came the social pressures, from factors extraneous to the Bible; some Afrikaners objected to having to drink from the same communion cup as the blacks.

There is no way of establishing from this distance whether those who did so were part of the minority who did believe in innate inferiority. Or whether they would have claimed that it was merely a matter of the 'culture', perhaps referring to hygienic considerations. But even if one gives lip service to the fact that all people, as descendants of Adam, are equal, reluctance to sit in the same pews as one's fellow believers suggests something deeper.

It is also hard to reconcile with God's repeatedly expressed desire throughout the Bible for such things as a humble, lowly spirit.[19] It brings to mind the ease with which notions of group superiority can readily morph from merely seeing the *status quo* as a happenstance cultural blip to seeing it as something innate. Something, that is, which for all practical purposes is not really different from biological racism.

It's important to note that the majority of Afrikaner Christians at the time did not feel that way at all about their fellow believers from other ethnic backgrounds. But the pressure from a minority was enough for the cracks of compromise to commence at the DRC's annual Synod in 1857.

The Synod recognized that the Bible taught that all believing Christians should worship together. Nevertheless, it recommended that "as a concession to the prejudice and weakness of a few" the churches could serve additional tables "to the European members after the non-white members have been served".

The Synod also recommended that if that same "weakness" required that the groups be separated, "the congregation from the heathen should enjoy its privilege in a separate building and a separate institution". Not surprisingly, concession to weakness soon grew into policy—separating white and non-white

---

19.   E.g. Psalm 18:27; 25:9; 51:17; Isaiah 57:15; 66:2; Matthew 11:29; Romans 12:6.

churches.[20]

To highlight my previous comment that things were never simple, the matter was complicated by the demands of some black believers for their own churches and congregations.[21] This may have been motivated by the desire to hear God's Word in their mother tongue.

Of the handful of reasons discussed at the Synod for this objection to joint fellowship, one was an attempted biblical justification for keeping 'basters' (the offspring of white–black liaisons) out of fellowship. Another was, as described in a recent doctoral thesis:

> "… a form of biological racism, which propagated keeping brown and black people separate because they represented a different human species marked by their colour and hair. It asserted that brown and black Christians stood on a much lower level of 'civilization' and often understood only the simplest of services".[22,23]

Note that this would have still been a pre-Darwinian belief in biological racism, since Darwin's book was yet two years away.

God wants separation?

For Christians, the acceptance of a notion such as apartheid would have been made easier to the extent that this segregationist ideology was presented in its 'idealized' form, as stated. One that was, from the statements of Verwoerd and others, meant to be 'separate but equal', with no exploitation of any group. But in addition to this, and the Afrikaners' desire for self-determination and self-identity, there was the specific idea that the Bible actually *supports*, if not mandates, the separation of people groups. As

---

20.   Manavhela, G.F., An Analysis of the Theological Justification of Apartheid in South Africa: A Reformed Theological Perspective, p. 30. Doctoral dissertation for Free University of Amsterdam, defended successfully 3 July 2009. Promoters: Professors A. van de Beek and J.M. Vorster at North-West University, South Africa.
21.   Ref. 20, p. 43.
22.   Ref. 20, p. 33.
23.   Giliomee, H., 'The weakness of some': The Dutch Reformed Church and white supremacy, *Scriptura* **83**: 212–224, 2003.

several South African whites have told me, this concept was a common background presence during that era.

Acts 17:26 featured prominently. This passage states that God has

"... made from one man every nation of mankind to live on all the face of the earth, having determined allotted periods and the boundaries of their dwelling place."

The first part of that passage makes it plain that all people on Earth are related through Adam. But remember that the socio-political pressure for 'separateness' was mostly not associated with any overt claims about biological inferiority/superiority. Ironically, one can speculate that had the notion of racial segregation arisen in a social setting of biological racism/evolutionism, the clash with the Bible's "made from one man" would likely have been more apparent. As it was, though, it may have been easy to skip through the first part of the verse with fleeting assent, to focus on the interpretation given to the latter parts of the verse. And it is there where the support for segregationism was supposed to reside.

This refers to God having determined when and where each nation would dwell. Instead of just seeing that as a reminder of God's sovereignty in human affairs, regardless of what we mortals propose, it has more than once in history been used as a justification for segregationism.

This is done by combining it with teaching concerning the Table of Nations in Genesis Chapter 10, and the subsequent Babel dispersion in the next chapter. In such an understanding, the passage is taken to mean that wherever we see national boundaries, any attempt to blur those boundaries is opposing God's will. And the Babel account is taken as punctuating God's desire that people should 'separate'. From there, it's easy for 'nations' to be conflated with 'races'. This is even easier in a setting where one can, with justification, speak of an ethnic group as the 'Xhosa nation' or 'Zulu nation'. Within more than one Christian-dominated culture, it has been a staple for those seeking to justify segregation that these passages taken together must indicate that God in general *wants* separation, rather than homogeneity.

Is this, however, a sound exegesis of the passages concerned? It is certainly not the simplest or most straightforward understanding. The Bible indicates that God was displeased at the post-Flood population in Babel for disobeying His command by refusing to spread out and again populate the earth. The statement in Acts about God determining boundaries says simply that *God is in charge* of whatever happens as far as national outcomes are concerned. The dispersion at Babel would, from a human perspective, have appeared to be random—but not to God. For reasons which may have to do with things to come only centuries later, wherever people ended up is where He wanted them.

But there is no indication that this was some sort of permanent arrangement, i.e. that the Chinese, for example, may only ever live in the place which their forefathers came to occupy. (The passage itself actually speaks against that, with its "allotted periods".) It is simply that, at any time in history, we can be sure that national boundaries are whatever God has determined for that point in time. This is how John Gill understands it in his famous 1909 *Exposition of the Entire Bible*, also Matthew Henry in his *Commentary*. The context of Paul's sermon actually makes it clear that God is in charge of human affairs. Despite the denser prose of earlier centuries, Gill's classic text is worth quoting at length (the **bold** is, following Gill, the biblical text; only the one *italic* emphasis was added):

> "And it is a certain truth that follows upon this, that no man has any reason to vaunt over another, and boast of his blood and family; and as little reason have any to have any dependence upon their being the children of believers, or to distinguish themselves from others, and reject them as the children of unbelievers, when *all belong to one family*, and are of one man's blood, whether Adam or Noah: of whom are **all nations of men, for to dwell on all the face of the earth**; for from Adam sprung a race of men, which multiplied on the face of the earth, and peopled the world before the flood; these being destroyed by the flood, and Noah and his family saved, his descendants were scattered all over the earth, and repeopled it: and this is the original of all the nations of men, and of all the inhabitants of the earth; and stands opposed to the fabulous accounts of the Heathens ... and particularly the Athenians boasted that they sprung out of the earth, which Diogenes ridiculed as common with mice and worms. But the apostle ascribes all

to one blood: **and hath determined the times before appointed**; how long the world he has made shall continue; and the several distinct periods, ages, and generations, in which such and such men should live, such and such nations should exist, and such monarchies should be in being, as the Assyrian, Persian, Grecian, and Roman, and how long they should subsist; as also the several seasons of the year, as seedtime and harvest, cold and heat, summer and winter, and day and night; and which are so bounded, and kept so distinct in their revolutions, as not to interfere with, and encroach upon each other; and likewise the several years, months, and days of every man's life; see Job 7:1 to which may be added, the times of the law and Gospel; the time of Christ's birth and death; the time of the conversion of particular persons; and all their times of desertion, temptation, affliction, and comfort; the times of the church's sufferings, both under Rome Pagan and Rome Papal; of the holy city being trodden under foot, of the witnesses prophesying in sackcloth, and of their being killed, and their bodies lying unburied, and of their resurrection and ascension to heaven ... Christ's personal coming, and the day of judgment … . All these are appointed times, and determined by the Creator and Governor of the world: **and the bounds of their habitation**; where men shall dwell, and how long they shall continue there the age or distinct period of time, in which every man was, or is to come into the world, is fixed and determined by God; nor can, nor does anyone come into the world sooner or later than that time; and also the particular country, city, town, and spot of ground where he shall dwell; and the term of time how long he shall dwell there, and then remove to another place, or be removed by death."

God is sovereign over national boundaries even where, as has happened repeatedly in history, the boundaries change. Modern-day examples would be the initial formation of Iraq, or the former Yugoslavia. This does not imply that families and ethno-linguistic groups need to remain passive in the face of this sovereignty, which encompasses our individual and corporate decisions. For example, there is no biblical proscription against a non-racist desire for political independence, whether of Afrikaners or Zulus. The problems arise when unjust and antibiblical agendas become involved.

Related to national boundaries are national rulers. The Afrikaner church appropriately emphasized that God's dealings are not solely with individuals, but with entire nations, and their rulers. Paul reminds us that whichever ruler is in authority over us at any point in time is only there by God's determination and authorization:

"Let every person be subject to the governing authorities. For there is no authority except from God, and those that exist have been instituted by God." (Romans 13:1)

Incidentally, it is likely that when we can review things from an eternal perspective, even evil rulers for a time, such as Hitler, will be seen in hindsight to have served an eternal purpose—though the Bible in no way indicates that we should therefore condone their evil. The pagan king Cyrus is seen to be carrying out God's purposes (Isaiah 44:28 & 45:1), and as Proverbs 21:1 reminds us:

> "The king's heart is a stream of water in the hand of the LORD; he turns it wherever he will."

By definition, therefore, God's sovereign will must have included both the rise of apartheid and its fall. As Christians, it is never wise to speculate in which particular direction His *sovereign* will (including over ethno-linguistic boundaries) is going to take human affairs in any individual socio-political situation. However, as people within the respective societies, we are meant to assess the actions of all the players according to the standards of His revealed *moral* will. This applies to the government of the apartheid era, as well as to the actions of its ANC successors.

In short, neither Acts 17:26 nor the Babel account, whether considered separately or jointly, give any indication of being intended as a prescription of God's once-for-all-time intention for particular nations (let alone races), and their ethno-linguistic or geographic boundaries—let alone how we are supposed to help Him implement any such intention.

Justifying supremacy

It is instructive to summarize the ways in which racial supremacy (and its frequent bedfellow, segregationism) can be justified in a Christian-dominated society that rejects outright evolution. Most involve adding to, distorting, or applying unsound exegesis, to Scripture. These can be held in various combinations with one another. They include:

1. Adam as the ancestor of only the white race. But this requires inventing pre-Adamic races in violation of Scripture. This did not seem to feature much, if at all, in southern Africa. It is a staple of some white supremacist groups in the US, notably the so-called 'Christian Identity' movement.

FEATURE

Gandhi and Race—Busting the Myth

It is widely believed that Mahatma Gandhi, famous for his successful non-violent overthrow of British rule in India, was opposed to racism. The story most people know has him organizing opposition to South Africa's pass laws as evidence for his alleged antiracism.

In fact, his own writings repeatedly make it clear that segregation only concerned him as it affected Indians. He was in fact strongly racially biased and antiblack, concerned with the purity of the Indian race. His struggle against the ruling powers in South Africa was driven by his concern that Indians would be dragged down to the level of "the Kaffirs" (a highly derogatory South African term for black people, derived from the Arabic *kafir*, a term used by Muslims to describe unbelievers). One example:

> "Ours is one continued struggle against degradation sought to be inflicted upon us by the European, who desire [*sic*] to degrade us to the level of the raw Kaffir, whose occupation is hunting and whose sole ambition is to collect a certain number of cattle to buy a wife with, and then pass his life in indolence and nakedness."*

Public domain

Gandhi also believed in the evolution of all life on Earth, albeit with spiritual pantheistic overtones. His true position on race appears to have been unknown to Martin Luther King, who publicly associated Gandhi with the struggle against racism and segregation.

*www.gandhism.net/hisownwords.php, accessed 29 October 2010.

2. All humanity descended from Adam, but then:

   a. One group was subsequently divinely degraded via the non-existent 'curse on Ham' (see p. 44). The fact that this blatant error was common in societies that practiced black–white racial segregation and even slavery suggests that its perpetuation and propagation in those societies was in response to a perceived need, subliminal or not, for justification of the practices. Note that it automatically relegates someone of the allegedly 'cursed' group to an inferior status—whether converted to Christ or not. It also puts one's focus on looking for the negatives in the other person's community, rather than any positives. OR:

   b. Some groups were subsequently degraded via culture and/or the environment. The fact that environment and culture both make a big difference is clear from the discussions in this book. But in its extreme form, such cultural/environmental determinism, as held also by some secularists in the past, holds that the impressions from these factors on the individual are more or less indelible. So it is then in practice indistinguishable from biological racism. A 'Lamarckian' version, so to speak.

Learning from history

Trying to hypothetically rerun history is largely pointless, unless it is to learn for the future. One can't help pondering, though, how different things might have been for South Africa if there had been, in that time, a great emphasis on something that is sorely needed in *all* modern cultures. By that I mean the maintenance and development of a truly biblical worldview, with believers—who were legion in South African culture—taught and encouraged to apply the Bible and its 'big picture' to *all* of life.

The Bible should be our starting point for reasoning, not a source of proof-texts to buttress the ideas of our time. Genesis history is the foundational key to understanding that 'big picture'—an originally good world, ruined by sin, to be restored in the future. And it includes the true history of humanity. That is, that we are not only made in the image of God, but are all related. And this was not that long ago—meaning we are not only related, but extremely *closely* related.

Vested interests, and human sin and fallibility, would have still played their part, as always. But common sense suggests that such an approach, particularly from pulpits across the land, might well have had a considerable impact on the course of events.

Of course, culture makes a huge difference, as does opportunity and historical disadvantage. Both can lead to very real differences between outcomes in various groups. There are at present concerns about the academic achievement levels of black South Africans. The current government seems to be addressing these using various 'affirmative action' policies, such as enforced hiring quotas, which can require employers to waive qualification requirements, or lowering academic standards in some instances. The positive intentions of many such policies are not in doubt, nor the historical imbalances and even injustices they are intended to overcome. But, as previous chapters have pointed out, there are intrinsic problems with what is in effect 'reverse racism', even where this is intended to be only temporary.

I understand how difficult it might be for a group such as South Africa's black population, still suffering the effects of major historical disadvantage, to accept such a designation for affirmative action, but reverse racism is what it is, nonetheless. And as shown earlier, it tends to exacerbate what it seeks to solve. One would hope for a wiser and more thoughtful approach to arise in time, to encourage and permit what is now a large black underclass to work its way out of abject poverty.

In addition, there has been a definite shift to a humanist/ secular social ethic. A missionary working there for years wrote to me that since the dismantling of apartheid, "There have been many adverse changes pertaining to abortion, homosexuality, pornography, and breakdown of the criminal justice system." Some of these issues had commenced their advance prior to 1990, as the struggle to dismantle apartheid intensified and such matters took second place to political survival. Of course, to the many South Africans (including Christians) for whom apartheid was often a life and death issue, the fact that the sexual morality of society was generally better in that time would have been cold comfort.

Unfortunately, white South Africans looking on could easily see their country's current social problems as reinforcement for any previous views they may have had on white supremacy. Perhaps especially so when they also see the failings of some other African nation-states since the departure of colonial influences— even though colonialism had mostly never nurtured the sorts of strong institutions we take for granted in the West.

If so, they would have overlooked the influence of culture and background. For example, the 'win at all costs' way in which the agendas of the revolutionary Marxists hijacked the struggle for liberation from apartheid meant that black Africans were encouraged to torch their schools in the name of 'freedom'.

This left many of their generation with a disrupted and fragmented education. In addition, large numbers of black Africans, trained by Cuban and Russian interests in guerilla warfare, were left at a loose end when the apartheid struggle was over. With little in the way of resources and training other than in weaponry, they would be a fertile breeding ground for the violent crime that has plagued post-apartheid South Africa. At one church in Johannesburg, the pastor told me that around half of the c. 200 families in his congregation had experienced an armed incursion and holdup in their homes. For many, such things will seem to be at least a partial demonstration of that which the 'idealized' version of the apartheid ideology sought to prevent for themselves and their children.

Selective outrage
Then, too, more than a little cynicism has unfortunately been fostered by hypocritical attitudes from the world outside South Africa. Walter Williams, an African-American economist who

spent some time living in apartheid-era South Africa, points out that in Africa as a whole, since 1960:

> "about 9 million black Africans have been slaughtered through genocide, politicide and mass murder. ... It turns out that about 5,000 South African blacks lost their lives [due to apartheid issues]. Do you see anything wrong with that picture: world silence in the wake of millions upon millions of black lives lost on the rest of the continent but world outrage in the case of South African apartheid and 5,000 lives lost? Might it be that white Africans are held to higher standards of civility; thus their mistreatment of blacks is unacceptable, while blacks and Arabs are held to a lower standard of civility and their mistreatment of blacks is less offensive?"[24]

Note how Williams highlights the fact that this actually reflects a subtle form of *antiblack racism*.

Apartheid and atheism

It's ironic that so many criticisms of apartheid came from atheistic sources, considering that atheism really provides no philosophical reference point from which to do so. Without an absolute reference point, who is to say that any action or policy is right or wrong, ultimately? Without a Creator God, how does the notion of 'human rights' obtain any meaning other than an arbitrary one, no different from a passing whim or fashion?

Yes, it is a tragedy that the voices of conservative Christians who sought to apply biblical standards in protesting apartheid were often ignored or suppressed—and from 'within the camp' at that. Christians in other nations need to take heed; if God's people are unwilling to stand up and be counted on matters of morality and justice, looking to secularism for the answers risks both individuals and nations paying a heavy price. South Africa's problems have not somehow disappeared with the (largely secular) dismantling of apartheid. Christians in that beautiful

24. Williams, W., Africa: a tragic continent, www.jewishworldreview.com/cols/williams081303.asp, 2003.

country (from all people groups) need our prayers and goodwill now as much as ever, as does the nation as a whole. The ongoing exodus of many skilled and qualified South Africans to overseas countries is not a good omen for the country's future.

AFRIKANER REACTIONS

I have had the privilege of engaging in several extensive speaking tours of South Africa on this topic of creation/evolution. Along with other CMI speakers, I often weave this important topic of Bible/science/race into my talks, whatever part of the world I'm in. In South Africa this is, for obvious reasons, an attention-grabber.

As a guest in another country, it was never appropriate to engage in public criticisms of any aspects of its complex history. I concentrated on the facts of the issue, both biblical and scientific. I would say how important it would have been for the history of 'race relations' in my own country of Australia if this way of thinking biblically about 'races' had been applied. I needed to remember, too, that South African whites, as a minority group, were from the outset in a quite different situation to those in Australia and elsewhere.

On a handful of occasions, one or two folk in the audience would pointedly march out in silent protest the minute I merely started on the topic. It seemed the word had spread in advance as to what I would say, and this was their way of making a point. But they were the exception.

The overall impact of each tour was tremendously positive. A lot of this was of course due to the powerful evidence for creation. But there were also not a few wonderfully encouraging reactions to the 'race' segment of the talks, the biological evidence for our relatedness as one human family. Interacting with these folk, it was clear that even though apartheid's founder and other Afrikaner intellectuals may have believed that there were no biological differences between races, *they* had clearly seen the differences as *major*. I recall more than once experiencing the situation when individual Afrikaners had the 'lights go on', often in tears, as they shed lifelong beliefs and understandings about racial differences (and thus, by way of unspoken corollary, white supremacism). It does not mean that they had been committed evolutionists prior to then. But the full implications of Genesis creation had never previously 'clicked' with them.

The highlight of all such tours was the evening lecture I had been invited to give at North West University in Potchefstroom[25] in March of 2006. At earlier venues on that particular tour, whenever locals heard that I would be giving the same sort of message in Potchefstroom, they seemed a little awestruck. I was informed that 'Potch', as it is often referred to, was the heart of conservative Afrikaner territory. I was even told that the region was 'the birthplace of apartheid', though that subsequently proved hard to confirm.[26] And positively, Potch was still known for its strong biblically Christian stance. So it was not likely, despite some years of evolution being pushed by the new ANC government, that this would be a hotbed of evolutionism. But even though apartheid had been effectively dismantled for over a decade, how would they receive *this* particular part of the message, about race, with its antiapartheid implications? Since they were likely to be aware of the general stance CMI was taking on race issues, would they stay away *en masse*, I wondered?

As it turned out, those fears were unfounded. Discussions with students from Potch after the talk indicated that they had been really looking for answers—a lot of them to do with creation/evolution. These were students from some very committed Christian families, concerned about church compromise on Genesis. But for some the answers they sought were specifically on race and apartheid in relation to the Bible. Remember that though brought up to love the Word of God, the family in which they grew up would often have also been inclined to see apartheid

25. Until 2004, the institution was known as Potchefstroom University for Christian Higher Education.
26. Upon the implementation of apartheid by the state, some voices from Potch were critical of the negative aspects of the policy.

(at least its idealized version) as normal, even decreed by the Bible.

The word certainly did seem to have gotten out. A lecture theatre designed to seat 380 ended up with well over 600, the overflow jammed into whatever patch of floor they could sit or stand on. According to the organizers, another 200 or so had to be turned away outside the doors.

The sounds of silence

With an audience that size, even when they are all very attentive, there is normally an inevitable level of background sound—just the combined breathing and slight rustling from clothing will ensure that. One's senses normally don't register this—until it is not there. The effect is striking, and makes one aware of the expression, 'You could have heard a pin drop'. That was what it was like that night, indicating the level of interest.

The 'race' portion of the message was no different from what my colleagues in this ministry and I have given hundreds of times all over the world. And the response to the whole lecture, to my relief, was not just positive, but enthusiastically so. Much more than at any other similar lecture, before or since, judging by the crowds excitedly discussing things afterwards inside, and outside at the book tables.

In the question time following the talk, there were one or two evolutionary-minded lecturers from that university who used the session to make comments designed to weaken the pro-creation impact of the

A portion of the crowd of over 600 at North West University, Potchefstroom campus, South Africa, gathered to hear the author on 9 March 2006.
Johan Kruger

talk.[27] But the students at that university made it very plain that they were unimpressed by these.

This *one human family* message can really radically change the way people look at the whole concept of 'race', and it did so repeatedly on those South African tours. I remember in particular the profound impact it had on one (university-educated) Afrikaner lady at a meeting prior to the one at Potch. With considerable emotion on display, she made it plain how drastically her ideas on race had changed. She said (emphases are hers—I will never forget the exact phrasing):

> "What you explained about the *melanin*… it's changed *everything!* I can never look at the world the same way again!"

It might surprise readers to hear that something so simple and straightforward as the facts already explained about skin and eye pigment could be so revolutionary in someone's life. But it's always been worldview, not the facts, which is the main issue. In addition to church venues, I have spoken at several universities and medical schools in South Africa. The medical students there would certainly have known of the simple facts about human pigmentation, for instance. And the majority probably believed, even if sometimes only vaguely, in God as Creator. Despite being taught evolution at university, many may well have still accepted the Bible's teaching that people are descended from Adam and Eve.

Nevertheless, a good number of the medical students had reactions similar to those of the above-mentioned lady, of the 'lights going on' about race. It was suddenly so obvious to them. In those circles, I never once had to deal with any objections from an alleged biblical basis, such as the supposed purpose of Babel being to separate races and so on. I did have one student say to me how ashamed he felt of having never examined the Bible carefully about this 'curse of Ham' (I dealt with it briefly in most of the talks), instead of just taking someone's word for it.

---

27.   Their aim was to defend evolution; there was no suggestion that they were pro-racism.

Given all the background to this issue, it's not surprising that knowing a few facts about human anatomy and physiology was not enough to change the way these medical students saw their fellow human beings, their relatives who happened to be Xhosa, Zulu or Tswana or whatever. That's not the way our minds normally work. What seems to have made the difference was seeing those familiar facts within a whole new framework of understanding—the big picture of biblical history. A framework which, incidentally, makes sense of the whole of reality.[28] And full marks to those who were willing to enthusiastically embrace what God's Word teaches about our *one human family*.

∞

---

28. A bold statement in this day and age, granted. But most people have never had the chance to see the 'big picture' of science in light of the Creation/Fall/Redemption framework of Scripture. Check out creation.com and its store for a wealth of information and resources, including books and DVDs, on every topic to do with the Bible, science, creation and evolution.

16 THE EFFECT OF RELIGION ON CULTURE

ARE ALL RELIGIONS EQUAL?

Religion (this incorporates all substantive world-and-life views, including atheism[1]) is both a part of, and a huge influence on, any culture.

Today, it's trendy to regard all religions (excluding atheism/humanism) as equal. By that is usually meant more than just 'equally worthy of respect and tolerance'. Of course, since virtually all religions make substantive truth-claims that are different from the truth-claims of other religions, they can't all be equally true. The often unspoken baseline assumption, in this evolutionized age that regards atheism/humanism/naturalism as the vantage point from which to judge everything else, is that they are all (including Christianity) equally wrong, i.e. *untrue* when it comes to any claims about ultimate reality. Something to observe and study, perhaps—but only out of sociological curiosity, as quaint relics of a pre-scientific past.

---

1.   See creation.com/atheism-a-religion, as well as: Leading anticreationist philosopher Michael Ruse admits that evolution is a religion, creation.com/ruse, after Ruse, M., How evolution became a religion: creationists correct? *National Post*, pp. B1, B3, B7, 13 May 2000.

Secular society can show its magnanimity by permitting all to exist side-by-side. But the fangs are bared, and all hell appears to break loose (perhaps not as purely metaphorical a comment as it might seem) should creationists dare to suggest that the Bible is actually true, *and that the scientific evidence is consistent with that*. In November 2010, our ministry was stunned to receive an invitation, the first in its history, from the Provost (Dean) of a secular university to hold a public seminar under the university's auspices. Richard Dawkins is perhaps the world's best-known atheist, and Darwin's chief living apostle. The Provost of this university had read Dr. Sarfati's powerful refutation of Dawkins' definitive book on evolution, *The Greatest Show on Earth*—a book titled *The Greatest Hoax on Earth? Refuting Dawkins on evolution.* For the first time ever, a secular university was saying something that to us was very obvious; that there clearly *was* a strong scientific case to be made for Genesis creation; that most people only ever heard the other (pro-evolution) side; and that it was therefore reasonable for a university interested in the free and fair exchange of ideas to give people in the community a chance to judge the debate for themselves.

Sadly, though not surprisingly, as soon as it began to be widely advertized, the hue and cry, led by the founder of an ironically named 'Freethinkers' group, forced the university to withdraw its sponsorship.

In George Orwell's famous 1945 book *Animal Farm*, a parody of communism in practice, all animals were equal, but some were more equal than others. The Western intelligentsia today seem to operate under a sort of reverse Orwellianism in regard to religions: 'all religions are equal, but one is less equal than others' (very similar to PC multiculturalism; cf. p. 239ff. As Thomas Sowell aptly summarized: "What 'multiculturalism' boils down to is that you can praise any culture in the world except Western culture—and you cannot blame any culture in the world except Western culture."[2])

---

2.   Sowell, T., in his column 'Random Thoughts' in *Jewish World Review*, 12 September 2002, accessed at www.jewishworldreview.com, 1 May 2011.

Religious selectivity

Christianity is not only singled out in an active sense but also passively. Something likely to offend Muslims, for instance, will generate strong media condemnation. A similar affront to Christians will most often be met by a loud media silence— unless, of course, it is to suggest that the Christians have no right to be offended. E.g. many outlets would not publish Danish cartoons about Muhammad, claiming 'sensitivity', but would have no problem reproducing 'art' like one image that featured Christ on the cross—submerged in urine, with a derogatory title to boot.

This tendency seems particularly strong in the US, perhaps partly in reaction to Christianity's history of cultural dominance there. It's also the same in Britain, another culture that has a strong Christian heritage. At a 2006 'impartiality' summit called by its chairman, Michael Grade:

> "Senior figures admitted that the BBC is guilty of promoting Left-wing views and an anti-Christian sentiment. … executives admitted they would happily broadcast the image of a Bible being thrown away—but would not do the same for the Koran."[3]

However, if by 'all religions are equal', it is meant they are 'equally worthy of respect and tolerance', this is self-evidently not true. Say that you are walking in an unfamiliar region, on a dark night, in a foreboding-looking alley. You see several large, hulking, strong men, holding objects in their hands, coming out of a building and then approaching you. Let's say that at this uneasy moment, you somehow had instant insight into what they were holding. I think that even if you were a rabid atheist, it would make a huge and positive difference to how you felt if they turned out to be Bibles. Obviously you would feel substantially better than if they were, say, knuckledusters, or beer bottles. But I suggest to you that 'Bibles' would also be more reassuring to you than if you knew that they were 'how to' manuals of voodoo

3. Revoir, P., Yes, we are biased on religion and politics, admit BBC executives, *Daily Mail*, 22 October 2006.

ritual—or Korans, for that matter.

Even Richard Dawkins might agree. To say that he is no friend of Christianity would be a masterful exercise in understatement. But in response to the decline of Christianity in Britain, he recently made this comment:

> "There are no Christians, as far as I know, blowing up buildings. I am not aware of any Christian suicide bombers. I am not aware of any major Christian denomination that believes the penalty for apostasy is death. I have mixed feelings about the decline of Christianity, in so far as Christianity might be a bulwark against something worse." [4]

Fiji: gimme *less* of that 'old-time religion'

I recall my first trip to the island nation of Fiji as a young man, several decades ago. Western influences, including Christianity, only really reached Fiji in the 1800s. The display in the national museum, complete with photographs of pre-Christian Fijian customs and dress, spoke of the coming of missionaries with disdain, even antagonism. It reflected the usual humanist approach that somehow this peaceful, pristine culture and its religion had been rudely overturned by Christianity—to the detriment of the native inhabitants.

The next day I went to a reconstructed village of pre-Christian Fiji. We went into the *bure kalou*, or temple, of the same type as pictured at right. Its purpose, said the guide, was the worship of 'spirits' of a particularly malevolent nature. These needed to be appeased frequently, and often in various bloodthirsty ways. Pointing out the large upright logs supporting the main structure, he described the standard approach of ensuring the temple was properly dedicated to these malign spirits. Before the base of each log was lowered into holes dug for that purpose, a Fijian, chosen at the whim of either the chieftain or high priest, would be seized and placed into the hole. The log would then be thrust

---

4. Gledhill, R., Scandal and schism leave Christians praying for a 'new Reformation', *The Times (UK)*, 2 April 2010.

into the hole alongside the hapless citizen, who, in addition to being crushed, would then be buried alive.

Then the guide turned to describing various practices that routinely took place in such temples. As he was talking in the building's dark interior, a drum outside began to beat furiously, building up to a crescendo. This was done, we were told, to convey to visitors some idea of the sheer terror experienced by captives bound in the temple awaiting their fate. These were people who had been chosen, again at whim, to be human sacrifices to those same demonic spirits. They would be tied up in pitch darkness, with similar frantic drumming going on outside. All to raise their level of terror while waiting for the application of the war-club that would in due course spill their brains all over an upright log installed for that purpose.

A reconstructed temple from pre-Christian Fiji.
Public domain

We also saw an authentic-looking full-size reconstruction of the hut of a chieftain in the old Fiji. Displayed inside with various other items were special carved wooden ceremonial forks. The chief would use these to eat certain chosen parts (such as the lips) of various of his subjects, selected as he saw fit. Cannibalism in Fiji was widely practiced. It was not that there was a shortage of food available on these tropical isles; we were told that the cannibalism was mostly associated with their religious practices and beliefs. Even the chieftain's own family was not immune from being capriciously clubbed to death. For example, if family members accidentally strayed into areas of the hut reserved for the big fella, the penalty was death by clubbing. Their lips, etc. could then, if he wished, form part of his subsequent dinner menu—and sometimes did.

For those, including pre-Darwinian evolutionists, inclined to seeing biology behind 'racial differences', tales of such savagery would tend to really reinforce the notion. When I heard them, I couldn't help but remember—from the previous night of our visit to those islands—the scores of fresh-faced Fijian high-school students who had spontaneously assembled around our resort lawns at sunset. Dressed in sparkling clean clothes, they were there to sing hymns and gospel songs in that uniquely melodious South Pacific *a capella* style. The tradition involved no financial incentives, no money from the resort, no offerings from the tourists, nothing of the sort. It was just their way of welcoming visitors to their land, sharing goodwill and joy. As we listened, it was being repeated in many other places on the island at sunset. So, had their great-grandparents been acting on racially based impulses, derived from being less-evolved savages? Or was it cultural behavior, driven by wrong-headed beliefs, and capable of radical transformation through the impact of the gospel? The answer seems clear.

After the gruesome demonstration in the temple, I spoke to the guide in private. Not surprisingly, his very positive assessment of the effects of Christianity didn't at all match the one the academics had set up in the museum.

Missionary contact commenced in the early 1800s, but the real change first came in 1854, when a prominent chieftain converted. Then in 1874 the process was firmly cemented when the islands were ceded to the British Crown. My conversation with the guide was in the 1970s, and he would have been born around 1920 or so. His own grandfather, perhaps even his father, would have still had vivid memories of living under the 'old ways'. The guide would have been well aware of the changes wrought by Western culture in general, and Christianity in particular. He spoke in the most glowing terms of the gratitude that Fijians in general had towards Christianity and the missionaries for liberating them from what was really a reign of terror.

I've been back to Fiji, mostly on ministry trips, since that time. The country today is still a mostly Christian nation, but the secularizing influences of evolution-soaked education are seeing a rapid departure—especially among the young. There has been a concomitant and accelerating social decay over the last few decades in particular.[5]

Torres Strait Islanders similarly have no incentive to hanker for the old ways. These are the indigenous inhabitants of a small chain of islands, part of Australia and just off the north-eastern tip of the continental mainland.[6] Islanders, as they are usually called by their fellow Australians, have much more in common ethnically with the Melanesian inhabitants of Papua New Guinea than with Aboriginal Australians.

Every year on 1 July, most of the Islanders enthusiastically celebrate the anniversary of the day in 1871 when missionaries from the London Missionary Society landed, bringing with them the life-and-culture-transforming good news of the gospel. The festival is appropriately called 'The Coming of the Light'.

COMPARATIVE OUTCOMES

Despite that sort of thing, it's not PC today to regard any particular culture—and especially any particular religion—as being 'better' than any other. Especially not Christianity—that would seem too much like the caricatures that associate Christianity with imposed cultural dominance and intolerance. Any suggestion to that effect would remind people of all of the ways in which the sins of colonialism, exaggerated or not, are sheeted home to the prevailing Christianity of the colonizers' culture. Even myths such as blaming Christianity for the enslavement of black Africans, as discussed earlier, are all too easily brought to the fore in such a context.

So to propose that Christianity might have major advantages

---

5.   Wieland, C., and Catchpoole, D., Creation among the coconut palms (Interview with Bible teacher Maurice Nicholson), *Creation* **28**(2):14–17, 2006, creation.com/fiji.
6.   A few islands in the group, close to the coast of mainland Papua New Guinea, belong to that country's Western Province.

over other religions is especially *verboten*. But this stance does not conform to reality. As we will see, even some prominent and well-informed non-Christians acknowledge that Christianity (even if it is, as they believe, untrue[7]) has huge positives for a culture in terms of sheer practical outcomes.

Voting with your (children's) feet

Sometimes, the acknowledgment of Christianity's cultural positives is inadvertent, in spite of what the person wants to believe. I recall when I was speaking on an Australian Christian radio station a few years ago. Lacking the equipment for talk-back, the station was taking calls off-air, and one young geology student had been put through to a former colleague (and still friend) of mine.[8] She told my colleague that Christianity was "not much good", and that she was drawn to religions like Buddhism or Islam. My colleague asked her what country in the world she would choose in which to raise her future children.

"Australia, of course", she replied.

He shot back, "If it couldn't be Australia, what would be your next choice?"

"Umm … America, I guess … or maybe England."

"And if that isn't possible?"

"Well," she replied, hesitating, "probably Germany … or Switzerland … ."

After she had been prodded to name several more, my colleague pointed out that her list included *none* that were predominantly Buddhist or Islamic. In fact, it was made up exclusively of countries which, despite the blatant secularism of many of them today, all historically shared a strong Christian social foundation.

Of course, our young lady's choices were neither unusual nor surprising. Not even the most vehement Christian-bashers would

---

7. The positives make even more sense once one realizes that the Christian's Bible speaks the truth about origins, history and indeed, all of reality. It also truthfully faces the flaws that even heroes of the faith demonstrated.

8. Warwick Armstrong, now retired.

prefer to bring their children up in Iran, Burma, Saudi Arabia or the like. But rarely would any of them make a connection between their choice of countries and the Bible.

Some time later, a young man I was discussing this with countered by saying, "In South America, Christianity conquered the local religions and reigned supreme; churches and crosses are everywhere. But I can't think of too many South American countries I would want my children brought up in, either."

I pointed out that the link was not about churchianity or public displays of 'religion'. It was about the real life-and-culture-transforming power of the Christ of the Bible. It was about a way of thinking which was based on the Bible, and which had changed the lives of millions. These had in turn affected others, so that even unbelievers were swept up in the positive benefits which flowed from it.[9]

It was easy to show how the countries he, too, had chosen for his children's upbringing had, like those on our geology student's list, all been at some stage powerfully affected by the Reformation and its strong emphasis on the Bible. Whereas this had bypassed the South American ones he had rejected.

On the surface, the reasons for such 'country' choices have nothing to do with Christianity. In the individual's mind, they involve such things as economic opportunity (associated with a high level of technology), reasonable expectations of justice in a society ruled by law, freedom of thought and expression, the relative absence of corruption, the dignity of the individual, human rights and so on. So why are high scores in all these things so heavily clustered in countries impacted strongly by the Bible?

Those of us of Western European extraction should consider that, to be brutally honest, our thinking on such matters is often associated with a degree of arrogance tinged with racism. We may have no intention of putting down other people groups, but somehow we find it unremarkable that the societies which are

9.   'Common grace'—a term not heard much today—refers to the benefits that flow to believers and unbelievers within a society with a predominantly Bible-honoring worldview.

the most 'advanced' in their economies, their technology, or their degree of 'civilized' behavior tend to be those whose people are the most like 'us' in their racial and ethnic attributes.

This is why most Westerners tend to see the correlation of such desirable cultural traits with the Bible as incidental. For them, Western Europe just happens to have had a strong Christian/ Protestant heritage. A more likely cause for the dominance of Western European cultures, they think, is that the same countries were also historically at the forefront of the development of science and technology, and it is these two factors which are seen as the true liberators of mankind. And in the background lies, unspoken (especially today when racism is unfashionable, not to mention politically incorrect) the overarching assumption with its whiff of biological/racial superiority: 'our kind of people' would naturally be the first ones to discover science, wouldn't they?

The reality is, though, that matters of racial or genetic endowment have nothing to do with the distribution of 'favored' countries and cultures. In reality, the common factor is the Bible, rediscovered and unchained at the Reformation, and the gospel preaching which flowed from its pages. This is what led naturally and consistently to *all* of the reasons why virtually everyone tends to rate cultures with such a heritage highly as a child-rearing preference. And it's a big reason why we don't see boatloads and trainloads of would-be immigrants rushing away from such countries, but the reverse.

SCIENCE AND TECHNOLOGY—THE BIBLICAL LINKS

Though many secular academics have long ago made the connection, even most Christians are still unaware of the way in which it was the Bible, rediscovered and refocused upon at the time of the Reformation, that led directly to the subsequent explosion of science and technology in Western Europe. Its people 'stole a march' in these areas (and reaped the associated economic rewards). They did so not because of any innate superiority, but because their culture was blessed with a way of thinking about the world which happened to be conducive to the flowering of scientific thought.

We look at the countries of Islam today, and often forget how advanced some of the great thinkers and scholars of the Arabic world were. Some of the finest mathematicians of antiquity were among their ranks, not to mention physicians. Yet modern science was not born there.

One of the most renowned of these mathematicians was the brilliant Persian Muslim Abu Ja'far ibn Musa al-Khwarizmi (780–850); he wrote the famous treatise on algebra. Even the word itself comes from his *al-jabr*, 'completing' or performing the same mathematical operation on both sides of an equation.[10] Also, the word 'algorithm' comes from his name itself, in Latinized form. Yet according to religious scholar and Islam critic Robert Spencer:

"the principles upon which al-Khwarizmi worked were discovered centuries before he was born—including the zero, which is often attributed to Muslims. Even what we know today as 'Arabic numerals' did not originate in Arabia, but in pre-Islamic India—and they are not used in the Arabic language today. … Al-Khwarizmi's work opened up new avenues of mathematical and scientific exploration in Europe, so why didn't it do the same in the Islamic world? The results are palpable: Europeans ultimately used algebra, in conjunction with other discoveries, to make significant technological advances; Muslims did not. Why?"[11]

The brilliance of the ancient Greeks needs no introduction—yet the way of thinking and investigating that we call science did not arise from their midst. Many ancient civilizations came close to making the leap; the Chinese made numerous discoveries and

10. His example, using modern notation instead of spelling it out in words as al-Khwarizmi did, was $x^2 = 40x - 4x^2$, and performing *al-jabr*, adding $4x^2$ to both sides, becomes $5x^2 = 40x$; then divide both sides by 5x, so x = 8.
11. Spencer, R., *The Politically Incorrect Guide to Islam (and the Crusades)*, p. 93, Regnery Publishing, Washington DC, 2005.

inventions long before the West. But the few intermittent signs of gestation of scientific thinking in such cultures led only to a series of stillbirths.

Modern scientific ways of thinking about the world are deeply ingrained in Western society, even in laypeople. So much so that we find it hard to see how people could think otherwise. For example, it seems obvious to us that there is an objective reality 'out there', ripe for us to uncover, gleaning ever more and deeper knowledge of the way it works. And we take for granted the idea that the world functions according to regular, unchanging and universally applicable laws that we can rely on absolutely, and thus harness for our benefit.

But consider someone brought up in a culture which believed that within every rock or tree there was an individual spirit. What motivation would they have for believing that there was an innate orderliness or predictability about the way in which rocks and trees behaved?

What if you had been brought up in a society which believed, as so many did and some still do, that the universe was an illusion of the mind,[12] or was itself one big thought? What sense is there in investigating something which may not even really, objectively exist? Why even think of looking for regular laws which govern the behavior of the universe if it is all just a big mind? The universe may well change its mind tomorrow.

By contrast, the notion of a Creator God independent of His creation readily leads to the idea of lawfulness in the world He made. The maker of nature is presumably the ruler of nature. Thus creation-based cultures were always more likely to discover the creation's lawfulness. But all Creator concepts are not the same. The law-giving God of the Christian Bible stands unique in the extent of His lawfulness. Jesus Christ, God the Son who made all things (Colossians 1:16) is 'the same yesterday, today and forever' (Hebrews 13:8), so His created laws can be expected to

---

12.   Another self-refuting philosophy: if everything is an illusion of the mind, then *this* thought is *itself* an illusion of the mind.

be likewise unchanging.

The fact that the one God made the entire universe is also a basis for expecting that the same laws would apply in all parts of His universe. All astronomers use this assumption continually, without acknowledging (often not even realizing) its Christian roots. They automatically assume in all their scientific reasoning that the same laws will apply on, say, Alpha Centauri as on Earth. This assumption can't be proved by science. For one thing, it is impossible to test the laws in every part of the universe. And for another, any experiment would presuppose the unity it's purporting to prove. But it *works* in practice.

That fickle bunch on Olympus

Had you been raised in ancient Greece, you would have been saturated with talk of 'the gods', but they could not be depended upon to ordain an unchanging lawfulness in the world. For one thing, they were not said to be the ultimate reality, in the way the Creator God of the Bible is. They did not always exist, but had themselves developed (evolved) from some pre-existent reality, some primordial ooze. And even though they had some sway over the forces of nature, Zeus and the gang on Olympus were renowned for being capricious, even deceptive. OK, so things fall down today—who's to say that tomorrow, the gods will not decree that they will henceforth go upwards? Or that they'll fall at a different rate? In addition, the Greek gods were not unified, but fought among each other, unlike the unbroken love-bond between the three Persons in Christianity's single Godhead.[13] So the decrees of Zeus might vary from those of Apollo, for example.

If you saw something in a rock that looked like a fish, then since experience and common sense say that fish don't live in rocks, it was probably the gods up to tricks. The medieval idea of fossils being manufactured by God or the Devil to fool us or test our faith did not derive from the Bible, but was inherited from Greek thought. Incidentally, Nicolas Steno (1638–1686),

---

13.   See creation.com/god#trinity for a number of articles defending this biblical doctrine.

the Danish founding father of modern geology and stratigraphy, avoided such Greek ideas in his (correct) reasoning about the connection between fossils and the processes of sedimentation. Like the founders of virtually all scientific disciplines, he was a believer in literal Genesis creation and a global Flood.[14] Such beliefs were not incidental to the rise of science, but a crucial part of it.

One of the fundamental principles upon which modern science is built is the general uniformity of natural law, also called the 'non-capriciousness of nature'. I.e. nature is not fickle or arbitrary. The whole of experimental science would be pointless if results could not be reliably repeated, or if the physical laws were prone to sudden variations at random. The God of the Bible, unlike the Greek gods, is not fickle or capricious (see Malachi 3:6). The pioneers of modern science understood this as guaranteeing the non-capriciousness of natural law, making the whole scientific enterprise possible.

iStockPhoto

Furthermore, people were given dominion over the world (Genesis 1:28). This passage has historically been understood as a mandate to be able to investigate, understand and even harness nature for good—with the implication of wise stewardship. Nature is worthy of respect as a creation of God, but is not sacred, "so we don't need to sacrifice to the forest god to cut down a tree, or

14.   Walker, T., Geological pioneer Nicolaus Steno was a biblical creationist, *Journal of Creation* **22**(1):93–98, 2008, creation.com/steno.

appease the water spirits to measure its boiling point".[15,16]

Many modern anticreationists charge that the notion of a miracle-working God (as in six-day fiat creation) is antiscience. They say it would destroy this crucial foundation of science, the assumption that things can always be expected to follow natural law. Their argument is used to justify redefining science in such a way as to exclude an original supernatural creation by definition, *a priori*.[17] But the (creationist) founders of modern science did not see it this way. They understood that there was no contradiction between the *general* uniformity of 'natural law' (God's normative activity in upholding and sustaining the creation) and the miracles He is recorded as having performed in the Bible. Since He is Himself responsible for the lawfulness of His creation, He has the sovereign right to add to it for His special purposes in one-off miracles, like raising Jesus from the dead.[18]

The miracles of Scripture are not arbitrary exercises happening at a whim, likely to recur at random intervals just when a scientist is about to make a measurement. They are rare events of very special significance and purpose. At the time of their occurrence, they are instantly identifiable as miraculous, precisely *because of* the general principle of non-capriciousness in all things. Generally, dead people don't come back to life, nor can living ones walk on water or indeed change it into wine. The Nativity accounts show that both Mary and Joseph were surprised at the Annunciation (of Jesus' virginal conception), precisely because they *did* know what normally needed to first take place.

In short, whatever the benefits that science (real, operational science in particular) has brought to the world can largely be traced back to belief in the Bible—in literal creation in particular. Even

15.   Sarfati, J., Why does science work at all? *Creation* **31**(3):12–14, 2009, creation.com/science-biblical-presuppositions; The biblical roots of modern science, *Creation* **32**(4), 2010, creation.com/roots.

16.   For a range of articles, with differing emphases, on Christianity and the environment, see creation.com/environmentalism.

17.   Wieland, C. Science: The Rules of the Game, *Creation* **11**(1):47–50, creation.com/rules.

18.   See creation.com/miracles and articles linked from there.

many secular scholars agree. An example is cited by Christian mathematician and Oxford professor John Lennox:

> "Some years ago, the scientist Joseph Needham made an epic study of technological development in China. He wanted to find out why China, for all its early gifts of innovation, had fallen so far behind Europe in the advancement of science.
>
> "He reluctantly came to the conclusion that European science had been spurred on by the widespread belief in a rational creative force, known as God, which made all scientific laws comprehensible."[19]

ECONOMIC OUTCOMES

The economic health of any group of people does of course depend on such predetermined factors as whether their place of abode has natural resources, fertile soil, etc. But it is also linked to culture and behavior. In a typical list of the countries in which most would want their children brought up, there is a strong correlation with capitalism and the free enterprise system. So it is hardly surprising that many see the capitalist economy *per se* as the real key to desirable living.

With the collapse of the Iron Curtain and the demise of socialism/communism, it was assumed that all Russia had to do was to adopt a Western-style capitalist system in order to rapidly reach a new era of peace, prosperity and personal freedom. Not many foresaw the nigh-catastrophic result. They did not take into account that free enterprise thrives on 'cultural morality'.

The notion of private property is repeatedly sanctioned and upheld in the Bible. ('Thou shalt not steal' only makes sense if an individual has private property capable of being stolen.) The virtuous woman of Proverbs 31, whose children 'rise up and call her blessed', is clearly running a business with 'merchandise'. But the Bible puts all this in the context of a society underpinned by

---

19.   Lennox, J., As a scientist I'm certain Stephen Hawking is wrong. You can't explain the universe without God, *Mail Online*, 3 September 2010.

strict moral law. It does so with no sense of dewy-eyed idealism, but rather a sober recognition of the capacity of all people for corruption and wrongdoing. Scripture requires a legal framework to prevent fraud and coercion, and to enforce contracts. Dealings must be just; weights and measures must be precise; the poor are not to be oppressed. And, despite what many liberal churchians (who often seem to defer more to Marx than the Bible, anyway) say, the poor are not to be shown legal favoritism, either, since it would contradict the following:

> "You shall do no injustice in court. You shall not be partial to the poor or defer to the great, but in righteousness shall you judge your neighbor (Leviticus 19:15)."

This is all part of a moral law eternally decreed by the Creator and stamped on the human heart and conscience (Romans 2), as well as to be enforced by the civil authorities (Romans 13).

By way of aside, the concept of such an immutable moral law, and the recognition of man's fallenness,[20] was also integral to the development of our strong Western systems and institutions of law and justice. These are, despite their imperfections, one important reason why Western culture 'works' and why its countries are seen as desirable places in which to live. Recent exercises in attempted 'nation-building' in both Iraq and Afghanistan have constantly come up against cultural roadblocks. It's fine to talk about the need for strong institutions—law enforcement, governments, courts, etc. But such institutions depend upon a certain type of underlying religious-cultural fabric, which is hard, if not impossible, to impose or manufacture at will.

In order to maximize its benefit to a society, the free enterprise

---

20.   The US Constitution's checks and balances on power largely reflect the keen awareness within their culture of the sin nature, whether or not each contributor held to biblical authority. In contrast, the French Revolution followed the philosopher Jean-Jacques Rousseau (1712–1778) in believing that man is basically good, and things would be well if the right people were in charge. And who could be more right than Maximilien Robespierre (1758–1794), known as 'The Incorruptible'? But his Reign of Terror resulted in 16,000 to 40,000 being guillotined. Whereas the American founders recognized that all people were flawed (Genesis 3), so trusted no man or group with too much power.

system needs such a cultural backbone of agreed-upon morality. Despite the West increasingly turning its back on God, there is still an embedded substrate of this morality. However, Russian society had just had seventy years of official atheism, reinforced and sustained by a relentless program of indoctrination in evolution/long-ages. So, especially since Russia was not part of the Reformation's main sphere of influence anyway, it had little Bible-derived foundation left. If everything just evolved, then there is nothing 'out there' to act as an absolute standard of right and wrong. Public order under the Soviet rule depended on the harshness of the state more than on the inherent social morality of the individual.

Without the proper, biblically mandated legal protection against force and fraud, a *laissez faire* system imposed upon such a substrate led to chaos, in which the law of the Darwinian jungle reigned. Generally, it was the most ruthless robber barons and 'mafia' types who prospered astronomically. Meanwhile, most of the rest of the population was plunged into such misery that large numbers yearned for the once unthinkable—a return to the days of iron-fisted communist rule.

Compare this to the economic foundation that made America great, the Protestant/Puritan ethic. In the society of that time, despite the shortcomings of sinful individuals, there was an overriding cultural consensus that one should work hard (and honestly) for one's employer. Hard work and integrity were equally cultural and moral obligations on business owners, including on their activity as employers. Doing business was to be regarded primarily as service to one's fellow man. Making money was a secondary issue—though important, it all belonged to God anyway.

A useful side effect is that this system encourages right behavior even if it is for the wrong motives. If force and fraud are precluded, the only way a greedy person can satisfy his greed is to find out what lots of people want, then supply it at a price people are willing to pay. And if he wants to beat his competition, he will need to keep improving the quality of his work and friendliness of service. Even if John Rockefeller, Henry Ford, Bill Gates, and Sam Walton were super-greedy, it is in one sense irrelevant. They never would have become multi-billionaires without making it possible for the masses to obtain oil, cars, computers and cheap everyday things, respectively. But as will be further seen, a large part of their success was the Christian worldview underpinning the American free market.

The more that this cultural morality crumbles away in the once-Christian West, incidentally, the more need there is for many more rules and regulations and red tape than ever before, ultimately stifling economies. Transactions that could once be done on a handshake now require complex contracts that are often later shown to be not worth the paper on which they are written.

Governments have a legitimate role in ensuring that transactions between free individuals in an open marketplace are honest and transparent. But anyone who has tried to file a complaint for dishonest business practice with a corporate regulator will agree that the regulator's commitment to the role seems more often honored in the breach. The basis on which a decision is made to pursue a case or not is rarely one of strict principle, but rather things such as cost-effectiveness and political pragmatism— including whether the case is likely to benefit or enhance the standing of the official in charge. In place of straightforward laws rigorously enforcing honesty we see a plethora of choking regulations which are often frustrating in the extent of their pettiness and complexity.

Dictators, prices and the Genesis Fall

But this itself is once more a problem with human nature: even the regulators are fallen, selfish human beings.[21] Those who have

---

21.   There is a whole field called 'Public Choice Theory', about how politicians and bureaucrats are seeking their own good rather than the public's. James M. Buchanan (1919–) won a Nobel Prize in economics for this. A detailed book is Thomas Sowell's *Knowledge and Decisions* (1980, 1996), which Buchanan himself highly praised and said should be "required reading". The 1980s UK comedy *Yes (Prime) Minister* is a brilliant satire on public choice theory, showing many ways in which politicians and bureaucrats increase their own power.

faith in more and more regulations overlook the following old question, going back to Plato: "Who regulates the regulators?" And regulation requires power, thus encouraging an increasing concentration of such governmental and bureaucratic might. The ultimate example is the central planning of Marxist economies. As noted in Chapter 13, it is no coincidence that such social philosophies (of which Nazism is just another variant[22]) are near-universally associated with tyrannical forms of government, despite their stated utopian ideals. Nor is it surprising that they regularly attract the sorts of ruthless personalities that make the lists of history's greatest butchers.

Leaving aside moral failings of bureaucrats, another problem is their lack of omniscience, again consistent with Scripture. What is called 'the dictates of the market' really represents the free choices of millions of buyers and sellers. No group of central planners can possibly have the wide-ranging diffused knowledge about the wants of all these people needed to decree how many of each of millions of different types of goods should be produced. It's thus no accident that communist countries were plagued by shortages of some things and surpluses of others.

Instead, prices, if freely set by buyers and sellers, immediately convey an enormous amount of information about the likes and dislikes of millions of people. E.g. a high price of oil is a signal that more people want it and that it's scarce—and there is then an incentive to supply more of it.[23]

People will readily aim their frustrations with things like increasing red tape and bureaucratic nightmares at 'the government', as if a change in politicians could unwind the result

---

22.   The fierce opposition of Hitler's National Socialism to, e.g., Bolshevik Socialism in pre-WWII Germany is perfectly understandable considering they were in effect struggling over the same ideological and political 'turf' in the dying days of the Weimar Republic.

23.   That's not to say unfettered markets always get it right. Joseph Stiglitz, who famously foresaw the Asian financial crisis and the 2008 bubble before it burst, won a Nobel Prize in economics for his work on the deficiencies of a purely market-based approach. Real life rarely rewards a 'one-size-fits-all' answer for the complex issues of human interactions.

of a decades-long shift in this cultural morality, and long-standing ignorance of man's universal fallenness and fallibility. And rarely will they see that the fault is also in the individual's dealings with government. Despite the biblical injunction to "give to Caesar that which is Caesar's" (see Matthew 22:15–21), this general decline in morality means that often even Christians think that it is fair game to evade taxation lawfully due (as opposed to the legitimate practice of arranging one's affairs lawfully to avoid paying Caesar more than is really his). It is as if there is an 'arms race' between the government's ability to plug loopholes in tax legislation and the ability of individuals and corporations to find and exploit them—or lobby the government for them. This generates the need for armies of bureaucrats on the one side, and legions of highly paid advisers on the other—even if only to unravel the baffling complexities. All parties in such a scenario are distracted from contributing productively to an economy.

In short, it is no coincidence that societies that have this post-Reformation heritage are more likely to have strong economic systems. Countries and cultures which missed out on this heritage are most often riddled with corruption, which holds back true economic advance. They also more readily substitute rule of bureaucrats for rule of law. It may also be no coincidence that with the decline of Christianity, Western economies once seen as invincible seem to be increasingly vulnerable.

China's rise

Modern China has, like Russia, also had years under communist materialism, but has exploded economically since the state-imposed economic system was largely discarded. For one thing, this shows that, contrary to many expectations, democracy is not a prerequisite for a functioning market economy. (Similarly, Britain's initial rise as a world economic power happened when it became a free economy, before it became democratic.) Its boom, however, is not the exception to our general rule about morality that one might think. Its unique system of combining a market economy with authoritarian rule is not comparable to post-communist Russia. The Chinese government may have loosened the economic fetters, but is still very much in charge, and seeks to exercise a significant level of 'imposed morality' through stern controls.

In addition to having provided the cheap manufacturing base for much of the world, China has a confluence of factors that have helped to make it uniquely primed for growth since around the turn of the millennium. For starters, its sheer size and other demographic factors. These include the unprecedented exodus, encouraged by government, of huge numbers of the rural population to coastal cities, where their consumption and production rises dramatically.

One bright spot for China's future, not often appreciated in the West, is that the Christian church has actually prospered behind the scenes. Estimates vary, but the size of the Christian population, while still a distinct minority, is likely to be double, or very nearly so, the entire population of Australia.(!)[24]

A Chinese government economist, Zhao Xiao, traveled around America to investigate the key to its market successes before publishing a paper on his conclusions in 2002. In it, he "argues that the key to America's commercial success is not its natural resources, its financial system or its technology but its churches, 'the very core that binds America together'".[25] The paper was titled 'Market Economies with Churches and Market Economies Without Churches'.[26] His conclusions are similar to those of this chapter, namely that the success of the free market system requires "a moral underpinning". Interestingly, he subsequently became a Christian.

Nor was this a one-off. Prolific secular economic historian Niall Ferguson (1964–), in his recent book *Civilisation: The West and the Rest*, quotes a member of the Chinese Academy of

---

24. Estimates vary wildly, but it's probably around 50 million.
25. Micklethwait J. and Wooldridge, A., *God is Back: How the Global Rise of Faith is Changing the World*, Allen Lane (the Penguin Group), London, p. 8, 2009.
26. English translation at www.danwei.org/business/churches_and_the_market_econom.php, 2006.

Social Sciences as saying:

"We were asked to look into what accounted for the West all over the world … . At first we thought it was because you had more powerful guns than we had. Then we thought it was because you had the best political system. Next we focused on your economic system. But in the past 20 years we have realised that the heart of your culture is your religion: Christianity. That is why the West has been so powerful. The Christian moral foundation of social and cultural life was what made possible the emergence of capitalism and then the successful transition to democratic politics. We don't have any doubts about this."

In an online review of Ferguson's book, former *Sunday Telegraph* editor Dominic Lawson explains how Ferguson goes on to back this up with empirical evidence:

"The most entrepreneurial city in China, Wenzhou, where the free market is given full rein and where the state's influence is minimal, is also home to almost 1,400 churches—half a century after Chairman Mao boasted that it was 'religion-free'. One of its most successful business leaders, Hanping Zhang, argues that an absence of trust had been one of the main factors holding China back; but he feels he can trust his fellow Christians because he knows that they will be honest in their dealings with him."[27]

Things in China are far from being all rosy, however, and despite draconian penalties, corruption still exercises a huge drag on the economy. In 2010, a front-page international news report[28] indicated that the problem of fraud and fakery was much greater

---

27.   Lawson, D., Review: Civilisation: The West and the Rest by Niall Ferguson— the prolific historian argues persuasively that western loss of power can only be resisted by rediscovering the work ethic. And he has the facts to prove it, www.thesundaytimes.co.uk, 27 February 2011, accessed 14 May 2011.
28.   Jacobs, A., Real problem for China: Robust culture of fakery, *International Herald Tribune*, 7 October 2010, p. 1.

than just that of the pirated DVDs and designer labels most Westerners are familiar with.[29] It stated that "in China, fakery is so pervasive that some worry it could make it harder for the country to take the next step in economic development." After a fatal plane crash, officials discovered that 100 pilots who worked for Shenzhen Airlines "had falsified their flying history".

In science, there has been "a deluge of plagiarized or fabricated Chinese research." In December 2009, says the report, a British journal withdrew "more than 70 papers by Chinese authors whose research was of questionable originality and rigor." Alan Feduccia, an evolutionary expert in fossil birds, referring to a famous 'feathered dinosaur' fossil, widely touted by *National Geographic,* that turned out to be a fake, stated:

> "*Archaeoraptor* is just the tip of the iceberg. *There are scores of fake fossils out there,* and they have cast a dark shadow over the whole field. When you go to these fossil shows, *it's difficult to tell which ones are faked and which ones are not.* I have heard that there is a fake-fossil factory in northeastern China, in Liaoning Province, near the deposits where many of these recent alleged feathered dinosaurs were found [emphases added]."[30]

And in a recent Chinese government study, "a third of the 6,000 scientists at six of China's top institutions admitted to engaging in plagiarism or outright fabrication of research data." A country's research and development will obviously have a major impact on its economic outcomes. The article also stated that the British medical journal *The Lancet* had warned that such matters threatened President Hu Jintao's vow of China being a "research superpower" by 2020.

Without wanting to propose any sort of a simplistic equation, or to suggest that other factors may not also be very important,

---

29. And which even Christians have unfortunately supported by purchasing such 'bargains'—despite knowing of the seller's flagrant breach of the Eighth Commandment.
30. Discover Dialogue: Ornithologist and evolutionary biologist Alan Feduccia plucking apart the Dino-Birds, *Discover* **24**(2), February 2003, creation.com/4wings.

the point is that there is clearly a strong and direct link between cultural morality and economic outcomes. Despite all the positive trend indicators, serious poverty is unfortunately still a huge problem for large portions of the Chinese population. Time will tell if China's economic miracle can be sustained long-term.

One further comment concerns the blessings that flow from the outworkings of the gospel and the effects of the Bible on culture. Some cultures have aspects in their own traditions (such as Confucianism for Chinese and Japanese societies) that have similar outworkings, stressing hard work and trustworthiness in business. The fact that such cultures are often more shame-driven than guilt-driven is of interest; the fear of being found out to have cheated, for instance, and thus 'losing face', can be a stronger motivator than the internal qualms more prevalent in the West. Nevertheless, the basic principle is that "righteousness exalts a nation" (Proverbs 13:4). The positive effects on a culture and society from doing things in the way recommended in the Maker's Handbook are not restricted to supernatural endowment of divine favor. It should not surprise us that applying God's principles, even if this is by non-believers, will lead to better outcomes in the world He made.

Before passing from a discussion of things sino-cultural, Singapore is worth a brief mention. Former Prime Minister Lee Kuan Yew is himself a declared agnostic. With relentless (some less kindly disposed to him might say ruthless) pragmatism, he put many things into practice based on what he had observed to 'work' (or otherwise) in his extensive time within Western society. One example was corporal punishment at his English school, and another was failures of certain aspects of the English welfare system. While emphasizing Asian values, he drew on common threads in Christian, Buddhist, and Confucian values to create a near-miraculous and much-admired economic outcome for a tiny city-state with no natural resources. Fearful of ethnic tensions in that multiracial society 'ejected' from the rest of Malaysia, Lee's government wisely focused on culture and religion to prevent racial strife, stressing harmony.

While sternly enforcing the policy of no religion criticizing another, Singapore's 'multiculturalism' was not some version of the postmodern PC trend discussed earlier, but quite removed from it. Far from being under siege there, Christianity blossomed. From the limited perspective of my own interactions over decades with churches in Singapore, its Christian leaders, in contrast to those in the US, are generally positive about their government's actions in regard to economic as well as racial and religious policies. Lee's much-vaunted crackdowns on corruption and crime have set the country apart from many other parts of Asia. These are issues with clear moral parameters, in line with biblical principles. It may be no coincidence that Lee's government, despite its imperfections, contained many staunch Christians (cf. p. 293).

Africa: stuck with the hand that's dealt

Naturally, geography and natural resources make a difference. If it were not so, there would have been less astonishment at Singapore's outcomes.

For example, one huge and often unrecognized disadvantage that sub-Saharan African nations have had concerns their waterways. Most of us know of the mighty rivers in those nations, such as the Zambezi. But a big factor in the history of trade and development of the interior of continents and nations is whether people could navigate major rivers deep inland from the sea. Unfortunately for sub-Saharan Africa, most of its rivers drop off sharply from escarpments as one approaches the coast, meaning that any trip inland is soon frustrated by cataracts.

Added to that has been the tremendous prevalence of many types of deadly diseases, particularly insect-borne ones, in Africa's swampy, steamy interior. While Europe was blossoming, it was, for centuries until the advent of modern medicine, literally a life-threatening exercise for outsiders to engage in any sort of significant economic activity in Africa. For one thing, they lacked the natural resistance of its inhabitants. And even this came at a price for Africans, as in our earlier discussion of sickle cell anemia (p. 138).

Thus Africa was economically behind the eight-ball—in addition to the religious–cultural factors already mentioned. When people consider the socio-economic contrast between Africa and various advanced nations of the world, there is always the convenient 'racial–biological' explanation at hand, even if just subliminally. I venture it is even present at some level in the thinking of many who are themselves of African stock—even though it has no basis in reality.

Nonetheless, 'cultural–religious' issues are probably much more significant to Africa's overall economic malaise than any geographic disadvantage. In today's world there are many additional ways of transporting freight. With this and modern disease control, there are countries in sub-Saharan Africa which should be more than prosperous. This is because they are rich in sought-after natural resources such as gold, copper, and diamonds. Yet most of the people in a nation such as the Congo—or Nigeria, for instance, with its substantial oil reserves—continue to live in abject poverty. A bright spot for the latter country is the astonishing transformation under way of the port city of Lagos under the pragmatic policies of state governor Babatunde Fashola (1963–).[31] Elected in 2007, Fashola (pictured overleaf) eschews the common 'big man' trappings of power and was re-elected in a landslide in 2011. Once more, race was not the issue that kept the Lagos of the past a 'city of despair'.

The Philippines and Indonesia are similarly examples of countries blessed with enough natural riches, fertile soil, etc. to ensure a good standard of living. Yet endemic corruption has greatly contributed to a yawning disparity between the super-rich and the very poor majority.

It's easy to see how some might look at the trouble and strife in various post-colonial regimes in Africa and make an 'obvious' racial connection. But the facts overall do not bear that out. Culture, including its links to religious heritage, is the main issue, not genes. In some African countries, of course, the situation was

31. Perry, A., Making over Lagos, *Time*, May 30, 2011, pp. 39–42, accessed at www.time.com 2 June 2011.

worsened by governmental Marxism—an antibiblical system[32] with a track record of failure when applied to real economies, for reasons explained already.

Some of these nations, disenchanted with failed socialism, have, like Russia, tried to graft capitalism onto significantly dysfunctional cultures—mostly without great results. The reasons are, once again, not racial, but involve the foundational worldview of any culture.

HOW WE SEE THE WORLD—IT MAKES A DIFFERENCE

I recall visiting my daughter Lara once in the Cape York community of Aboriginal people she most identifies with. Walking through the ramshackle, heavily damaged houses, here and there one or two stood out as well cared for—no piles of trash or broken windows, even flowers in the garden. She told me that they were the houses that belonged to the handful of strong Christian believers in the community.[33]

Babatunde Fashola, 13th Governor of Lagos State, Nigeria. Fashola is a lawyer with a passion for practical economics aimed at ending poverty and anarchy. His dramatic vision for transformation of Lagos, substantially underway, includes the biblically appropriate notions of property rights for all, and the extension of the rule of law. In his own words, a dysfunctional city "creates desperate conditions for people and reduces their ability to resist temptation."
Public domain

---

32. For one thing, the commandment not to steal the private property of another makes no sense in a system ostensibly doing away with the notion of private property altogether.

33. The situation has improved since then—along with, not coincidentally, the number of Christians.

This reminded me of what my colleague Dr. Don Batten told me about when he extensively visited India as part of his scientific work for our government's agricultural authorities. His visit covered several states of India, including the one called Kerala. This is a state which, unusually for India, has a historically high proportion of Christians (at nearly 20%, it is about ten times the national average). That Christian influence goes back a very long way, and the church there is said to have been commenced by the Apostle Thomas. Not surprisingly, there is a lot of nominal Christianity, too. But Don noticed a tremendous difference, virtually the minute he crossed the border into Kerala. The streets were cleaner, communities were neater, there was less poverty, less begging, everything seemed different. It has the highest literacy rate as well. It seems that worldview makes a difference.

To a Hindu who sees someone with a horrible deformity in a destitute condition begging on the street, well, that person is likely working out his karma for something done in a past life, or whatever. The aspects of Indian culture that lead to so much misery are not some inevitable consequence of their racial predisposition, but have in large part grown out of a different way of looking at the world. And that's not locked in to any genes.

Atheists crediting Christianity

Even non-Christians can recognize and acknowledge this sort of thing. Africa, as we've seen in part, is a place where many dysfunctional aspects of culture hold society back and reinforce racist perceptions of black Africans. Matthew Parris, a well-known UK politician, author and journalist, wrote a remarkable piece in London's *The Times* titled, "As an atheist, I truly believe Africa needs God" and subtitled: "Missionaries, not aid money, are the solution to Africa's biggest problem—the crushing passivity of the people's mindset."[34]

Parris was writing from a background of personal experience

---

34.   Parris, M., As an atheist, I truly believe Africa needs God, *The Times Online*, 27 December 2008. See also Catchpoole, D., creation.com/atheists-credit-christianity, 13 April 2010.

in various countries in southern Africa where he grew up, as well as an extensive tour across the continent in his twenties. And of a more recent visit to see a village well development project, he wrote:

> "It inspired me, renewing my flagging faith in development charities. But travelling in Malawi refreshed another belief, too: one I've been trying to banish all my life, but an observation I've been unable to avoid since my African childhood. It confounds my ideological beliefs, stubbornly refuses to fit my world view, and has embarrassed my growing belief that there is no God.

> "Now a confirmed atheist, I've become convinced of the enormous contribution that Christian evangelism makes in Africa: sharply distinct from the work of secular NGOs, government projects and international aid efforts. These alone will not do. Education and training alone will not do. In Africa Christianity changes people's hearts. It brings a spiritual transformation. The rebirth is real. The change is good."

Parris says that he used to say it was a pity that "salvation is part of the package", and though he could see how "Christians black and white, working in Africa, do heal the sick, do teach people to read and write", he "would allow that if faith was needed to motivate missionaries to help, then, fine: but what counted was the help, not the faith."

However, Parris now says, "This doesn't fit the facts." He explains how Christian faith helps the poor not just because it motivates the missionary to help in practical ways, but because "it is also transferred to his flock. This is the effect that matters so immensely, and which I cannot help observing."

When he conducted an extensive driving tour in his twenties, from Algeria to Niger, Nigeria, Cameroon, the Central African Republic, through the Congo to Rwanda, Tanzania and to Kenya, Matthew Parris says he could not escape the same observation. Christians, whether black or white, were "different" from other people. And his recent trip to Malawi once again reminded him of this, something he says he'd been trying to "banish" all his life:

> "The Christians were always different. Far from having cowed or confined its converts, their faith appeared to have liberated and relaxed them."

He also observed that Christians had a certain "liveliness, a curiosity, an engagement with the world—a directness in their dealings with others" that was lacking in non-believers. "They stood tall", he writes. He states that the difference between Christians and non-Christians was particularly striking in "lawless" parts of the sub-Sahara.

> "Whenever we entered a territory worked by missionaries, we had to acknowledge that something changed in the faces of the people we passed and spoke to: something in their eyes, the way they approached you direct, man-to-man, without looking down or away. They had not become more deferential towards strangers—in some ways less so—but more open."

In short, Parris acknowledges that through transforming the individual, Christianity transforms the individual's immediate culture. Then, on his recent visit to a village development project in Malawi, he came in close contact with charity workers. Parris admits that it would suit him to believe that their "honesty, diligence and optimism in their work" was not connected to their obvious personal faith, but he says he had to concede that there was no doubt that they were "influenced by a conception of man's place in the Universe that Christianity had taught."

Then he makes this astute observation:

> "There's long been a fashion among Western academic sociologists for placing tribal value systems within a ring fence, beyond critiques founded in our own culture: 'theirs' and therefore best for 'them'; authentic and of intrinsically equal worth to ours. I don't follow this. I observe that tribal belief is no more peaceable than ours; and that it suppresses individuality."

He goes on to say that such a mindset "feeds into the 'big man' and gangster politics of the African city: the exaggerated respect for a swaggering leader" and that it does nothing to allay fear of evil spirits, ancestors and nature that so burden many in Africa. (Which is interesting in light of our earlier observations concerning Aboriginal people going 'back to the culture'). He says that in non-Christian Africans,

> "a great weight grinds down the individual spirit, stunting curiosity. People won't take the initiative, won't take things into their own hands or on their own shoulders."

By contrast, he says, Christianity,

> "with its teaching of a direct, personal, two-way link between the individual and God, unmediated by the collective, and unsubordinate to any other human being, smashes straight through the philosophical/spiritual framework I've just described. It offers something to hold on to, to those anxious to cast off a crushing tribal groupthink. That is why and how it liberates."

Parris ends with the warning that aid which provides only material supplies and technical knowledge is unlikely to succeed.

> "Removing Christian evangelism from the African equation may leave the continent at the mercy of a malign fusion of Nike, the witch doctor, the mobile phone and the machete."

Machete massacres and witch doctors are of course precisely the sorts of things that are often associated in people's minds with racist assumptions about why Africa has so many problems. What a difference it makes when we realize that these problems for members of our *one human family* are not because they are in some way biologically 'backward', or have not moved as far yet from their ape-like ancestors!

Though our Western society still lives off the accumulated 'capital' of its biblical heritage, this is rapidly being depleted. The influential people in any culture, the movers and shakers, are the ones most likely to have been exposed to higher education.

Nowadays, that means they are the most exposed to the sort of teaching that reinforces an evolutionized, antiChristian worldview. This is likely the greatest single factor behind the decline of Christian influence in the West.

SOCIAL COMPASSION

When it comes to social compassion, too, not many people realize just how many of the things we take for granted in our culture are really the consistent outcomes of the way in which our societies were once based upon the Bible. Back when I used to practice medicine, it was brought home to me through some of my patients from countries like Malta, Iran—even parts of Greece—telling me what it was like in hospitals 'back home'. It was, they said, standard and accepted practice for the families of patients to have to bribe the hospital authorities in order to ensure that the patient was adequately fed. If the patient needed to have shots of a narcotic painkiller, then an amount approaching the street value of the drug would first need to be paid 'under the table' to the head nurse.

We tend to take for granted that countries that are more associated with 'white European civilization' will have a higher level of social compassion. We are often unaware of the racial overtones of such assumptions, even in our own thinking. But social compassion is not something that happens to be intrinsic to the Anglo-Saxon character or racial makeup. Rather, it largely results, again, from historical belief in the Bible and the Christian gospel. It came especially through the massive social transformations wrought by the gospel preaching of giants like John Wesley, George Whitefield and Jonathan Edwards.

The genuine revivals that swept England and America, and touched the continent, were so different from what is called 'revival' today. I don't want to imply that anything involving lots of Christians would have been all sweetness bathed in warm rosy light (we are all fallen sinners after all, though redeemed). The overall reality, though, is that millions surrendered their lives

FEATURE

Where are all the Atheist Aid Organizations?

High-profile British politician and author Roy Hattersley (pictured) has published a biography of the Salvation Army's founders, even though he himself is an atheist. On a recent BBC program concerning the Salvation Army, Hattersley was effusive about the Army, saying:

> "… it remains a vibrant organization because of its convictions. I'm an atheist. But I can only look with amazement at the devotion of the Salvation Army workers. I've been out with them on the streets and the way they work amongst the people, the most deprived and disadvantaged and sometimes pretty repugnant characters. I don't believe they would do that were it not for the religious impulse. And I often say I never hear of atheist organizations taking food to the poor. You don't hear of 'Atheist Aid' rather like Christian aid, and, I think, despite my inability to believe myself, I'm deeply impressed by what belief does for people like the Salvation Army." *

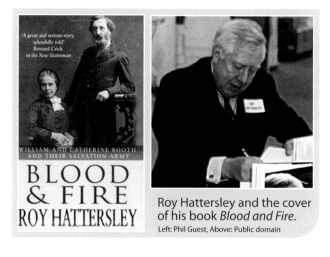

Roy Hattersley and the cover of his book *Blood and Fire*.
Left: Phil Guest, Above: Public domain

Since the publication of his biography of William and Catherine

Booth, Roy Hattersley has written further of the positive influence of Christian evangelists:

"My view of society is very different from that which was held by Booth and [Evangelist John] Wesley. I am an atheist. But that does not prevent me from admiring the strength of their different convictions. Nor did it stop me from realising the crucial part that Wesley's 'respectable' Christianity played in the development of modern Britain."[†]

Other atheists, seemingly 'stung' by the increase in similar comments over the years, have launched their own charitable organizations, but mostly these just highlight the contrast. In preparing this book, I googled 'atheist aid', and the website www.atheistaid.org.uk popped up prominently. Under the heading "Compassion without religion", it stated on the front page (12 October 2010):

"This site highlights current charity work and philanthropy by atheists and agnostics. Please mail me if you'd like to publicise your good works."

The rest of the front page had two entries, one highlighting the Haiti Appeal by Richard Dawkins' foundation and listing a good number of other atheist groups that had declared their support for it. The other was an atheist writing in to tell of how she and other atheists were helping edit a book, *The Atheist's Guide to Christmas*, in aid of an HIV charity.

That's it. There was nothing else on the site. When I checked again on 19 July 2011, it seemed to have gone defunct.

*Broadcast on BBC World Service, 2 January 2010, the Hattersley interview is in the segment 3.00–4.42, www.bbc.co.uk/iplayer/episode/p005hzr2/Global_Business_Organising_Salvation/. See also Catchpoole, D., creation.com/atheists-credit-christianity, 13 April 2010.
†See textualities.net/author/roy-hattersley.

to Christ's loving mercy and grace, acknowledging the affront of their sin-stained lives in the sight of a holy Creator God.

Like a spreading flame, this 18th-century Great Awakening, as it is called, surged across Great Britain and the United States. Many of the individuals thus transformed became the movers and shakers of their day. In England, a few of these converts to Christ became parliamentarians with names that still reverberate down to our time. This includes William Wilberforce, mentioned in Chapter 4 in relation to slavery. He was the prime mover behind its abolition. As we saw before, he was directly motivated by his born-again, Bible-based Christianity.

Many have first become aware of the activities of Wilberforce and his compatriots through the Hollywood film *Amazing Grace*. Unfortunately, despite its many pluses, the film could have left one thinking that Wilberforce's ultimate triumph was due mainly to his dogged perseverance and political skills. The reality is that his biblical convictions, *plus* a background Christian consensus in the culture which voted parliamentarians into power, were crucial. Without these, no amount of argument and rhetoric would have enabled Wilberforce to get the politicians to agree to vote to overturn the whole institution of slavery throughout the British Empire.[35] It was secularists and anti-Christians who strongly opposed the abolitionist movement.

The surprise Oscar-winning film *Slumdog Millionaire* graphically portrayed some of the horrors commonly inflicted on impoverished people, particularly children, in India. The average Westerner looking on from the confines of their own culture would tend to react with disbelief. The politically correct view that all cultures are 'equally worthy of respect' would somehow not likely spring to mind when watching the section that shows a child being deliberately blinded to make money through begging.

Biology no answer

Any explanations in most Westerners' minds for the differences between the society they were viewing in this movie and their own would easily gravitate to racist assumptions. Perhaps a shrug of the mental shoulders, with something like, 'That's just the way they are over there'. It sounds innocuous enough. But mostly, that sort of thinking is a sanitized way of expressing to oneself what are really deep-seated suspicions or even convictions— namely, that those belonging to the other group are biologically

---

35. See Sarfati, J., Antislavery activist William Wilberforce: Christian hero, 20 February 2007, creation.com/wilberforce.

and racially less capable of creating 'our sort of society'. But pre-Revival England was a pretty horrible and heartless place, too. Children were routinely being forced to labor in mines, and to perform similar brutal and hazardous tasks that made money for others—and were tortured if they resisted. The influence of the gospel on Western society brought about not just the abolition of slavery, but prison reform, hospital reform, orphanage reform, and much more.

All this was not driven by emotion so much as by a robust Christian worldview, based on belief in a totally trustworthy and historically accurate Bible. Because it extended to all levels of class and education, it also reached the lawmakers and other influential people. Today, by contrast, it is the influential strata of society who, being the most 'evolutionized', are most 'immune' to gospel preaching.

Fortunately, the Great Awakening arrived *before* the views of Darwin (and the long-agers that preceded him) had captured the public mind and seduced the bulk of the church into surrendering biblical authority. One can only shudder at the direction our world might have taken had it been otherwise. If the bulk of the population had believed then, as now, that science made nonsense of the Bible's history, would millions of them have believed its gospel message, so inextricably rooted in that history? Would countless thousands upon thousands have repented, often in tears, for their sin if they'd believed that sin was just some left-over collection of instincts from their animal ancestry? And where would that have left us in regard to slavery, and all of the social reforms and liberties held dear by even the most ardent humanist today?

It's also not just a matter of what our modern world owes to the Christian faith, but how quickly we might be capable of descending to new forms of brutality without what pastor and theologian Peter Barnes calls "the restraining influence of the revelation of the true God". Germany's Nazi era, occurring in one of the world's foremost civilizations, is just one reminder.

Barnes writes further:

"The Aztecs practised human sacrifice—they would cut out the hearts of their still living victims. In India widows were thrown on their husband's funeral pyre, and unwanted infants were thrown into the Ganges River. In the Pacific Islands, for example on Aneityum in Vanuatu (formerly known as the New Hebrides), brides were given a cord to wear around their necks. Should they outlive their husbands, the cord would be tightened by family and friends, and the widow would be strangled."[36]

WOMEN IN SOCIETY

Part of the sinful tendency in humanity is for men to frequently pervert their God-given headship role into a corrupt exploitation, even oppression, of women. History shows that nowhere has this been more *minimized* than in Bible-centered, gospel-transformed cultures. Famous antislavery activist Harriet Beecher Stowe (1811–1896), author of *Uncle Tom's Cabin* (1852), is less well known for her book *Woman in Sacred History* (1873), where she stated:

"The object of the following pages will be to show, in a series of biographical sketches, a history of *womanhood under divine culture*, tending toward the development of that high ideal of woman which we find in modern Christian countries."

Genesis tells us that people were given dominion over the rest of creation—but not over each other. There is no biblical justification for one person having dominion over or exploiting another (as opposed to being in an authority *role*, such as an employer–employee relationship or parent–child—a different issue altogether). Paul says, in Galatians 3:28, that in Christ there

---

36.   Barnes, P., If the Foundations are destroyed—what we owe to the Christian faith, *Evangelical Times*, February 2011, p. 31. See also creation.com/what-good-is-christianity, 2007.

is no male nor female, just as there is no Jew nor Greek, slave nor free—even though all these categories existed. His point is clear: we all come to Christ equally through faith in Christ Jesus.

Islam and the boy who cried wolf

By way of aside, it is ironic to see how it has become trendy today, in the same circles which would passionately defend the rights of women (albeit mainly to slaughter their own babies in the womb), to defend Islam—regardless of its track record on that subject. I'm not criticizing anyone for defending another's right to practice this or any other religion. What I mean is that many today who are fierce in their critiques of Christianity simultaneously seek to shield Islam from having any sort of spotlight shone on its teaching or practices. Anyone who does otherwise is immediately decried as either 'Islamophobic'—or, surprisingly often, as 'racist'.

The more that we have unfounded charges of racism, the harder it is to deal with that odious residue of *real* racism in our world—somewhat like the boy who cried wolf. Islam is of course a religious/cultural issue, even a political issue; but not a racial one. I recently saw it implied in the media that people are down on Islam because of prejudice against Arabs. But the world's most populous Muslim nation today is Indonesia, and its people are ethnically quite different from Muslims in the Arabian sphere. And there are many whites who are Muslims, as well as many Christian Arabs.

HUMAN RIGHTS

Today there is more emphasis on our 'rights' than ever. If we are just evolved effervescences of nature, however, what possible basis can there be for any absolute 'rights'? Our opinion? What if my perceived 'right' infringes upon yours—does it not then simply boil down to which of us is 'stronger' in our society?

In those cultures which have reached the greatest levels of human freedom of expression and respect for human rights, the notion of rights was tightly bound up with the fact of biblical creation. As we saw in the chapter on slavery, the United States Declaration of Independence eloquently declares (emphasis added) that the signers "hold these truths to be self-evident, that all men are created equal, that they are endowed *by their Creator* with certain unalienable Rights…".[37] Despite the huge aberration of the slavery era and its aftermath, that remains a major reason why there is so much more freedom, and why human rights are nearly always better protected, in countries and cultures which once had a biblical, creation-based foundation. Once again, it has nothing to do with any 'racial' factors.

Christian pedophiles, atrocities and more

Christian culture has skeletons in its cupboard, too, of course. The sins of pedophilia may be rampant outside of church circles as well as within them, but the fact that it still happens with tragic regularity 'inside the camp' (and in all denominations) is horrible, and totally unacceptable. For millions, it is a shuddering indictment of the Christian church. This is especially widespread since the drawn-out global scandal concerning priests in the Roman Catholic church. It creates a special public cynicism, because individuals inclined to sexually abuse children have a strong propensity to seek out roles in organizations like churches where they have the trust and confidence of parents. The fact that there are far more pedophiles in the public schools than in the RC church is worthy of mention, if only because it rarely comes to light. It does not of course excuse a single instance of this horrific sin against little ones within Christendom. People rightly decry hypocrisy, as does God in His Word. Such offenders may in fact not even be true believers. Jesus predicted in Matthew 13 that there would always be those he depicted as 'tares' within His church, acting as contaminants among the 'wheat' of God's real

---

37. Some of the signers were deists, not biblical creationists, but the societal context in which all expressed this notion very much grew out of the biblical notion of creation. And even the most anti-Christian of them, Thomas Paine, appealed strongly to the Bible in his *Common Sense*, e.g.: "These portions of scripture are direct and positive. They admit of no equivocal construction. That the Almighty hath here entered his protest against monarchical government is true, or the scripture is false."

children. But in any case, those who profess a biblical standard should not find it surprising that they will be judged more harshly than those who do not.

Then there are the dubious military adventures, and atrocities, carried out in times past in Christianity's name or under its cover. And of course the Inquisition, 'witch' burnings, and so on. Many fail to consider, however, that there were literally hundreds of millions killed in the 20th century by openly anti-Christian or atheistic regimes, the ideologies of which were squarely based on evolution-as-fact. This makes the just over 3,000 who were sentenced to death in an Inquisition spanning three and a half centuries fade into insignificance. The numbers killed by such anti-God regimes are far more than have died in all the religious wars of history put together. Also, most of those that died at the hands of these regimes were their own citizens, killed by their own government.

This does not excuse Christian failings, of course. But as the late evangelical philosopher Francis Schaeffer pointed out, when professing Christians do such things, they are being *inconsistent* with the principles enunciated by the Lord Jesus Himself. But when an openly anti-Christian or atheistic regime like Nazi Germany, Stalinist Russia, or the Khmer Rouge of Pol Pot's Kampuchea engages in atrocities in the name of its evolution-based naturalistic ideology, it is being utterly *consistent* with its foundational assumptions—no God, no absolute basis for right or wrong, no retribution in any afterlife, and might is right.

∞

17 RACISM TODAY— AND HOPE FOR TOMORROW

As stated before, the point of this whole book has been less about Darwin or evolution than it is about the Genesis history of mankind. Rejecting or distorting that truth (which in most situations worldwide has been and still is greatly facilitated by Darwinian evolution) makes it easier to believe that some people are intrinsically inferior.

The racist excesses of the past could have been greatly mitigated, if not averted, if the ruling worldview in any given society had incorporated the clear teaching of the Bible in Genesis. Believing and emphasizing that truth, that we are very closely related—*one human family*— would have prevented a lot of pain over the centuries. Especially if it had been accompanied by highlighting its straightforward implications. Based on the Bible, people *had* to be very closely related, whether this had yet been shown scientifically or not. In this way, the church would have anticipated, even been able to predict, the outcome of modern biological investigations. If the church had resoundingly proclaimed that close relatedness of all humanity from the pulpit within Western societies, especially at a time when the church's view still mattered a great deal in many countries, what a difference it would have made.

RACISM—ALIVE AND KICKING

What a difference can still be made today, too, because as we've seen and as will be further shown below, the subtle (and many not-so-subtle) influences of evolutionary racism are with us today.

Consider the average person today of European extraction, confronted with television images of mass starvation in a famine in Africa. Now imagine that they were to see on film the same horrors, but this time affecting children that looked 'just like them'. Could one really maintain that it would make no difference, or that there would be no subliminal effects of evolutionary racist thinking within most of them? My colleague Gary Bates, CEO of CMI in the United States, says that when he was still an evolutionist, he would rationalize away the images of 'starving kids in Africa' as simply 'Darwinian natural selection in action'. It was therefore also somehow for the greater good. When he became a Christian (in large part through seeing the evidence for creation), he says, "Everything changed. I saw the suffering of Africans in a completely different light. These were part of my extended family, and it was no longer possible or natural to 'harden the heart' like before." Another CMI colleague, Dr. David Catchpoole, while he was still an evolutionist, had similarly seen famine in Africa or India as a removal of the weak, and thus a 'good thing'.

If you think that because of the popularity of antiracism in the media and among the intelligentsia, racism is no longer an issue; ask the average African American. Sure, they'll tell you, these last few years they no longer get asked by 'whites' at hotels to bring them towels. But when it comes to feelings and attitudes, many will confirm that there's still a way to go. When CMI speakers in the US go to 'all-black' churches, the extremely positive reaction they get to this message of *one human family* tells its own story.

However, I need to stress that I'm talking here about feelings and attitudes. The common belief that the relatively poor economic and social outcomes for African Americans are largely the result of racism is not shared by African Americans like Thomas Sowell and Walter Williams, both cited in these pages. And being both born in the 1930s, they are old enough to remember Jim Crow laws. They point out a fact which is uncomfortable for some ideologues more committed to their 'vision' than to reality. That is that in the US there is little difference in income between black married families and white ones, and between black and white single-parent families; but married families are far wealthier on average than single-parent ones. The main difference, then, is that far more black families are headed by single parents.

They also answer the obvious question—of whether this dominance of single-parenting is itself the result of either racism or the legacy of slavery—in the negative. This is because the data shows that a few decades ago, most black families were headed by married parents, despite being a generation or three *closer* to slavery, and experiencing far *worse* racism, discrimination and poverty. Sowell and Williams both argue that while the black family in America stood firm in the face of slavery, lynching and virulent racism, it has been devastated by welfare policies that, for example, in effect 'reward' teenage girls for having babies out of wedlock. This might sound like something coming from an absence of compassion, but the facts and figures make their argument compelling. It seems the more things head in antibiblical directions, what mostly happens is that the very ones society purports to help are the main ones harmed.

Note that when a Bible-believing Christian acts in a way that shows they believe that another person is intrinsically inferior due to membership of another ethnic group, it's *inconsistent* with what they claim to believe. But the charge of inconsistency could not be easily leveled at a person who is overtly racist and believes evolution. This is so, regardless of the antiracist stance of most of evolution's promoters today. They can often be commended on their approach to racial issues, but it is *not a natural outgrowth of their evolutionary presuppositions*. Unfortunately, their ability to separate their views on evolution from their ideas on racism does not extend to most of the general population. And that's a big reason why racist notions, though deeply non-trendy, and despite the best efforts of Hollywood, still smolder on.

The bit about Hollywood is not meant sarcastically, by the way. In spite of the social negatives of various of the trendy causes taken up by Hollywood, there is no doubt that on many occasions film makers have used their great power to help bring about good. One only has to think of how films like the 1962 Gregory Peck classic *To Kill a Mockingbird* helped to bring home the evils and injustices of racist attitudes. And certain film and popular music celebrities, both by fundraising and by example (including personal donations), have on occasion used their privileged social position in ways that Christians would surely want to commend. I think for instance of the huge sums personally donated by software mogul Bill Gates to the fight against malaria—a disease that mostly afflicts people of a different ethnicity to his own.

Evolution and religion—a deadly cocktail

Most of the time, the racist attitudes of today are not from some neo-Nazi skinhead consciously applying evolution, but are just something sitting quietly below the surface in that average person next door. Such a person often holds a poorly thought-out mix of ideas that reflect both a vague understanding of evolution and the religious influences of their childhood.

Just a few months ago my wife and I were being served food in an Australian cafeteria by a lady familiar to us, our having been regular customers over the years. She is an unfailingly pleasant and warm lady, probably in her early 50s. There was no-one else waiting, and we chatted briefly over the counter. The subject of the then-current devastating floods in Pakistan came up. She said, "Yes, it's so sad, isn't it ..." .Then, as if to relieve herself of the burden of either thinking, feeling or perhaps especially *doing* anything about it, she immediately went on to say (emphasis hers), "I really think it must be God's method of keeping the population down in *those* places". I suspect she really meant, "You know, places where the sorts of people live who obviously need to be kept from over-breeding." Because it was clear that she saw them as inferior to 'us'—even to the extent of being less worthy to live. They required a divine cull via something akin to natural selection.

A while back, while traveling in a taxi in the capital city of Australia's Northern Territory, I was chatting to the driver about how things were in that sweltering tropical metropolis. Occasionally he would mutter something about the things he didn't like about "the racapes". It took me a while to realize that he was referring to the local Aboriginal people, and what I was mishearing was his pronunciation of "the rock apes", his term for them. The evolutionary implications are not difficult to discern. It gave me cause to reflect on the name of that city—Darwin, of all things.

Evolutionary racism, sport and the White House

In the second half of 2010, the news outlet of Australia's government broadcaster, the ABC, announced that the country's communications watchdog had found football commentator Sam Newman guilty of breaching its code by ridiculing a man "on the basis of color and race".[1] In a show that had aired twelve months prior to that, Newman had "held up a photo of a 107-year-old Malaysian woman and made repeated references to her new husband being 'a monkey'." Panelist Brendan Fevola said: "You can't call him a monkey", but Newman then said the man was "not long out of the forest" and also appeared to compare him to (African-American tennis champion) Serena Williams.

Not long ago, the International Cricket Council (ICC) banned a player for the first time ever for 'racial abuse'. The banned player was India's off-spinner Harbhajan Singh. The racial slur was calling Australia's all-rounder Andrew Symonds a 'monkey'. Symonds is of Caribbean descent and was at that time the only 'black' player on the Australian team.

My CMI colleague David Catchpoole wrote, in a web article

---

1.   Newman's monkey slur may cost [Channel] Nine $200k, abc.net.au/news, updated 7 September 2010, accessed 3 October 2010.

on the subject, that despite the wide media coverage, he had been unable to find:

> "any news report or official commentary on exactly *why* the term 'monkey', directed against Symonds, constitutes 'racial abuse'. And it's not just in relation to this latest 'event'—in recent months the media have widely reported similar 'racial abuse' instances against Symonds and other 'black' participants in international cricket."[2]

He went on to detail several instances of such things as 'monkey noises' aimed against players with clear racial intent. For example, during a test match between South Africa and Pakistan in October 2007, four spectators were arrested for racially abusing three members of the South African team, via 'monkey chants'. The one distinguishing feature of all of the three South Africans thus singled out was that they were all black.

The media, however, never, ever seems to want to mention the obvious 'evolutionary' link. David's article pointed out that at the time of the Andrew Symonds incident, several bloggers on it, though opposed to racism, were puzzled as to why 'monkey' had racist overtones. One asked whether it would be racist to call someone a donkey, for example. Some of the more knowledgeable bloggers understood very well, despite the media blackout on discussions of racism's evolutionary link. David's article listed and referenced several of these blog comments as follows (the emphases were all in the originals):

> '"Monkey" is a very old racial slur that suggests that someone is sub-human.'

> '[I]f I was to taunt someone who was black and say they were a monkey to suggest that they were sub human, considering that according to the evolution path many believe that monkeys are human ancestors, then this is considered a racial taunt.'

> '"The monkey slur is used against ANYONE of dark skin

---

2. Catchpoole, D., It's just not cricket, 8 January 2008, creation.com/cricket (references in article).

coloration ... to infer that they have not yet evolved beyond the ape stage.'

"'THE BLACK people of African origin are sometimes sensitive to being called MONKEY because the ANGLOSAXON WHITES have used the term MONKEY as a term to PUT down AFRICAN-ORIGIN people using Darwin's Theory of Evolution.'

"'If anyone thinks monkey is not a racist taunt, you should watch soccer matches in Eastern Europe and (on occasion) Spain and Italy, where fans make monkey noises and throw bananas when black players touch the ball. You may think differently then.'"

Indeed. Similarly, there was a 'racist row' in November 2009, concerning Michelle Obama, the wife of US President Barack Obama. It involved a photo appearing on the internet which had been doctored to make her features look like a monkey. It was, not surprisingly, slammed as disgustingly racist and offensive.[3] The photo had, till removed, been at the top of Google's image search list for the First Lady's name. Google made a public apology, even though such listings depend on popularity, for which the company is not responsible.

Once more, the media did not dare to discuss the obvious reason *why* such an image associated with a dark-skinned person is

First Lady of the USA, Michelle Obama was the subject of a 2009 racist attack that generated wide media attention--but discussion of its obvious evolutionary undertones was a media taboo.
Public domain

---

3.   Catchpoole, D., Michelle Obama racism row—what's it based on? 8 December 2009, creation.com/obama-racism-row.

considered racist. President George Bush was more than once depicted as a chimpanzee. And Darwin, likewise, has been caricatured as an ape, in both earlier and more recent times. Yet very few ever thought, or think now, that such images are 'racist'. Offensive they might be, but not racist.

In this case, too, it was bloggers who came out and stated the obvious. The reason the Michelle Obama depiction was quite properly regarded as racist is, of course, the whole idea of evolution in the public mind. Its portrayal over generations has deeply entered the consciousness of the masses. The British science publication *New Scientist* (no friend of creation) recently pointed out some of these lingering influences, which then go on to influence more, in scientific diagrams. The publication showed how, even today, diagrams of 'ape to man' evolution show apes with a dark exterior becoming progressively lighter as they advance more and more toward becoming 'fully human'. That position, at the far right of such diagrams, is invariably occupied by someone looking like a modern European.[4]

It's no coincidence that Charles Darwin predicted that the fossil remains of man's remote ape-like ancestors would be found in Africa. For one thing, Africa was home to apes that closely resembled people. At the same time, he believed, it was home to people that resembled apes more than Europeans did. As shown earlier, he believed they had not yet evolved as far towards humanness.

Ape-men and black pride

It's both sad and ironic, then, to see the stance of the current government of South Africa on human evolution. Elected by the black majority following the dismantling of apartheid, it is mostly composed of black Africans. This government is strongly pushing the idea of human evolution as something to be welcomed and embraced—by black Africans in particular!

Of the discoveries in Africa of alleged 'transitional forms' or

---

4.   Editorial, Racism still runs deep: Even the most well-meaning liberal can harbour hidden prejudice, *New Scientist* 197(2643):5, 2008.

'hominids', not all by any means have been unearthed in South Africa. And certainly not the major ones like the famous Lucy. Yet sufficient of these types of creatures, the australopiths, have been found in the Sterkfontein area in that country to warrant the government labeling it 'The Cradle of Humankind'. It seems that South Africa's government wants it to be a source of 'black pride' that 'all were once Africans'. One can almost hear the ghostly sniggers of white supremacists and eugenicists of the past—and their present-day counterparts.

KEY TO THE FUTURE

The real antidote to all this residual racism, even while this fallen world persists, does not lie in the politically correct remedies that our Western world is applying at present. Language can be a tool for perpetuating attitudes, but merely sanitizing our language is not likely to make a real long-term difference. Nor is throwing large amounts of money at problems without understanding their causes. And the reverse racism of affirmative action has already been tried in many places around the world and found wanting.

What *would* make a crucial difference would be to make it widely known that both the Bible and science unite to tell us that we really are *one human family*. And a very close family at that. We are *not* separated by even tens of thousands of years of 'separate development', let alone hundreds of thousands of years. It bears repeating often enough to drum into the collective subconscious of every society: **forget what you think you know from evolutionary conditioning—there is absolutely no scientific justification for the belief that someone is inferior or is to be treated differently because of belonging to people group A instead of group B.**

Of course, widespread acceptance of this would be far more likely to happen if accompanied by a similarly far-reaching acceptance of the truth and authority of the Bible. Which would in turn be accompanied by the wonderful reality of large numbers of people *eternally* changed—forever co-heirs with Christ of

God's eternal Kingdom, part of His royal family.

Unequal people with equal value

As previously pointed out, we are *not* all equal—that much is clear from just a casual glance. Some people are shorter than others; and you can substitute for 'shorter' in that sentence words like 'smarter' or 'more athletic' or 101 others. So to talk of the 'equality of man' can lead to misunderstanding. All of us are either inferior or superior to other people in many different things. At school, I was always inferior to just about everyone in sport, just as some of my classmates were inferior to me in academic things. That's just facing reality. But racism, real racism of the sort that causes harm in a society, involves a starting assumption that a person is inferior *in the very nature of their being*—simply by virtue of their belonging to a different group.

The opposite is what we may call the 'Genesis assumption'—we are all equally made in God's image, and therefore have equal *intrinsic* value as people. It automatically means that, regardless which group of people we come from (or which branch of the family, might be a good way of putting it), we are all equally deserving of dignity and respect *a priori*.

Obviously, people from whatever 'race' can, through their behavior, undermine their own likelihood of being regarded or treated with dignity and/or respect—but that is a different issue. So is the fact that substantial clusters of individuals can, through their actions and attitudes, negatively affect perceptions of (and behavior towards) their entire group.

Genesis history also indicates that we are all closely related, all members of this *one human family*. So, no group of people is going to be *intrinsically* superior or inferior to any other group of people in any area that matters.

All of us are indelibly influenced by our culture. All of us have the potential, however, to break free of aspects of that culture which are not honoring to God and are harmful to our fellow human beings. And we can help others do the same. We all have equal 'rights' as human beings before God—which rights can only exist anyway if they have been bestowed by our Creator, as the framers of the US Declaration of Independence recognized.

More than animals

With rights come responsibilities and accountability. We are not just some highly evolved animals accountable only to the law of the jungle. We are all moral creatures, having the knowledge of right and wrong. The Nazi defendants in the famed Nuremberg war crimes trials challenged the judge's right to try them, since they were obeying the laws of their government at the time. By what legal standard, other than sheer victors' power of retribution, could he possibly hold them accountable?[5] Lead prosecutor Robert Jackson (USA) reminded them of the existence of a higher moral law than any man-made system. But what could this be, if not the precepts and standards of the Creator of humanity? And how could we reliably know what these were, unless He had inerrantly revealed them to us?

As with so much else, it all comes back to the one watershed issue—the truth and authority of the Bible as God's Word to us. And nowhere is this more under assault than in the area of the Bible's Genesis foundations, allegedly in the name of 'science'. Fewer and fewer people in this evolutionized age acknowledge a Creator, so by definition they do not acknowledge any absolute standard of right and wrong. The Bible assures us that one day *all* will have no choice but to acknowledge their Creator, who is none other than the Lord Jesus Christ, God the Son, the eternal Word made flesh (John 1:1–3, 14).[6] Philippians 2:10 tells us that one day "at the name of Jesus every knee should bow, in heaven and on earth and under the earth". In the meantime, acknowledged or not, the reality is that such an absolute standard exists.

At some level, we all know this, and know that we have

---

5.   Though it doesn't affect their monstrous guilt in the Holocaust and more, they had a point in one respect—one indictment was: "Conspiracy to wage aggressive war". Yet one of the four nations judging them was their *co-conspirator*, the Soviet Union (Molotov–Ribbentrop Pact to carve up Poland).
6.   See creation.com/incarnation, 2010.

violated it repeatedly (Romans 2:15). But the Bible also explains that the conscience is no longer an infallible guide because of the Fall, because it can be seared (Titus 2:4). Thus our consciences now must be *properly informed*, and we do that by studying God's Word (Psalm 1:2).

The evolutionary notion that some groups are less able to grasp these truths does not correspond to reality. You've seen how Darwin described the natives of Tierra del Fuego, regarding them as low-lifes beyond hope. Yet a radical transformation was brought about in the Fuegians and their culture by the work of the gospel through the South American Missionary Society (SAMS).[7] So impressed was Darwin with the change that in later years, though as convinced an unbeliever as ever,[8] he became a financial supporter of SAMS till his death.

God(s)—more or less?

The fact is, we all fall short, measured against God's holiness. The Bible says, "For all have sinned and fall short of the glory of God" (Romans 3:23). The evolutionary theory of how religion developed goes something like this: when the brains of our ape-like ancestors had finally evolved far enough to be able to think such abstract thoughts, at first came the worship of multiple spirits (animism). Then this became the worship of many gods/idols, then fewer and fewer gods were worshipped. Until, much later still, only one was worshipped. And, say many evolutionists, the inevitable progression will lead to the elimination of god-worship altogether as we become sufficiently far removed from our more primitive ways of thinking.

If this notion of how religion progressed were true, then digging into archaeological layers at various ancient centers of civilization should reveal *more and more* gods the deeper one goes. By contrast, the whole history of humanity from Genesis indicates that the worship of the one (true) God, by the immediate

---

7.   Originally the Patagonian Missionary Society—see samsusa.org.
8.   The story of Darwin recanting on his deathbed is almost certainly apocryphal—see creation.com/recant.

descendants of Noah, became corrupted into the worship of many gods and idols. So this, in direct contrast to the evolutionary model, would argue for *fewer and fewer* gods as one digs deeper into the layers. Archaeologist and friend of CMI Dr. Clifford Wilson, when I interviewed him for *Creation* magazine,[9] indicated that archaeology basically confirms the biblical picture. As you dig deeper through the layers of the Ancient Near East, you don't come up with more and more gods, but fewer and fewer, essentially. The worship of the one true God did indeed become corrupted into the worship of many gods.

This is further highlighted in Romans Chapter 1, the early part of the Apostle Paul's letter to the Christians in Rome. He indicates that at some level, all people understand that there is a Creator God. This complex and amazing world, though corrupted by sin, clearly did not make itself. He writes (vv. 20–21):

> "For his invisible attributes, namely, his eternal power and divine nature, have been clearly perceived, ever since the creation of the world, in the things that have been made. So they are without excuse. For although they knew God, they did not honor him as God or give thanks to him, but they became futile in their thinking, and their foolish hearts were darkened."

A skilled diagnosis

What follows from Paul is as applicable to today's worship of evolutionary nature, with the alleged power to create itself, as it is to those in the past who abandoned the knowledge of the Creator to worship multiple idols (vv. 22–23):

> "Claiming to be wise, they became fools, and exchanged the glory of the immortal God for images resembling mortal man and birds and animals and creeping things."

The Bible says (v. 25) that these are those who:

> "exchanged the truth about God for a lie and worshiped

9.   Wieland, C., Archaeologist confirms creation and the Bible: interview with archaeologist Dr. Clifford Wilson, *Creation* **14**(4):46–50, 1992, creation.com/clifford-wilson.

and served the creature rather than the Creator, who is blessed forever! Amen."

Three times in that section, Paul refers to the fact that this willful rejection led to God giving them up. In verse 28:

"And since they did not see fit to acknowledge God, God gave them up to a debased mind to do what ought not to be done."

Everything Paul writes is based upon his implicit belief in that real Genesis history, which he takes for granted. And this is so clear and plain in the Word of God. That same Genesis history explains *why* we are 'naturally' biased against God. It's all tied up with the account of how people came to be. The first man, Adam, rebelled against His Maker, bringing the Curse of sin and death.

The Genesis history about that Curse tells us, too, why this world, for all its beauty and marvel, is also a world of agony, suffering and death. Paul describes this whole creation[10] as "groaning" under the weight of this Curse, and as subject to "the bondage of corruption" (Romans 8:21–22). This is why Jesus, whom the New Testament calls "the last Adam" (1 Corinthians 15:45), came to shed His blood in death—ultimately to overcome that Curse of sin and death brought in by the disobedience of the first Adam.

Hope that's really real

Jesus, the Creator of the universe, wept at the death of His friend Lazarus (John 11:35). This was not the way He had made the world, full of death and sorrow—sin had ruined it. Death is not some normal part of the natural order, with countless trillions of creatures suffering and dying over billions of years, as the traditional interpretation of the fossil record would have us believe. In 1 Corinthians 15:26, death is called "the last enemy". This enemy, the Bible declares, will be overcome because of the

---

10. This is another problem for the idea of intelligent life on other worlds: Adam's sin would have brought the Curse upon the Vulcan and Klingon home planets as well as ours. See also Bates. G., *Alien Intrusion* (book) and creation.com/did-god-create-life-on-other-planets.

sacrificial death of Jesus Christ. This overcoming is only because He bore the sin of the world, in atonement for the offense of our sin against a holy God. On the Cross, God the Father laid upon the Son "the iniquities of us all", so our sin was imputed (credited) to His account (Isaiah 53:6–10). And His perfect life enabled His righteousness to be imputed to believers in Him (2 Corinthians 5:21).

It's because of what happened at the Cross that all things will be *restored* (Acts 3:21). They won't be put back to billions of years of death and bloodshed, because that's not how things began, despite how the evolutionary/long-age philosophy would have us interpret the fossil record.[11] The fossils are a clear testimony to the year-long global catastrophic Flood described in Genesis.[12]

Things will be restored to (= put back to) a sinless, deathless condition, because that's how things were originally. Revelation 21:4 tells us that in this restoration to come, there will be no more death. Why? It's because there will be no more curse, as Revelation 22:3 tells us. That's referring to the Genesis Curse. The whole framework within which the gospel message exists concerns the creation of a good world, ruined by sin, to be restored in the future because of the Cross. If Genesis is not taken as the history it was so obviously meant to be, all of the logic of the gospel unravels. Rather, in the last chapters of the Bible, we see this current world history come full circle, with such allusions to the original Edenic paradise as the return of "the tree of life" from which the first couple was separated (Revelation 22:2, cf. Genesis 3:22 ff.).

Sin will have no place in this new creation, in God's Heaven. We could not be allowed to enter in our old state, carrying our load of sin and our old nature (Revelation 21:27), or we might spoil it all over again. We can only enter once the sin burden has been lifted, once its stain is washed away (Revelation 22:14) by

---

11.   See also Grigg, R., The future—some issues for 'long-age' Christians, *Creation* **25**(4):50–51, September 2003, creation.com/future.

12.   There is a wealth of materials on creation.com and its store, including books and DVDs, on this and a host of related topics to do with the Bible, science and evolution.

the precious blood of Jesus.

It's only by having a glimpse of the utter holiness of God, who is unable to countenance sin in any shape or form (Habbakuk 1:13), that we have some understanding of sin's true awfulness, and of what has happened to a once-perfect world in consequence. And it's as we contemplate this that we come to understand the incredible thing that Christ has done for those prepared to take up their cross, and follow Him—totally trusting in His perfect, once-for-all-time blood sacrifice for the complete forgiveness of all their sin.

What's the reason for it all?

Why did God ordain things this way—what is behind all this cosmic drama? God is outside of time. He knows all things and knows the end from the beginning. So, as someone said, God was not caught napping by the Fall. Salvation via the Cross was therefore not God's plan B. It was His plan A from the beginning. Isaiah 46:9–10 says:

> "Remember the former things of old: for I am God, and there is none else; I am God, and there is none like me, declaring the end from the beginning, and from ancient times the things that are not yet done, saying, My counsel shall stand, and I will do all my pleasure."

Furthermore, we are told that our names were "written from the foundation of the world in the book of the slain lamb" (Revelation 13:8, 17:8), and that "he chose us in him before the creation of the world" (Ephesians 1:4).[6]

So why this way—why the temptation, the Fall, leading to the sacrifice of Jesus, "the Lamb of God who takes away the sin of the world" (John 1:29), on the Cross? People have often asked me things like that. I have to say that the Bible does not stoop to satisfy all our human curiosity on this and many other points. Let me, though, just throw in something that I've found to be a helpful speculation, and it's not entirely original.

God is omnipotent, yes—but there are some things He cannot

do. One is to do something contrary to His nature—for example, to lie (Numbers 23:19). Another is to do something that is a logical absurdity. For instance, God cannot make a rock so heavy that He cannot lift it.[13] Similarly, God cannot create married bachelors. A logically absurd proposition doesn't become meaningful just because we add the words 'God can'.[14] What I'm getting at is this: perhaps this whole cosmic drama of Creation/Fall/Redemption was the only way a lasting true-love relationship could be brought about. (Let me go a little bit further before outlining who the parties in this relationship of true love will be.)

True love requires the possibility of rejection. Imagine that you, if a young lady, are engaged to be married to a wonderful man. You are convinced that this is definitely true love, in the fullest meaning of this word that you can imagine. One day you are at the beach together, and as you are applying suntan lotion to the back of your fiancé's neck, you notice a metallic plaque embedded in the skin there which reads "made in Taiwan." Slowly the truth begins to dawn that this is a clever humanoid bio-robot. Your fiancé was *programmed* to love you.

If this techno-fantasy were true, think on this: up to that point, your belief that it really *was* true love required that he also be free to reject you. As far as you were concerned, he chose to love you in spite of the fact that he was totally free to *not* love you, to reject you. Once you know that he has *no choice* but to love you—that it is not possible for him to reject you—the illusion of true love disappears. You know it wasn't true love at all. So God could never have had a truly loving relationship with people who were simply *programmed* to love Him.

Now we can't know for sure whether the direction this discussion is heading is truly relevant to the question of why God did things this way. But we can know from Scripture something of the relationship that is the focus and the ultimate goal of God's

13.   This is the fallacy of contradictory premises—something requiring too much power for an all-powerful being to perform.
14.   Omnipotence was traditionally defined negatively: God is not restricted by anything *outside* of Himself; it was never intended to rule out *self*-restriction because of His goodness or logical nature. See also creation.com/omnipotence, 2008.

creative purpose. It is the marriage bond between Christ and His Bride, the Church. It is a relationship that is meant to be true love in the deepest sense of the word. And yet it has to be such as to never again leave open the possibility of future breakdown, of future rejection of that love—even though true love, in our conception, requires the possibility of rejection.

How God will reconcile the seemingly irreconcilable is something that our finite minds might not be able to grasp, even if it were explained to us this side of eternity. But what is being suggested is that the need to resolve this mystery is what made it not just an option, but an absolute necessity, to do things in the way that God did it. Perhaps the package *had* to involve both man's rejection and God's sacrificial, redeeming love through becoming our relative.

Whether that is so or not, there is no doubt that what Creation/Fall/Redemption, the biblical big picture, is really all about is this eternal marriage. Through all of it, God will have achieved a Bride for His Son. There will be an unbreakable and everlasting and indescribable love relationship between the Lord Jesus Christ and the redeemed who make up His Church, something He could never have had with angels. His 'Church' is not any building or denomination, it's the true believers from many different denominations, some even from no denomination at all. The Church has been called out of the world to become Christ's Bride as He reigns over the New Heavens and New Earth for all the ages to come.

You'll notice that, as much as I hope you would receive Christ right now (if you are not one of His already), I haven't spent a lot of time on what salvation can do for you. That's because I need to tell it like it is—that ultimately, it's not really about you so much as it's about God. You may have heard messages promising you health, wealth and happiness through coming to Jesus. Sure, in the Bible's 66 books, an isolated verse here and there can be found to bolster many different emphases. But there is plenty of evidence, both in Scripture and the lives of Christians, including the Apostles, that God did not promise us a rose garden in this life. One only has to see, in context, the New Testament's description of things that happened to those whom it holds up as examples of great faith:

> "They were stoned, they were sawn in two, they were killed with the sword.... destitute, afflicted, mistreated" (Hebrews 11:37).

There *is* happiness that comes from the abundant life God promises to the believer (John 10:10). And we've already seen in this book the benefits and blessings that can flow to entire societies and nations. There is peace, too, and joy—sometimes described as 'peace dancing'—that comes from knowing that sins are totally forgiven. *Forever.* But in a real sense these benefits are a side effect of the gospel. They are an adjunct to the main game, which is all about God and the eternal relationship He desires.

In the end—celebration

All whose names are in the Lamb's Book of Life (Revelation 21:27) will be part of His Bride. They will be present at that great Marriage Supper of the Lamb, described in Revelation 19:9, when Christ, God's Lamb, has come for His bride, the church. There will be people there from every ethnic group imaginable. Whether we call their subdivisions 'races' or any other name, they will be "from every tribe and language and people and nation" (Revelation 5:9). All part of this *one human family* while on Earth. All descended from our first parents, Adam and Eve—forever to be joined to their Creator in the bonds of everlasting love, now as *one heavenly family.*[15]

If you're not certain that you'll be there, there is nothing stopping you from casting yourself on God's mercy right now and asking Him to forgive your sin(s). Jesus Himself said in John 3:16, and 6:37:

---

15.   Note that Jesus is no polygamist, which is yet another powerful argument against intelligent life on other planets. Jesus will have *only* a human bride, not a Vulcan or Klingon bride as well. See also Bates. G., *Alien Intrusion* (book) and creation.com/did-god-create-life-on-other-planets.

"For God so loved the world, that he gave his only begotten Son, that whosoever believes in him should not perish, but have everlasting life."

"All that the Father gives me will come to me, and whoever comes to me I will never cast out."

There's His promise. Believe it—act on it. I hope to see you at The Wedding Celebration.

∞

ABOUT THE AUTHOR

Carl Wieland

Carl Wieland is currently the Managing Director of *Creation Ministries International* in Brisbane, Australia. Dr. Wieland has been involved in creation ministry since 1974, and in 1978 commenced *Creation* magazine, which now has subscribers in over 110 countries.

Carl is well known for his passion for making otherwise complex scientific subjects accessible to a wide range of people. While doing creation ministry part-time, he practiced as a family doctor for 13 years before becoming the fulltime head of the Australian ministry from 1987 till the present.

An accomplished public speaker on creation/evolution, he has ministered widely in both Australia and overseas. Dr. Wieland was also the executive producer of CMI's acclaimed 2009 year-of-Darwin documentary, *The Voyage that Shook the World*.

He has written extensively for CMI's website creation.com, as well as for *Creation* magazine and occasionally also for its peer-reviewed companion, CMI's *Journal of Creation*. He has authored or coauthored several layman's creation books, including contributing to one of the most popular creation resources of all time, *The Creation Answers Book*.

OTHER CBP RESOURCES BY THE AUTHOR

Books

- Beyond the Shadows: making sense of personal tragedy
- Stones and Bones: powerful evidence against evolution
- Creation Answers Book (contributor—Ed. D. Batten)

DVDs

- Creation: key to dynamic witnessing
- Dynamic Life: changes in living things
- Walking through Shadows: a personal testimony
- Why it Matters: the relevance of creation
- Clash over Origins: debate with Dr. Mark Farmer

CREATION
BOOK PUBLISHERS
www.creationbookpublishers.com

For further information on creation/evolution

CREATION.com